Introductory Physical Science

9th Edition

URI HABER-SCHAIM

PETER GENDEL

H. GRADEN KIRKSEY

HAROLD A. PRATT

ROBERT D. STAIR

SCIENCE CURRICULUM INC., LAKEWOOD, COLORADO 80228

Introductory Physical Science
Ninth Edition

Uri Haber-Schaim, Peter Gendel, H. Graden Kirksey,
Harold A. Pratt, Robert D. Stair

Published by Science Curriculum Inc., Lakewood, CO 80228. All
rights reserved. No part of this book may be reproduced in any
form or by any means without permission in writing from the
publisher. This edition of *Introductory Physical Science* is a revision
under free licensing of the work under the same title copyrighted
originally by Education Development Center, Inc. The publication
does not imply approval or disapproval by the original copyright
holder.

Editor: Linda Bevard
Book Design and Production: SYP Design & Production, Inc.
Photo researcher: Susan van Etten
Photography:
    Benoit Photography: pages 1, 14, 27, 53, 57, 62, 71, 84, 95, 97
    146, 147, 157, 221, 226, 239, 242, 249, 261, 262, 263, 264, 269,
    280, 283, 292, 294, 295, 296, 298, 318
    Corbis Images: pages 323, 345
    David Topping: pages 4, 27, 37, 115, 117, 181, 182, 183, 185, 186,
    191, 196,197, 207, 261, 268, 275
    Douglas Christian: pages 3, 85, 86, 123, 124, 127
    H. Nakagone, M. Hotta, T. Takahashi: page 323
    Jan Sullivan/PDPhoto.org: page 157
    Martha Svatek: page 303
    Robert Stair: pages, 197, 275, 285, 286, 304, 317, 319
    Stevie Grand/Science Photo Library: page 139
    Susan van Etten: pages 1, 16, 18, 19, 43, 53, 71, 95, 101, 107 115,
    142, 160, 161, 162, 164, 221, 239,
    USGS: page 43
Graphics:
    Ashley van Etten: pages 11, 12, 213, 214, 217
    Robert Stair: pages 9, 10, 32, 33, 167, 188, 199, 200, 243, 245, 310,
    313, 316, 335

Printed in the United States of America
By Quad/Graphics USA

ISBN 1-882057-29-5

10 9 8 7 6 5 4

4QGT15

Preface to the Ninth Edition

The objective of the *IPS* program is to guide all students to knowledge of physical science and the way scientific knowledge is acquired. Rather than surveying the entire field of physical science, *IPS* defines a path toward this objective, with options for achieving it. The result is a course that avoids being dogmatic and "a mile wide and an inch deep." These attributes and extensive reliance on experimental results to guide student learning make *IPS* a unique physical science course.

Inquiry and guided reasoning based on the results of student experiments are used to achieve these outcomes. Students acquire laboratory skills, reasoning skills, and the ability to communicate by participating in a cooperative learning process. *IPS* students learn from nature, the text, their teacher, and each other.

This edition combines instructional material from previous editions of *IPS* with that from *Force Motion and Energy (FM&E)*, another course by the same team of authors. This combination provides the breadth of material needed to meet the local, state, and national physical science standards.

Part One, the first six chapters, provides an overview of macroscopic properties of matter and is the foundation for the next two parts. Part Two, Chapters 7–11, presents atomicity and the classification of elements. Part Three, Chapters 12–16, guides the study of energy, forces, and Newton's laws.

This edition continues the use of formative assessment questions, designated by a light yellow background at the end of each section. Additional formative assessment questions are included in the *Teacher's Guide and Resource Book*. Comprehension Guide Questions™ (CGQs) are new to this edition. They are placed in the margin for students to use in assessing their own comprehension as they read the text.

Acknowledgements

This edition was field tested during the entire school year of 2008–2009, by close to 650 students of a range of abilities in both 8th and 9th grades. We are very much indebted to their teachers for providing detailed and continuous feedback:

Sheila R Askham, Oberon Middle School, Arvada, CO
Peter Gendel, Isidore Newman School, New Orleans, LA
Raymond Larson, Mercersburg Academy, Mercersburg, PA
Gery Morey, Independent Day School, Tampa, FL
Kent Roberts, Colville Junior High School, Colville, WA

We also appreciated receiving feedback on selected chapters from the following teachers during the fall of 2009:

Stephanie Geyfman, Giunta Middle School, Riverview, FL
Nicole Jacquay, Wilson Middle School, Tampa, FL
Rodger Lawson, Bartels Middle School, Tampa, FL

February 2010

Uri Haber-Schaim
Peter Gendel
H. Graden Kirksey
Harold A. Pratt
Robert D. Stair

CONTENTS

Part 1 – Properties of Matter

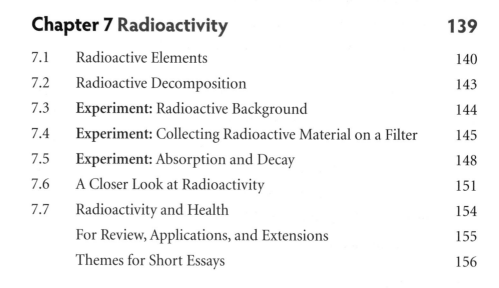

Chapter 11 Sizes and Masses of Molecules and Atoms

Part 3 – Energy and Forces

Chapter 12 Heating and Cooling

To The Student

You will have a different experience in this course than you have had in other science courses. You and your classmates will work together to do experiments, evaluate data, draw graphs, write, read, develop arguments, defend conclusions, and solve problems. Although you may find that it takes time to adjust to learning this way, you will find it a satisfying and productive way to gain knowledge.

To arrive at meaningful conclusions, you need large amounts of data. Rather than depending only on the data that your team collects, you will share your team's data with the entire class and reach conclusions based on this larger pool of data. Your classmates will be depending on your data, just as you will be depending on theirs. A well-kept notebook will be of great help in organizing your data and helping you learn from your experiments.

This course will also help you learn science through the written word, a valuable skill that you will need throughout your life. Comprehension Guide Questions™ (CGQs) located in blue boxes in the margins will allow you to check your understanding of the material you have just read.

What you learn from your experiments and reading becomes truly useful when you can apply it successfully to new situations. The many problems at the ends of sections and chapters will help you sharpen your problem-solving skills and build a solid foundation of science content and skills for future learning.

The Authors

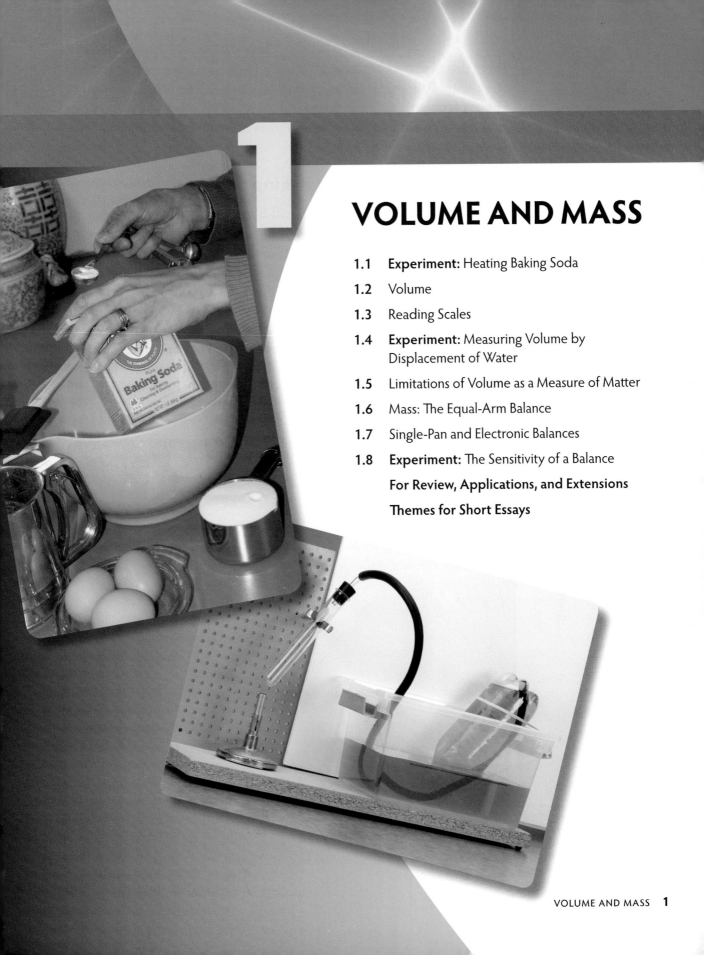

VOLUME AND MASS

There are many ways to begin the study of physical science. We will begin with a simple experiment that produces some surprising results. The experiment may raise some questions in your mind. At the same time, you will learn very useful laboratory skills.

1.1 Heating Baking Soda

EXPERIMENT
E

What do you think will happen if you heat some baking soda in a test tube? Will the baking soda change color? Will anything come out of the test tube? Before you read on, try to predict what will happen and be prepared to explain what you based your prediction on.

Put some baking soda into a dry test tube to a height of about 0.5 cm. In case a gas is produced, it will be useful to be able to collect it. You can do that with the apparatus shown in Figure 1.1. The bent glass tube may already have been inserted into the rubber stopper. If you have to insert the tube yourself, look closely at Figure 1.2 and its caption for useful advice on how to do it safely.

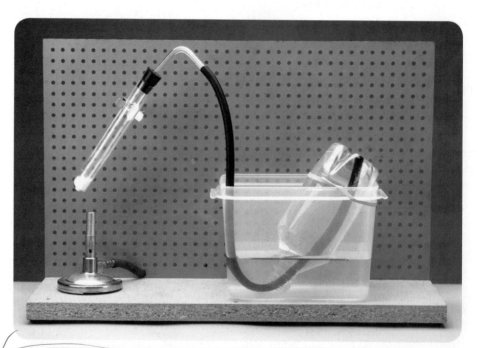

Figure 1.1

The apparatus used in heating baking soda. To be sure that no water will spill during the experiment, fill the large plastic container only up to the marker. Fill the bottle with water and hold your hand over the mouth of the bottle as you invert it, and place it in the container. Use a rubber band to hold the bottle in place. Finally, insert the rubber tube all the way up to the bottom of the inverted bottle.

After your teacher has checked your setup, you may begin heating the baking soda over either a microburner or an alcohol burner. Look at Figure 1.3 to see how the flame on the burner you are using should appear.

CAUTION: Always wear safety glasses when you use a burner or work with gases.

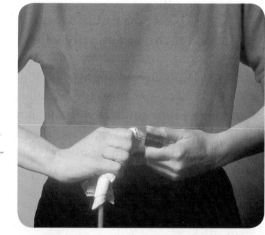

Figure 1.2

Lubricate the glass tube with glycerin or water before pushing it into the stopper. Hold the tube with a towel as close to the stopper as possible while pushing it in. This will prevent the tube from hurting you in case it breaks.

Figure 1.3

The proper size and color of the flame for a microburner (left) and for an alcohol burner.

Watch the test tube and collecting bottle as you heat the baking soda.

- What do you observe at the bottom of the test tube?*
- What do you observe near the top of the test tube?
- What do you observe in the inverted bottle?

When it appears that no further changes are taking place, pull the rubber tube completely out of the water while the flame is still on. Only then turn off the flame. (Why is the order of these steps important?)

> **(!) CAUTION: Do not blow out the flame of a microburner; turn off the gas supply valve.**

Even without measuring, you can see that there is more gas in the bottle than there was air in the test tube. To make sure of this, we heated an empty test tube connected to the same collecting bottle shown in Figure 1.1. All the air that was driven out of the heated test tube shows up as the small bubble in the bottle in Figure 1.4.

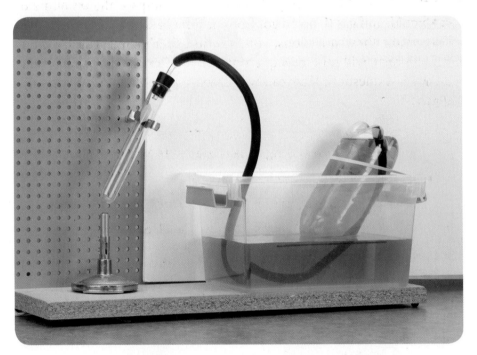

Figure 1.4
The result of heating an empty test tube for a few minutes. Blue food coloring has been added to the water to make the bubble at the top of the inverted bottle more visible. Clearly, the gas in your experiment was not just air from the test tube.

*Answer all bulleted questions in complete sentences. Restate enough of the information in the question so that it is clear which question is being answered.

- Where do you think the gas came from? *Compressed from Baking soda?*
- Where did the droplets on the test tube come from?

As far as you can tell by looking, the baking soda in the test tube remained unchanged. But did it really? You can answer this question with the following test.

First let the test tube in which you heated the baking soda cool down. Then put about an equal amount of baking soda in a second test tube. Pour some tea into each of the two test tubes (about a quarter tube will do). Gently shake both test tubes or use a stirring rod to dissolve the powders. You have now treated the contents of the two test tubes equally.

- Describe the color of the liquid in each test tube.
- Are the two white powders the same substance? What is your evidence?

Do you think you can get the baking soda back by mixing all the substances that you collected? Were these substances there all the time, or were they formed by heating? How can you compare the amounts of solid, liquid, and gas that you got from heating baking soda?

To answer these questions, you will do experiments. These experiments, in turn, will raise new questions. In the next section we will start with the last question: How can we compare amounts of solids, liquids, and gases?

---

1. Why do you think baking soda is used in baking?

2. List some tools that you have used

   a. to extend your vision to see distant objects.

   b. to extend your vision to see very small objects.

   c. to tell how hot something is.

1.2 Volume

Suppose that you have several stacks of pennies of different heights. How can you find the number of pennies in each stack? The obvious answer is to count them. But if you had to count the pennies in many stacks, it would take you quite awhile. You could speed up the counting by making a scale like that shown in Figure 1.5 (on the next page), marking it off in spaces equal to the thickness of one penny. You can then place this scale alongside each stack and read off the number of pennies.

Figure 1.5

A scale for counting the number of pennies in a vertical stack. The distance between marks is the thickness of one penny.

You can't do the same to Count bars of copper

Suppose that each penny is pure copper. If you want to measure the amount of copper in each stack of pennies, you must first decide on a unit to use in your measurement. If you choose as a unit the amount of copper in one penny, you simply count the number of pennies.

Could you use the same unit to find out how much copper there is in a solid rectangular bar of copper? You might think of making a box that is the same size and shape as the copper bar and then counting the number of pennies needed to fill the box. This idea will not work, though, because when you place pennies next to one another in a rectangular box, there will always be empty space between them.

A better way to find out how much copper there is in a solid rectangular bar of copper is to choose a new unit of measure, the volume of a small cube. We will call it a unit cube (Figure 1.6). Cubes have the advantage that you can place them next to one another without air spaces.

Suppose you had a box the same size and shape as the copper bar, and you could fill it with unit cubes. You could simply count the number of cubes to find the amount of copper in the bar. Of course, you do not have to count each cube. If a cubes fit along the length of the box, b along the width, and c along the height, then the total number of cubes in the box (and bar) is $a \times b \times c$. (See Figure 1.6.) This is the amount of copper in the solid bar, expressed in unit cubes. This amount is also the *volume* of the bar, expressed as the number of the unit cubes.

What we choose for the length of each side of this unit cube is a matter of convenience. We shall choose a unit of length based on the meter (m), the international standard of length in the metric system. In this case, as in much of this course, we shall use the centimeter (cm). A centimeter is 0.01 m. The volume of our unit cube would then become 1.0 cm × 1.0 cm × 1.0 cm or one *cubic centimeter* (cm³), a small cube 1 cm on an edge.

To summarize, we can compare different amounts of the same substance by comparing their volumes—that is, the amounts of space they occupy. For a rectangular solid, we find that volume by measuring the length of its three edges and calculating the product of these numbers.

Using volume to compare amounts of substances is easier with liquids, because liquids take the shape of their containers. Suppose you wish to compare the amounts of water in two bottles that have very different shapes. You simply pour the contents of each bottle separately into a graduated cylinder that has already been marked with the desired

How do you calculate the volume of a rectangular box or bar?

How many centimeters are there in one meter?

Why is the volume of a liquid often easier to measure than the volume of a solid?

0.01.

units, and read the volumes (Figure 1.7). This way of measuring volume is very much like counting pennies in a stack.

You can use the property of a liquid to take the shape of its container when you want to find the volume of a solid of irregular shape, such as a small stone. After pouring some water into a graduated cylinder and reading the volume of the water, you can put the stone in the water. The stone will sink to the bottom, and the water level will rise. You can then read the combined volume of the water and the stone. The difference between the two readings is the volume of the stone.

To find the volume of an irregular solid, what two measurements must be subtracted from each other?

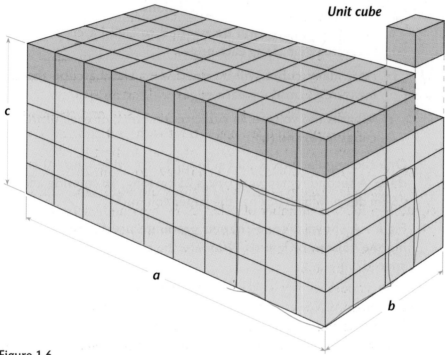

Unit cube

Figure 1.6

A bar of copper 10 cubes long, 4 cubes wide, and 5 cubes high. One layer of the bar contains 10 rows of 4 cubes each, or 10 × 4 cubes. There are 5 layers in the bar. Each layer contains 10 × 4 cubes. Therefore, the number of unit cubes in the bar is 10 × 4 × 5 = 200. If the unit cube is 1 cm on an edge, the volume of the bar is 200 cm³ (cubic centimeters). For any rectangular solid, therefore, the volume is the product of the three dimensions, $a \times b \times c$.

Figure 1.7

A graduated cylinder marked off in units of volume. The cubic-centimeter marks could be made by filling the cylinder with liquid from a small cubic container, 1 cm on an edge, and making a mark at the liquid level each time a container full of the liquid is poured in. Many graduated cylinders are marked off in *milliliters* (mL). A milliliter is the same volume as a cubic centimeter. (1 mL = 1 cm³.)

3. How many cubic centimeters of water are required to fill a graduated cylinder to the 50.0-mL mark?

4. Rectangular box A has a greater volume than rectangular box B but the length of box A is less than the length of Box B. How is this possible?

5. Adding a stone to a graduated cylinder containing 25.0 cm^3 of water raises the water level in the cylinder to the 32.0-cm^3 mark. What is the volume of the stone?

6. A student has a large number of cubes that measure 1 cm along each edge. (If you find it helpful, use a drawing or a set of cubes to answer the following questions.)

   a. How many cubes will be needed to build a cube that measures 2 cm along each edge?

   b. How many cubes will be needed to build a cube that measures 3 cm along each edge?

   c. What is the volume, in cubic centimeters, of each of the cubes in (a) and (b)?

7. One rectangular box is 30 cm long, 15 cm wide, and 10 cm deep. A second rectangular box is 25 cm long, 16 cm wide and 15 cm deep. Which box has the larger volume?

8. Figure A shows a cone-shaped graduate used for measuring the volume of liquids. Why are the divisions not equally spaced?

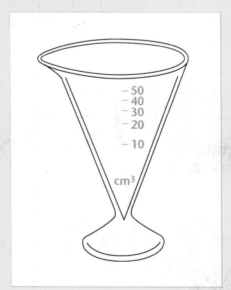

Figure A
For Problem 8

1.3 Reading Scales

To measure length with a ruler, volume with a graduated cylinder, or temperature with a thermometer, you must be able to read a scale. Begin by reading a metric ruler (Figure 1.8). The smallest divisions on such a ruler are 0.1 cm, or one *millimeter* (mm), apart.

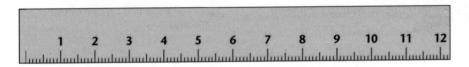

Figure 1.8
A metric ruler. The numbered divisions are centimeters. The small divisions are 0.1 cm, or millimeters.

When the object you wish to measure has sharp edges, you can clearly see where the edge lines up with the ruler. Most often the edge of the object falls between two lines. To record the length, you can estimate the position of the edge. In Figure 1.9, it is clear that the length of the object is between 4.8 and 4.9 cm. In fact, you cannot tell whether the edge is closer to one line or the other, so it is best to report it as halfway between the two lines. In this case, the length is reported as 4.85 cm.

In Figure 1.10 the edge falls closer to the line on the left than to the line on right. So you know that your estimate should be more than 4.80 cm and less than 4.85 cm. In other words, the possible values range from 4.81 cm to 4.84 cm. The best estimate here is a value near the center of this range. Report the length as 4.82 cm or 4.83 cm. (Remember that it is not possible to read thousandths of a centimeter with a ruler, so do not report the length as "4.825 cm.")

> Why is it not useful to have divisions 0.01 cm (or 0.1 mm) apart on a ruler?

> Suppose you measure the length of an object, and it appears to be halfway between 2.6 cm and 2.7 cm. How should you report the length?

Figure 1.9
Reading the position of the edge of an object. Here the edge falls halfway between two of the millimeter marks.

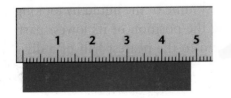

Figure 1.10
Here the edge is closer to the line on the left.

Figure 1.11

Here the edge is closer to the line on the right.

Figure 1.12

Here the edge falls on one of the millimeter marks.

Why is it important to estimate the position of the edge of an object if it falls between two marks on the ruler?

Figure 1.11 shows a different situation. Here the edge of the object falls closer to the line on the right than to the line on the left. Its length must be more than 4.85 cm and less than 4.90 cm. It is best to report this measurement as 4.87 cm or 4.88 cm.

In Figure 1.12 the edge falls on a line. In this case, you should report the reading as 3.20 cm, rather than just 3.2 cm. This will indicate that the reading is closer to 3.20 cm than to either 3.22 cm or 3.18 cm. Here the "0" gives us information that would have been lost if you had written only "3.2 cm." Notice, however, that you should not report the length as "3.200 cm." The additional zero would suggest that you can tell the difference between 3.200 cm and either 3.199 cm or 3.201 cm. This is not possible with this ruler.

Your reading of the last digit on a ruler is an estimate. Others might measure the same object and estimate slightly different values. How far apart might those estimates be? To find out, consider the object shown in Figure 1.10. You know that the possible values for its length range from 4.81 cm to 4.84 cm. That means that if you estimate the length to be 4.82 cm, your estimate might be as much as 0.02 cm too low (4.84 cm − 4.82 cm = 0.02 cm).

If you estimate the length of the object to be 4.83 cm, you might still be off by as much as 0.02 cm. In this case, your estimate might be 0.02 cm too high (4.83 cm − 4.81 cm = 0.02 cm).

With either estimate, you will not be more than 0.02 cm too high or too low. We write this as ±0.02 cm. (The symbol ± is read "plus or minus.") This value is called the *uncertainty* of your scale reading.

Reading the level of a liquid in a graduated cylinder poses a special problem because the top of the liquid is curved. The curved surface is called a *meniscus*. Generally, we read the volume of the liquid by looking at the meniscus at eye level and reading the position of its lowest part. Measurements of volume can be reported to the nearest half of a division. For the same reasons as discussed for the ruler, reading the scale on the graduated cylinder also introduces uncertainty in the reported value.

How do you read the volume of a liquid in a graduated cylinder?

9. The scale in Figure B is in centimeters.

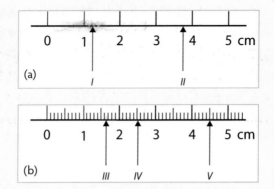

Figure B
For Problem 9

a. Estimate the positions of arrows *I* and *II* in Figure B(a) to the nearest 0.1 cm. Can you estimate their positions to 0.01 cm?

b. Estimate the positions of arrows *III*, *IV*, and *V* in Figure B(b) to the nearest 0.01 cm. Can you estimate their positions to 0.001 cm?

c. Why should you report the positions of the arrows in part (b) to the nearest 0.01 cm and not to the nearest 0.1 cm?

10. What part of a cubic centimeter do the smallest divisions on each of the graduated cylinders in Figure C represent? Express your answer as a decimal.

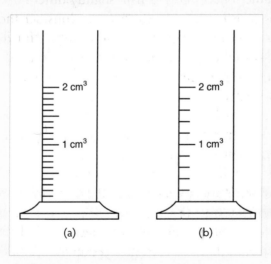

Figure C
For Problem 10

11. What is the level of the liquid in Figure D(a) to the nearest half division? What is the level in Figure D(b) to the nearest half division?

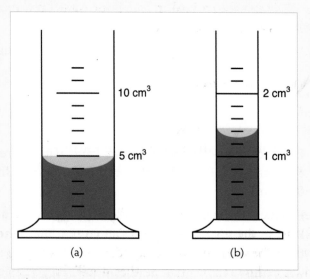

Figure D
For Problem 11

12. Three students reported the length of a pencil to be 12 cm, 12.0 cm, and 12.00 cm. Do all three readings contain the same information?

13. What advantage is there to making graduated cylinders narrow and tall rather than short and wide?

1.4 Measuring Volume by Displacement of Water

EXPERIMENT
E

A granular solid like sand, although it does not flow as well as a liquid, can be measured by the same method in the last section. Suppose you have some sand in a cup. To find the volume of the sand, you could simply pour the sand into a graduated cylinder. But does the level of the sand in the graduated cylinder really show the volume of the sand alone? What about the air spaces between the loosely packed grains? The graduated cylinder measures the combined volume of the sand plus the air spaces. However, you can do a simple experiment to find the volume of the sand alone.

Pour some sand into a dry graduated cylinder until it is about two-thirds full.

- What is the volume reading on the scale?

Now pour the sand into a beaker, and pour water into the graduated cylinder until it is about one-third full.

- What is the volume of the water?

Add the sand to the water. What is the volume of the sand plus the water?

- What is the volume of the sand alone?
- What is the volume of the air space(s) in the sand?
- What fraction of the dry sand is just air space? Express your answer as a decimal.

The experiment you have just done shows that we must be careful when we talk about the volume of a sample of a dry substance like sand. We must say how the volume was measured. If you have a bag of dry sand and want to know how many quart bottles it will fill, you need to know its volume dry. You need to know the volume of both the sand and the air spaces. But if you want to know the volume of sand alone, then you must use a procedure like that in the experiment you have just done. This is similar to measuring the volume of an irregular solid. You measure the volume of the sand alone by the volume of the liquid that is displaced.

14. The volume of a marble is 1.0 cm³. Of the following choices, which tells how many identical marbles are needed to fill an empty graduated cylinder to the 100-cm³ mark?

   A. 100   B. More than 100   C. Less than 100

15. A volume of 50 cm³ of dry sand is added to 30 cm³ of water for a total volume of 60 cm³.
   a. What is the volume of water that does not go into air spaces between the sand particles?
   b. What is the volume of water that does fill air spaces between the sand particles?
   c. What is the volume of the air spaces between the particles in the dry sand?
   d. What is the volume of the sand particles alone?
   e. What fraction of the total volume of the dry sand is sand particles? Express your answer as a decimal.

1.5 Limitations of Volume as a Measure of Matter

Whenever we measure the volume of a solid by displacement of water, we make an assumption. We assume that the volumes of the solid alone and of the water alone add up to the volume of the solid and water together after they are mixed. This assumption may or may not be correct, depending on the kind of solid we have. For example, suppose you measure the volume of a few chunks of rock salt by the displacement of water. You will see in Figure 1.13 that the total volume of rock salt and water decreases as the salt dissolves.

Why is the test tube containing only water included in the photos in Figure 1.13?

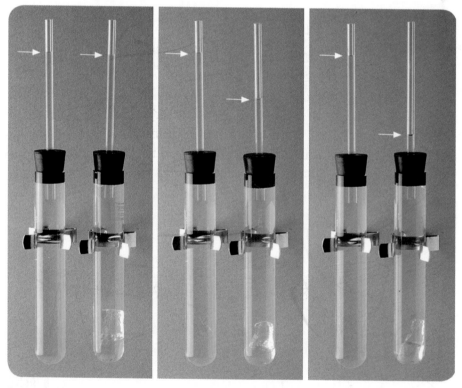

Figure 1.13

(a) Two test tubes. The one on the left contains only water. The one on the right contains water and two pieces of rock salt that have just been added. Notice that the total volume is the same for both, as shown by the water levels in the narrow tubes that extend above each test tube. (b) The same test tubes are shown 15 minutes later, after the salt has begun to dissolve. (c) The same test tubes 30 minutes after the rock salt was added. Notice the decrease in the total volume of the rock salt and water, as shown by the water level in the narrow glass tube.

The results of the experiment shown in Figure 1.13 strongly suggest that volume is not always a good measure of the amount of a substance. Here are some other difficulties with the use of volume to measure the amount of a substance. If you have ever pumped up a bicycle tire, you know that a gas is very compressible. As you pump more and more air into the tire, the volume of the tire remains almost unchanged. Does this mean that the amount of gas in the tire remains almost unchanged, too? If you compressed the gas obtained from heating baking soda by forcing it into a container of smaller volume, would there be less of the gas?

Finally, can we really use volume to compare the amounts of different substances, some of which are solids, some liquids, and others gases? Consider the heating of baking soda. Does measuring the volume of the baking soda, the liquid condensed near the top of the test tube, and the gas collected in the bottle really tell us how much of each of these substances we have?

1.6 Mass: The Equal-Arm Balance

The limitations of volume as a measure of the amount of matter must have been known to people many centuries ago. They developed a method for measuring the amounts of different substances without measuring their volumes. Archaeologists have recovered from an Egyptian tomb several thousand years old a little balance beam made of carved stone (Figure 1.14), along with carefully made stone masses. The balance was

(b)

(a)

Figure 1.14

(a) This balance, the earliest known, comes from a prehistoric grave at Naqada, Egypt, and may be 7,000 years old. It uses limestone masses and has a red limestone beam 8.5 cm long. The balance is shown at its true size.

(b) The standard masses shown are in units of beqa (BEK-ah). The letters and numbers on these four masses were placed there by archaeologists. *(Courtesy of Science Museum, London)*

probably used for the careful measurement of gold dust. Goldsmiths knew even then that the balance was the best way to determine the amount of solid gold they had.

The balance was hung by the upper loop so that the horizontal beam was divided exactly into two arms of equal length. With no objects suspended from either arm, the balance bar would hang horizontally. An object hung from the loop on the end of one arm could be balanced by hanging masses shown in Figure 1.14(b) from the end of the other arm.

People soon learned that the bar would remain horizontal even if there were drastic changes in the shapes of the objects being balanced. Cutting up a chunk of iron into several pieces or filing it into a pile of small grains does not affect the balance. A balance responds to something quite independent of the form of an object. It responds to what we call *mass*.

Suppose a piece of gold balances a piece of wood, and the piece of wood balances a piece of brass. Then we say that the masses of all three are equal. If something else balances the piece of brass, it also balances the wood and the gold and therefore has the same mass. The equal-arm balance gives us a way of comparing the masses of objects of any kind, regardless of volume, shape, color, or the substance they are made of.

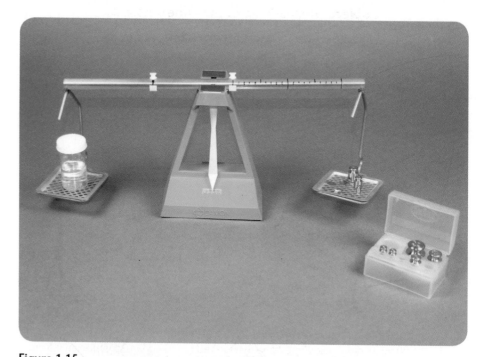

Figure 1.15

An equal-arm laboratory balance. The object to be massed is placed on the pan at the left. The standard gram masses are placed on the pan at the right. The tip of the pointer is at the middle of the scale on the base.

To use the balance, people used standard units of mass, something like those in Figure 1.14(b). They compared their gold or other objects to these standard masses.

A modern equal-arm balance is shown in Figure 1.15. The standard unit of mass being used with this balance is the *gram* (g), a unit of mass in the metric system.

The international standard of mass in the metric system is a carefully made cylinder of platinum kept at Sèvres, France, near Paris. This cylinder has a mass of 1 *kilogram* (kg), or 1,000 g. All other kilogram masses are compared, directly or indirectly, with the standard. If you were to place an object with a mass of 1 kilogram on a supermarket scale in the United States, the scale would read 2.2 pounds.

18. Suppose two objects with different shapes were hung from opposite ends of an equal-arm balance. The bar remained horizontal. Which of the following statements about the properties of the objects are true?

    A. The volumes of the objects are the same.

    B. The masses of the objects are the same.

    C. The objects are made up of the same substance.

    D. The colors of the objects are the same.

19. For each of the following objects, tell whether you would you use a count, a volume measurement, or a mass measurement to describe how much the object could hold. Explain.

    a. Elevator

    b. Stadium

    c. Bridge

    d. Bus

    e. Water tank ✓

    f. Train car

    g. Theater

    h. Saucepan

20. Are items you buy at a grocery store measured more often by volume or by mass? Give some examples.

21. What is your mass in kilograms?

1.7 Single-Pan and Electronic Balances

An alternative to an equal-arm balance with a set of standard masses is a balance with a pan on one side of the support and beams with sliding masses, called *riders*, on the other side (Figure 1.16). Such a balance is known as a *single-pan balance*. These balances are very common. You have probably seen one in your physician's office or in your school's health clinic (Figure 1.17).

Both the equal-arm and the single-pan balances compare the mass of the object on the pan with standard masses. The standard masses are placed either on the second pan of an equal-arm balance or as riders on the beams of the single-pan balance. An electronic balance (Figure 1.18) does not look at all like a balance. It has neither a second pan nor beams carrying riders.

Electronic balances have two advantages. First, it takes only seconds to mass an object. Thus, many teams in the laboratory can share one balance. Second, in many experiments you will need to find the mass of a liquid or powder in a container. An electronic balance can subtract the mass of the container and give you the mass of the contents alone. To use this feature, you press the *tare* button with the empty container on the pan. Then you mass the container and its contents.

Electronic balances are delicate instruments and must be handled with care. Use them only within the range they were designed to handle. Your balance should probably not be loaded with more than 200 g.

> What does the tare button on an electronic balance do?

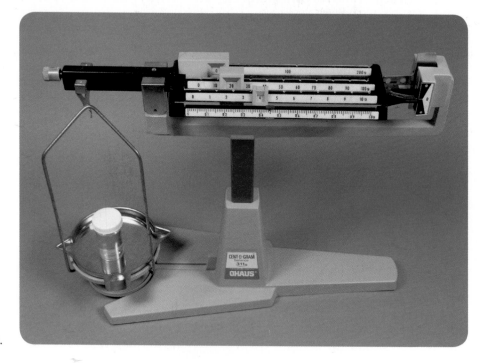

Figure 1.16

A single-pan balance with four beams and four riders.

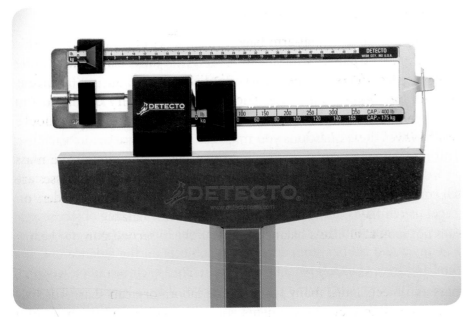

Figure 1.17

The top of a common balance in a physician's office. The scale is shown in both kilograms and pounds. *(Courtesy of Detecto, a Division of Cardinal Scale Mfg. Co.)*

Figure 1.18

An electronic balance with the 100-g calibration mass on the pan.

22. What is the advantage of using a single-pan balance rather than an equal-arm balance when massing a person?

EXPERIMENT E

1.8 The Sensitivity of a Balance

If you mass the same object several times on the same balance, will you find the same mass each time? And a related question: How much must the masses of two objects differ before your balance is able to tell the difference between them? The purpose of this experiment is to answer these questions.

To answer these questions you must zero the balance before each use. This means that the balance must be adjusted so that it correctly displays a reading of "zero" when there is zero mass on its pan. Your teacher will tell you how to zero the balance you are using.

Let us return to the first question: If you mass the same object several times, will you find the same mass each time? Mass two objects, such as a penny and a rubber stopper. Place the objects on the balance one at a time and have your lab partner read and record each result. Now switch roles with your lab partner, mass the two objects again, and record these results. Repeat this procedure as many times as specified by your teacher. Compare the results for each object obtained by you and your lab partner.

- Does your balance give the same results to the nearest 0.01 g? the nearest 0.001 g? or something in between?

Now for the second question: How much must the masses of two objects differ before your balance is able to tell the difference between them? To answer this question you can add small, known masses to an object already massed on your balance. A set of such small masses can be obtained using the squares from a piece of graph paper.

To obtain small, known masses, cut a group of smaller squares from a large square of graph paper that you have massed. Begin by neatly cutting a large square of graph paper that has 20 squares along each edge. This large square is made up of 400 small squares.

Estimate the mass of the large square to the nearest 0.1 g. You can write your estimate on the square and compare it with the estimates made by your classmates. Now mass the large square.

- What is the mass of your large square of graph paper?
- What is your calculated mass of a single small square?

For the purpose of this experiment, it will be convenient to have rectangular pieces of graph paper made up of small squares with a total mass between 0.003 and 0.007 g.

- How many of the small squares are in a group that has a mass between 0.003 and 0.007 g?
- What is the mass of this group of small squares?

These groups of squares are the known mass that you will add to an object massed on your balance.

Prepare ten of these groups of small squares. With a penny or rubber stopper already balanced, add the groups of small squares one by one and observe the effect on the balance.

- How many groups of squares did you have to add before the balance gave you an observable response?

The smallest change in mass that a balance can detect in a reproducible way is called the *sensitivity* of the balance.

- What is the sensitivity of your balance?
- How does this value for the sensitivity of the balance compare with your answer to the first bulleted question in this experiment?

23. A rectangle made from two squares of graph paper has a mass of 0.0045 g. The results of adding 10 such rectangles, one at a time, to an electronic balance are given below along with the mass readings on the scale.

Initial mass on the balance = 2.64 g

Number of rectangles	Was there a change from the previous reading?	Mass reading (g)
1	No	2.64
2	No	2.64
3	Yes	2.65
4	No	2.65
5	Yes	2.66
6	No	2.66
7	No	2.66
8	Yes	2.67
9	No	2.67
10	Yes	2.68

Based on these results, what should you report for the sensitivity of the balance?

24. Karen massed an object three times, using the same equal-arm balance and gram masses. Her results were 18.324 g, 18.308 g, and 18.342 g. How could she best report the mass of the object?

25. Five students in turn used the same equal-arm balance to measure the mass of a small dish. None knew what results the others obtained. The masses they found are given in the table below.

Student	Mass (g)
1	3.752
2	3.755
3	3.752
4	3.756
5	3.760

   a. Can you tell whether any student made an incorrect measurement?

   b. Do you think there is anything wrong with the balance?

   c. What do you think is the best way to report the mass of the dish?

26. Susan massed an object three times, using the same single-pan balance. Her results were 21.420 g, 21.425 g, and 21.410 g. How could she best report the mass of the object?

27. Five students in turn used the same single-pan balance to measure the mass of a small dish. None knew the results the others obtained. The masses they found are given in the table below.

Student	Mass (g)
1	4.360
2	4.370
3	4.365
4	4.360
5	4.355

a. Can you tell whether any student made an incorrect measurement?

b. Do you think there is anything wrong with the balance?

c. What do you think is the best way to report the mass of the dish?

28. Five students in turn used the same electronic balance to measure the mass of a small dish. None knew the results of the others. The masses are given in the table below.

Student	Mass (g)
1	4.36
2	4.37
3	4.36
4	4.37
5	4.36

a. Can you tell whether any student made an incorrect measurement?

b. Do you think there is anything wrong with the balance?

c. What do you think is the best way to report the mass of the dish?

29. Suppose the volume of a piece of glass is measured by displacement of water and by displacement of burner fuel. How would the two measurements compare?

30. In determining the volume of a rectangular box, five cubes were found to fit exactly along one edge, and four cubes to fit exactly along another edge. However, after six horizontal layers had been stacked in the box, a space at the top was left unfilled.

    a. If the height of the space was half the length of an edge of a cube, what was the volume of the box?

    b. If the height of the space was 0.23 of the length of an edge of a cube, what was the volume of the box?

31. What is the total number of cubes that will fit in the space enclosed by the dashed lines in Figure E? Is there more than one way to find an answer?

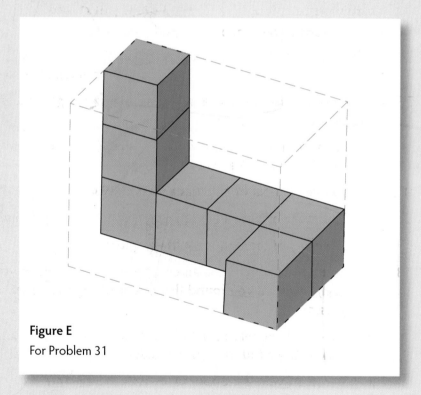

Figure E
For Problem 31

32. In an experiment in which the volume of sand is measured by the displacement of water, the sand was slightly wet to begin with. What effect would this have on the volume of air space that was calculated? On the percentage of the volume that was air space?

33. a. How would you measure the volume of a sponge?

    b. What have you actually measured by your method?

    c. Does this differ from your measurement of the volume of sand?

34. Fuel oil usually is sold by the gallon, gas for cooking by the cubic foot, and coal by the ton. What are the advantages of selling the first two by volume and the last by mass?

35. In the following list of ingredients for a recipe, which are measured by volume, which by mass, and which by other means?

    1 ½ pounds ground chuck   pinch of pepper

    1 medium-size onion   3 drops steak sauce

    ½ cup chopped green pepper   oregano to taste

    4 slices day-old bread   3 tablespoons oil

    1 teaspoon salt   1 1-pound can tomato sauce

36. a. What is the volume of an aluminum cube with edges that are 10 cm long?

    b. What is the mass of the aluminum cube? (One cubic centimeter of aluminum has a mass of 2.7 g.)

37. One cubic centimeter of gold has a mass of 19 g.

    a. What is the mass of a gold bar 1.0 cm × 2.0 cm × 25 cm?

    b. How many of these bars could you carry?

38. Suppose that you took home an equal-arm balance. When you were ready to use it, you found that you had forgotten a set of gram masses.

    a. How could you make a set of uniform masses from materials likely to be found in your home?

    b. How could you relate your unit of mass to a gram?

39. Suppose you balance a piece of modeling clay on the balance. Then you reshape it. Will it still balance? If you shape it into a hollow sphere, will it still balance?

40. Estimate in grams the mass of a watch. Now find the mass of a nickel (5¢) on your balance. Estimate the mass of the watch again. Did you change your estimate? Does knowing the mass of a nickel help you to better estimate your own mass? Why?

41. How could a person easily tell which envelopes contained four sheets of paper and which contained five sheets without opening the envelopes? What assumption did you make in arriving at your answer?

THEMES FOR SHORT ESSAYS

1. Suppose you are employed as a technical writer by a company that manufactures graduated cylinders. Printed instructions are to be included in packages sent out by the company. Write instructions telling customers how to use the cylinders correctly to measure the volumes of liquids.

2. A friend wants to use your balance during the summer. Write a complete set of instructions for her so that she will be able to do so successfully on her own without anybody being present to help her.

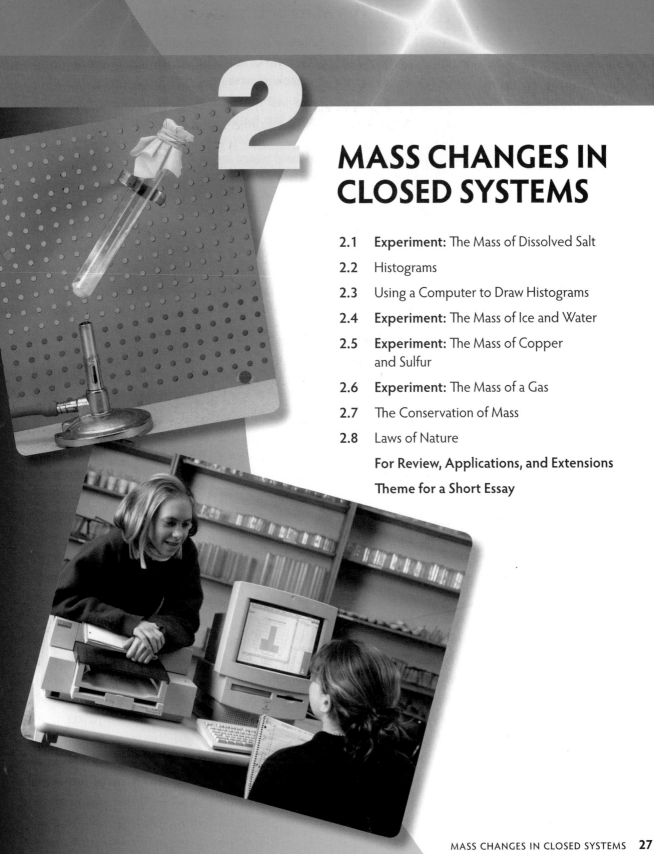

2

MASS CHANGES IN CLOSED SYSTEMS

EXPERIMENT
E

2.1 The Mass of Dissolved Salt

In Section 1.5, you learned that as salt dissolves in water, the combined volume of salt plus water decreases. Does mass also change when salt is dissolved in water?

Pour about 2 g of salt into the cap of a small plastic bottle, and carefully put it aside. Pour water into the bottle until it is about two-thirds full. Find the total mass of the bottle, water, cap, and salt when all are on the balance together but the salt and water are not mixed.

Carefully pour the salt into the bottle, and put the cap on. Shake the bottle occasionally to speed up the dissolving of the salt. After the salt has dissolved, mass the capped bottle.

- Taking into consideration the sensitivity of the balance, what do you conclude about the mass of salt and water as the salt dissolves?

Answering this question calls for a comparison between two mass measurements, before and after dissolving. A good way to do that is to subtract the earlier value from the later value. This difference is called the *change* in mass. Suppose that the earlier mass was 28.36 g and the later mass was 28.37 g. Then the change is

$$28.37 \text{ g} - 28.36 \text{ g} = +0.01 \text{ g}.$$

In this example, the later mass was greater than the earlier one. The positive sign (+) indicates that the mass increased. Suppose the earlier mass were 26.12 g and the later mass were 26.10 g. The change would still be calculated by subtracting the earlier value from the later value:

$$26.10 \text{ g} - 26.12 \text{ g} = -0.02 \text{ g}.$$

The negative sign (−) indicates that the mass decreased. Thus, change is expressed by a signed number; it can be positive, zero, or negative.

Your measurements sum up the result of a single experiment. To have more confidence in your conclusion, you would have to repeat the experiment several times to be sure that you have not spilled any salt or made an error in reading a scale. Many repetitions would use up much time and would be boring. So, instead of asking you to repeat this experiment, we shall bring together the results of all the experiments done by the whole class. We shall follow the same procedure with other experiments.

The first step is to gather the data from all the lab groups in the class. For future reference, copy the class results in your notebook.

- Considering the sensitivity of the balance, and the results of the entire class, what does your class conclude about the mass of salt and water as the salt dissolves?

> Why should a change be expressed as a signed number?

• Can you suggest any reasons why all the members of the class do not find the same change in mass?

final - initial = change

1. Here are the results of several experiments similar to the one you did. For which team(s) is the change of mass stated correctly?

Team	Mass Before Dissolving (g)	Mass After Dissolving (g)	Change In Mass (g)
1	42.67	42.65	+0.02
2	69.05	65.05	0
3	43.12	43.22	+0.10
4	43.10	42.95	−1.15
5	25.64	25.61	−0.03

2. Why is it important to always subtract the earlier value from the later value when finding the change in mass, instead of always subtracting the smaller value from the larger one?

3. Do you need to know the individual masses of the samples of water and salt to determine the change in mass when the two samples are mixed? Why or why not?

4. In Experiment 2.1, The Mass of Dissolved Salt, how could you get the dissolved salt back? How do you think its mass would compare with the mass of dry salt you started with?

5. If the change in mass in Experiment 2.1, The Mass of Dissolved Salt, were −0.0001 g, would you have observed this change using your balance? Explain.

6. a. In daily language we use various words to express the positive or negative sign of a change. For example, Elizabeth gained 1 kg; Tom lost 2 kg. Use positive and negative symbols to express these statements in terms of change in mass.

   b. In the morning the temperature rose from 10°C to 14°C. In the afternoon the temperature fell from 16°C to 11°C. What were the changes in temperature in the morning and in the afternoon?

2.2 Histograms

You probably have heard the proverb "a picture is worth a thousand words." It is just as true to say "a picture is worth a thousand numbers." To see for yourself, we will start with the data in Table 2.1. They were taken by a large class. The picture or histogram comes later.

Team Number	Mass before (g)	Mass after (g)	Change in mass (g)	Team Number	Mass before (g)	Mass after (g)	Change in mass (g)
1	32.17	32.24	+ 0.07	11	31.31	31.26	– 0.05
2	29.57	29.36	– 0.21	12	32.55	32.38	– 0.17
3	28.67	28.67	0	13	32.26	32.21	– 0.05
4	38.02	38.02	0	14	34.29	34.27	– 0.02
5	27.67	27.64	– 0.03	15	31.43	31.39	– 0.04
6	31.55	31.55	0	16	31.86	31.86	0
7	31.45	31.43	– 0.02	17	30.86	30.87	+ 0.01
8	35.12	35.12	0	18	30.29	30.29	0
9	31.45	31.45	0	19	29.14	29.15	+ 0.01
10	28.67	28.65	– 0.02	20	30.86	30.64	– 0.22

Table 2.1 Class Data from Experiment 2.1, The Mass of Dissolved Salt

Suppose we want to use the results shown in Table 2.1 to answer the question from the previous experiment: "Is there a change in mass when salt dissolves in water?" All of the data are there, but it is difficult to understand the entire table all at once. Are the results of teams 1 and 2 typical of the entire class? Are the results of other teams close to either of them? Are the results of other teams somewhere in between the results of teams 1 and 2?

The data in the "Change in mass" columns show that the value of the change in mass that occurs most often is zero. There are also a few entries of +0.01 g and –0.02 g. Are they really very different from zero?

The change in mass was calculated by subtracting the mass before dissolving from the mass after dissolving. Because the sensitivity of the balance is about 0.01 g, each of these measurements could be 0.01 g greater or 0.01 g less than what is reported. This means that the uncertainty in each measurement is ±0.01 g. When the two measurements are subtracted to find the change in mass, the possible uncertainty in the difference becomes ±0.02 g. This can be shown by the following example. The results of Team 3 could have been 28.68 g instead of the reported

> Why is the uncertainty in the difference of two measurements twice the uncertainty of a single measurement?

28.67 g before the salt dissolved, and 28.66 g after instead of 28.67 g after. In this case the reported change would have been –0.02 g. It would also have been possible for the mass measurement before dissolving to have been 28.66 g and the mass after dissolving to have been 28.68 g, giving a change in mass of +0.02 g. Thus, calculating the difference between two measurements doubles the uncertainty.

To be able to draw conclusions from the data, we need to present them as a picture that will emphasize an overall trend. We want a picture with less detail—one that ignores small differences that could be within the uncertainty of the results.

To do that, imagine we use several containers or bins to sort the data. We label each bin with a range of values. How wide should the bins be? If the bins are too large, then all of the values will be lumped together and appear to be the same. If the bins are too small, values that differ by less than the uncertainty in the experimental results will appear to be different when we really don't know that they are. In our case, a width of 0.02 makes sense. For example, we label them "–0.03 to –0.01," "–0.01 to +0.01," and so on.

Each team writes its result for the change in mass on a card and deposits the card in the bin labeled with the appropriate interval (Figure 2.1). If a group's values are on the border between two bins, the simplest solution is to always put them in the bin to the right, as was done in Figure 2.1.

Where should you put a measured value that falls on the boundary between two bins?

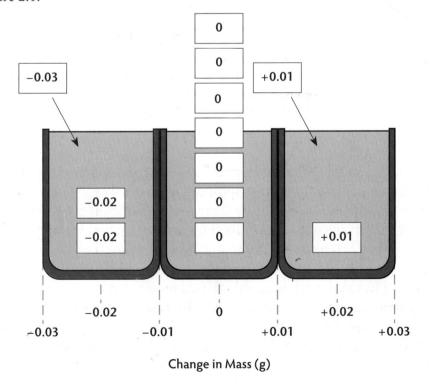

Change in Mass (g)

Figure 2.1

"Bins" for depositing data. Below the bins, the numbers in the upper row show the centers of the intervals represented by the bins. The numbers in the lower row show the borders between bins. One value, 0.01 g, fell on a border, so it was placed to the right in the bin representing the higher interval.

Once all the cards have been placed in the bins, we count the cards in each bin. Of course, we do not need real bins. We can use squares on graph paper instead, and plot a bar graph of the results. As with all graphs, find the largest and smallest values to help you decide how to mark the scale on the horizontal axis (Figure 2.2).

Figure 2.2

The starting points of a histogram: fitting the horizontal scale to the largest and smallest data values. Each square represents a bin. Just as in Figure 2.1, the labels in the upper row are at the centers of the bins, and those in the lower row show borders.

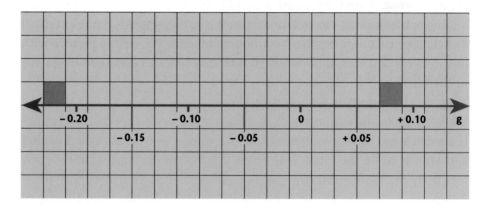

Now go through Table 2.1 (on page 30) and mark a square for each value in the table. If a value has already appeared, we draw its square on top of the one below it. The final result is shown in Figure 2.3. The height of each column tells us the number of measurements placed in each bin. A plot like Figure 2.3 that presents data by the number of times a value appears in an interval or bin is called a *histogram*. This is our picture that is worth a thousand numbers.

A histogram enables us to make several observations: First, most of the data are bunched around zero, with zero being the most frequent result. Also, some bins on both sides of zero have no data at all. Of the few readings far from zero, there are more on the left, indicating a loss, than on the right, indicating a gain.

Figure 2.3

A histogram of the data in Table 2.1, with an interval width of 0.02 g and with zero at the center of an interval.

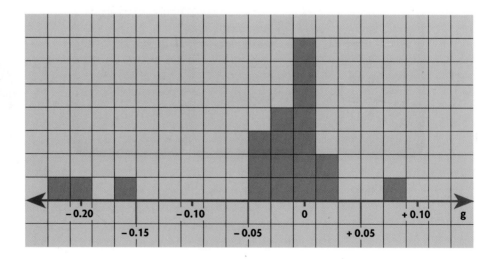

How would a histogram of the data in Table 2.1 look if we had placed the zero point at the border between two intervals (Figure 2.4)? Following the rule that a border value is placed in the interval to the right, we get the histogram in Figure 2.5. The histograms in Figures 2.3 and 2.5 have the same general appearance. However, the histogram in Figure 2.5 seems to suggest that the most frequent result is a small gain in mass. This apparent gain in mass is the result of having chosen the zero point at the border between intervals. The result shifts many values to the right. To avoid drawing misleading conclusions from histograms, try to set the borders between intervals so the results that occur most often fit into intervals rather than on their borders.

Why is it important to place results that occur most frequently within intervals rather than on a border between intervals?

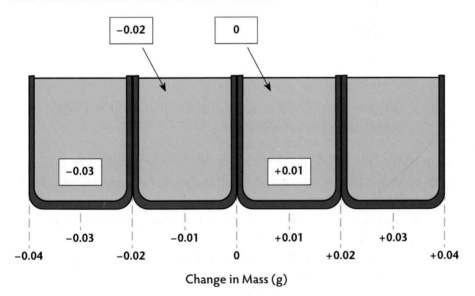

Figure 2.4
The arrangement of bins with the zero point at a border.

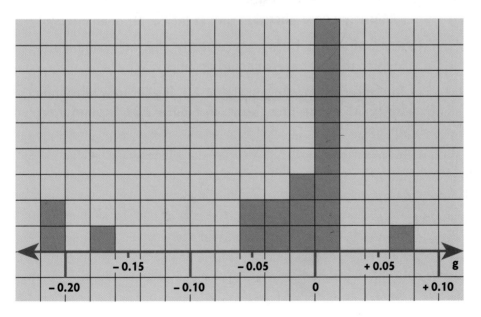

Figure 2.5
A complete histogram of the data in Table 2.1, with an interval width of 0.02 g and with zero at a border.

7. Suppose you had to add the results of two mass measurements made on your balance. Would the sum have a greater or smaller uncertainty than the individual measurements? Explain.

8. Consider a histogram having an interval or bin with boundaries of –0.01 g and +0.01 g. Which of the values given below should be counted in this bin or interval?

    A. –0.002 g

    B. –0.001 g

    C. 0 g

    D. +0.006 g

    E. +0.01 g

    F. +0.02 g

9. a. What is the interval immediately to the left of the interval containing zero in Figure 2.1?

    b. Identify the teams whose data appear in this column.

10. a. What is the interval immediately to the right of zero in Figure 2.5?

    b. Identify the teams whose data appear in this column.

    c. Identify the teams whose data are in the last column on the left in Figure 2.5.

11. a. Draw a histogram of the data in Table 2.1. Use intervals with a width of 0.01 g and place zero at the center of an interval.

    b. If you drew the histogram correctly, the interval immediately to the left of zero should be empty. Why?

    c. This observation is lost in Figure 2.3. Is your new histogram better than the one shown in Figure 2.3? Explain your answer.

2.3 Using a Computer to Draw Histograms

Drawing a histogram can be divided into two main steps: (1) deciding the width of the intervals and the value of the center of one interval, and (2) placing the values in the intervals, counting them, and plotting the histogram. The first step requires decisions on your part that were discussed in the previous section. These decisions are best made by you. Once the bins have been set up, the second step—counting and plotting—is routine. This step can be done by computer.

Figure 2.6 shows a histogram of the data in Table 2.1 created by a computer using a program written for *IPS*. Notice that the number of entries in each column must be read on the vertical axis at the left. Having the computer do the counting and drawing has an advantage. It allows you to try different interval sizes and make several histograms in a short time and find the one that in your opinion best summarizes the data.

> What advantage is there to having a computer count the values within each interval and draw the histogram?

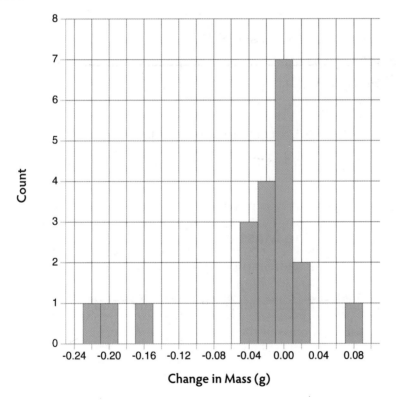

Figure 2.6

A computer-generated histogram of the data in Table 2.1. Note that the computer program shows only the centers of the bins and not both the centers and borders.

12. a. What is the width of an interval in the histogram shown in Figure 2.6?

b. Is zero at the center or at the border of the interval?

13. Figures A and B show histograms made from the data in Table 2.1. In each of these histograms,

  a. what is the width of the intervals?

  b. is zero at the center of an interval or at a border?

Figure A
For Problem 13

Figure B
For Problem 13

2.4 The Mass of Ice and Water

EXPERIMENT E

Here is another process involving a volume change. When ice melts, its volume decreases. Does its mass also change? Put an ice cube in a small container and put the lid on the container.

• What is the total mass of the ice and the container?

Allow all the ice to melt. If the container is not transparent, you can tell when the ice has melted by shaking it.

• Do you notice any condensation of water on the outside of the container?
• If so, what should you do about it?
• What is the total mass of the melted ice and the container now?
• From a histogram of class data, what do you conclude about change in mass when ice melts?

14. Between the time that a lab group measured the mass of the ice and container before melting and after melting, a second lab group spilled a few drops of water on the balance. What is the effect of this spill on the calculated change in mass

    a. if the balance has been tared before the second measurement was made?

    b. if the balance was not tared?

EXPERIMENT E · 2.5 The Mass of Copper and Sulfur

The changes you have examined so far were quite mild. A more dramatic change in matter takes place when sulfur and copper are heated together. Does the total mass change when these substances are heated together?

Put about 2 g of granular copper and about 1 g of sulfur in a test tube.

⚠️ **CAUTION: Do *not* use copper powder or copper dust. Always wear safety glasses when you use a burner.**

Stir the mixture with a glass rod or by shaking it gently. Then close the end of the test tube with a piece of rubber sheet held in place by a rubber band (Figure 2.7). Record the total mass of the closed tube and its

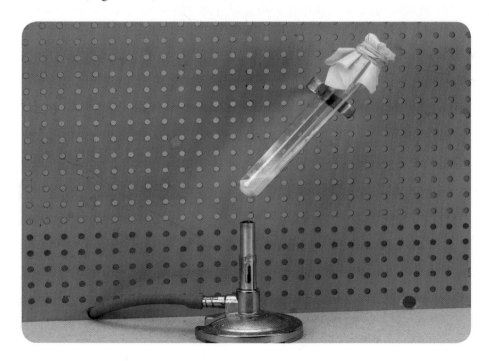

Figure 2.7
The setup for Experiment 2.5.

contents. Heat the mixture gently until it begins to glow; **then remove the flame immediately.**

 CAUTION: Do *not* touch the test tube until it has cooled.

- Has the total mass of copper and sulfur changed?
- Describe the appearance of the material in the test tube.
- Do you think the substance in the bottom of the test tube is sulfur, copper, or a new substance? Why? explain

---

15. The following data were recorded in an experiment in which copper and sulfur were reacted.

	Mass (g)
Tube and cover	20.484
Tube, cover, copper, and sulfur before reaction	23.440
Tube, cover, and products after reaction	23.386

a. What is the mass of the copper and sulfur before the reaction?

b. What is the change in mass of the reacting substances?

c. What is the percentage change in mass of the reacting substances?

16. A test tube containing 4.00 g of iron and 2.40 g of sulfur was heated in the same way that you heated the copper and sulfur. Before heating, the total mass of the tube and contents was 36.50 g. After heating, the mass was measured again. The mass of the tube and contents was 36.48 g.

a. Is it reasonable to think that mass remained the same during this experiment? Why or why not?

b. What additional steps would you take to increase your confidence in your answer to part (a)?

2.6 The Mass of a Gas

In this experiment, a solid and a liquid produce a gas. Is there a change in mass when this happens?

> **CAUTION: Be sure to use only the small *thick-walled* bottle wrapped with tape that your teacher has provided. Always wear safety glasses when you work with gases.**

Fill the bottle one-third full of water, then mass the bottle, its cap, and *one-eighth* of an Alka-Seltzer tablet. Place the piece of tablet in the bottle and immediately screw the cap on very tightly. Put it back on the balance.

- Does what happens inside the bottle affect the mass of the bottle and its contents?

Slowly loosen the cap.

- Describe what happens.

Again mass the cap, the bottle, and its contents.

- What do you conclude?"

2.7 The Conservation of Mass

What have the last four experiments shown? To answer this question, it is useful to remember that in each experiment great care was taken to ensure that nothing was added to or escaped from the containers. For example, in the experiment with ice and water, the condensation was removed from the outside of the closed container. In the last experiment the container was quickly capped to prevent the escape of gas. An experimental setup in which nothing is added or lost is called a *closed system*. When you worked carefully to maintain a closed system in each experiment, you found that most of the changes in mass that you observed were zero or close to zero. The results that were not zero were often less than the uncertainty in your measurements. Therefore, your results indicated that there was no change in mass that you could measure.

But from these experiments alone, you cannot predict with confidence that there will be no change in mass under other circumstances. For example, if you use larger amounts of matter in the experiments and use a balance of higher sensitivity, you might measure a change greater than the uncertainty in the measurements. If so, you would conclude

> What are the conditions that create a closed system?

that mass really does not remain the same. Furthermore, although you checked four kinds of change, there is an endless variety of other reactions you could have tried, some even more violent than the reaction of copper and sulfur.

What would happen, for example, if you set off a small explosion inside a heavy steel case, making sure nothing escaped? The experiments you have already done give no direct answer to this question, since it is not something you have tested in your experiments. Nevertheless, we can guess that the results of the four experiments you did can be generalized in the following way: In all changes that take place in a closed system, mass is exactly conserved; it remains exactly the same.

The generalization that we have just stated is known as *the law of conservation of mass.* It has been checked in many experiments to one part in a billion* for a large variety of changes. That is, experiments have been done in which a change in mass of one billionth of the total mass would have been observed if it had occurred. No such change has ever been observed.

Still, all this vast amount of evidence in favor of the law of conservation of mass does not prove that it will hold forever under all conditions. It does, however, give us a great deal of confidence in the law. If someone claimed that he or she had done an experiment in which as much as one millionth of the mass was lost or was created, we should treat the results with great suspicion. First of all, we should be sure that there has not been a leak of some sort in the apparatus that has allowed gas to escape. The chances are that we would find such a leak.

Our confidence in the law is very high, but there is one other possibility to consider. Suppose an experiment was done in which a change in mass of one part in 100 billion was reported. We might have to conclude, after a thorough examination of the experiment, that the law of conservation of mass has its limitations, that it holds to one part in a billion but not to one part in 100 billion (10^{11}). To date, no exceptions to the law of conservation of mass have been observed.

We have seen in this chapter that volume is very often a convenient way to measure the amount of matter. But we have also found that, when matter changes form (when ice melts, salt dissolves, and so on),

Is one-millionth larger or smaller than one-billionth? Explain.

Why should we be suspicious if someone says they found that one millionth of the mass was lost or gained in an experiment?

Why is mass often better than volume as a measure of the amount of substance in an object?

*A billion is 1,000,000,000. Such a number is clumsy to write. Most of the zeros can be dispensed with by writing the number as 10^9 and reading it "ten to the ninth." The 9 is called an exponent and tells how many times we multiply 1 by 10 to get the number. For example, $1 \times 10 \times 10 = 10^2$, $1 \times 10 \times 10 \times 10 = 10^3$, and so on. We shall use this way of expressing numbers, called *powers-of-10 notation*, whenever it is convenient.

there may be a change in volume but no observable change in mass. Unlike volume, mass is conserved. It is the law of conservation of mass that makes mass such a useful measure of matter.

17. A student wished to add a new experiment to Chapter 2 by investigating whether the mass of water changes when it is heated. The mass of a beaker containing a sample of water at 20°C was 109.44 g. After heating the sample to 60°C, the combined mass of the beaker and water was 109.08 g. Do these results contradict the law of conservation of mass? Explain your reasoning.

18. Can the law of conservation of mass ever be absolutely *proven* to be true? Why or why not

2.8 Laws of Nature

The law of conservation of mass is the first of several laws of nature that you will study in this course. It is worthwhile to pause at this point and compare the laws of nature with the laws of society. Laws of society are legislated; that is, they are agreed on through a voting process and then enforced. If evidence is presented that you have broken such a law, you are punished. The laws of society can be changed or repealed; this is also accomplished by a vote.

Laws of nature are different. Some laws are generalizations that began as lucky guesses based on a few crude experiments. Other laws started as consistent descriptions of patterns in nature or generalizations based on the analysis of many carefully conducted experiments. Regardless of how it comes about, a person takes a risk in announcing what he or she believes to be a law of nature. Before it is recognized as a law of nature, such a statement must stand up to criticism and testing by many other people doing additional experiments.

If you do an experiment that appears to violate a law of nature, you are not punished. On the contrary, if you present convincing evidence that the law is not quite true, the law is changed to take your new data into account. Only rarely does this lead to a complete repeal of the law. In most cases, the change is recognition that the law has limits.

How are the laws of society made? How are they changed?

How are laws of nature created?

19. There is an old saying: "What goes up must come down." Does this express a law of nature? Why or why not?

20. On a sunny day the sky is blue. Is this a law of nature? Why or why not?

FOR REVIEW, APPLICATIONS, AND EXTENSIONS

21. Suggest a reason for putting the lid on the small container that you used to study the mass of ice and water.

22. In Experiment 2.4, The Mass of Ice and Water, you melted ice. Would the mass of the container and its contents stay the same if you started with water and froze it? Try it.

23. Suppose you placed the entire setup used in Experiment 1.1, Heating Baking Soda (see Figure 1.1) on a balance and recorded the mass before and after heating. What would you expect to find?

THEME FOR A SHORT ESSAY

The terms "conserve" and "conservation" have different meanings in science and in everyday life. In a dry summer we are urged to conserve water. Driving at moderate speeds helps in the conservation of fuel. Write a brief essay explaining the difference in the meaning of "conservation" in this chapter and in daily life.

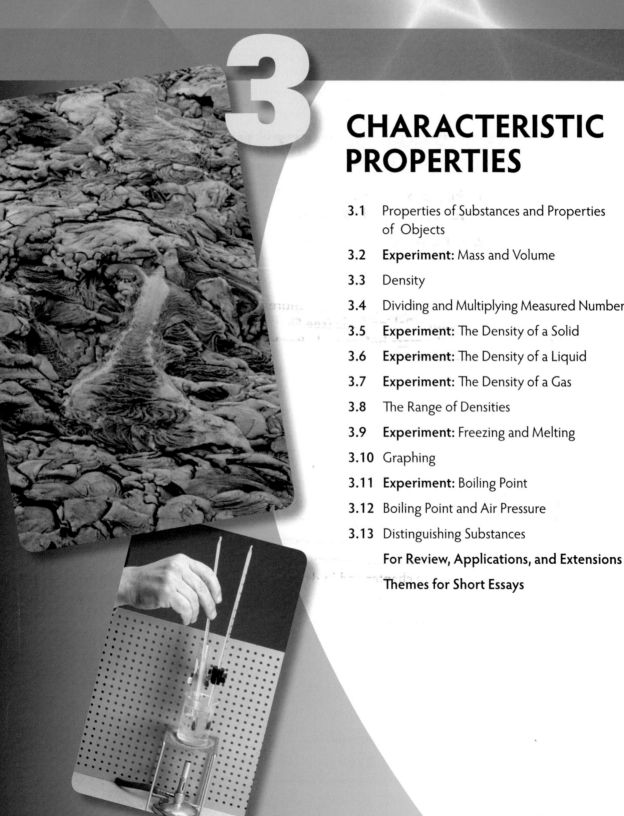

3

CHARACTERISTIC PROPERTIES

3.1 Properties of Substances and Properties of Objects

How do you know when two substances are different? It is easy enough to distinguish among wood, iron, and rock, or between water and milk; but there are other cases in which it is not so easy. Suppose that you are given two rings. Both rings look very much alike. They are equally shiny and feel equally hard. Are they made of the same metal? Or think of samples of two liquids. Both liquids are transparent and have no smell. Are they the same or different?

To be able to tell if two substances are the same or different, we have to do things to the substances to observe properties that are not obvious. Consider the two rings. Merely massing them will not help us tell whether they are made of the same or different metals. Two rings can be made of different substances and still have the same mass. On the other hand, two objects can have different masses and be made of the same substance. For example, consider two hammers, both made of steel but one much larger and with a greater mass than the other. Mass is a property of an object. It is not a property of the substance used to make the object.

To find out if two pieces of metal that look alike are made of the same substance, you may try to bend them. One may be thick and hard to bend, and the other may be thin and easy to bend; yet they both may be made of the same substance. On the other hand, you may find that two pieces of metal of different thicknesses but made of different substances bend with equal ease. Again, ease of bending, like mass and volume, is a property of the object and not of the substance.

Suppose we want to find out whether two objects are made of the same substance or of different ones. We have to look for properties that show differences between substances and do not depend on mass, size, or shape of the object or sample. We call such properties *characteristic properties*. You will investigate several characteristic properties in this chapter.

> Why is mass a property of an object and not a property of a substance?

1. How would you know if a property you observed is a property of a substance and not a property of an object made from the substance?

2. Which words in the following descriptions refer to substances and which refer to objects?

   a. A sharp, heavy, shiny, stainless-steel knife

   b. A small chunk of black tar

   c. A beautifully carved wooden chair

3.2 Mass and Volume

EXPERIMENT E

In the first two chapters you measured the masses and volumes of different objects. In this experiment you will answer the following questions. Does the mass of one cubic centimeter of an object depend on its shape? Does the mass of one cubic centimeter of an object depend on the substance it is made of?

To answer these questions you will use five metal cylinders, shown in Figure 3.1. Four of the cylinders are made from aluminum and the fifth is made from brass. The three thin cylinders shown in Figure 3.1 were cut from a much longer uniform cylinder of aluminum. Using a 10-mL graduated cylinder, you can verify that each of the three cylinders has a volume of 1.0 cm³.

1. a. Do you expect the mass of these three cylinders to be the same? b. Why or why not? Mass each of the three cylinders to check your expectation.

Suppose that you have a cylinder twice as long as each of the three long cylinders you have been using. Assume that this new cylinder was cut from the same aluminum rod that was used to make the three long cylinders.

2. What would the mass of this new cylinder be?
3. What would the volume of this new cylinder be?
4. How can you find the mass of one cubic centimeter of this new cylinder without cutting it in half?

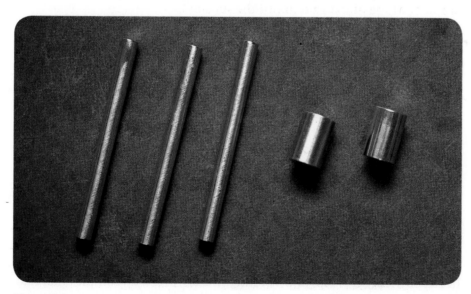

Figure 3.1
Five cylinders—four made of aluminum and one of brass. Each has a volume of 1.0 cm³.

The three long cylinders that you have been working with have the same shape. This raises another question: Does the mass of a piece of aluminum depend on the shape of the piece or only on its volume? To answer this question, you will use another aluminum cylinder. Its volume is also 1.0 cm³.

What is the mass of the short aluminum cylinder?

Does the shape of the piece affect the mass?

A piece of aluminum and a piece of brass can be cut so they have the same mass or the same volume. Can a piece of brass have both the same mass and the same volume as a piece of aluminum? To help answer this question, you can use the 1.0-cm³ brass cylinder shown in Figure 3.1.

Can the brass cylinder have the same mass and volume as a piece of aluminum?

3. If the mass of your aluminum cylinder with a volume of 1.0 cm³ is 2.7 g, which of the following is the mass of an aluminum cylinder with a volume of 3.0 cm³?

   A. 0.9 g

   B. 2.7 g

   C. 8.1 g

4. If the mass of your brass cylinder is 8.5 g, which of the following is the mass of a brass cylinder with a volume of 0.6 cm³?

   A. 5.1 g

   B. 8.5 g

   C. 14.2 g

5. If samples of brass and aluminum both have the same mass, which one has the greater volume?

   A. Brass

   B. Aluminum

   C. The volume is the same for both cylinders

3.3 Density

In Experiment 3.2, Mass and Volume, you worked with samples that had a volume of 1.0 cm³. Rarely do we find samples of matter with a volume of exactly 1 cm³, which we call a *unit volume*. In the laboratory, we usually work with samples that have a volume larger or smaller than one unit volume. However, we can always determine the mass of a unit volume of a substance. To do so, we measure the mass and volume of any size sample of the substance. The mass of one unit volume can then be calculated from these measurements by dividing the mass of the sample by its volume.

For example, suppose a sample of aluminum was measured and found to have a volume of 4.8 cm^3 and a mass of 13 g. We calculate the mass of a unit volume of aluminum in the following way:

$$\frac{13 \text{ g}}{4.8 \text{ cm}^3} = 2.7 \text{ g/cm}^3.$$

We calculated the mass of a unit volume by dividing mass by volume. Therefore, we refer to the mass of a unit volume as "mass *per* unit volume." The word "per" means a division by the quantity that follows it. For example, the speed of a car is stated in miles per hour—that is, a distance measurement divided by a time measurement. The mass per unit volume of a substance is called the *density* of that substance.

The units for density are g/cm^3 (grams per cubic centimeter). In the example shown above, the density of the aluminum is 2.7 g/cm^3. The two statements "The mass of 1 cm^3 of aluminum is 2.7 g" and "The density of aluminum is 2.7 g/cm^3" mean the same thing. The second statement is shorter and is used more often.

Density is a characteristic property of a substance. No matter what its size or shape, every sample or object made of that substance will have the same density.

Suppose that you know the mass and volume of a sample of a substance. State, in words, how you would calculate the density of the substance.

6. A parking lot is filled with automobiles.

   a. Does the number of wheels in the lot depend on the number of automobiles?

   b. Does the number of wheels per automobile depend on the number of automobiles?

   c. Is the number of wheels per automobile a characteristic property of automobiles that distinguishes them from other vehicles?

7. a. Draw a graph with the number of cars in a parking lot on the horizontal axis and the number of wheels in the same parking lot on the vertical axis.

> **b.** Draw a graph with the number of cars in the lot on the horizontal axis and the number of wheels per car on the vertical axis.
>
> **8.** Suppose you were to plot the mass of several samples of aluminum on the horizontal axis, and the density of aluminum on the vertical axis. Describe the appearance of the resulting graph.

3.4 Dividing and Multiplying Measured Numbers

As we saw in Sections 1.3 and 1.8, all measurements have some uncertainty in the last digit reported. So if the mass of a pebble is reported as 12.36 g, we are certain of the 12.3. But the 6 is estimated and contains some uncertainty. When the volume of the pebble is reported as 4.7 cm^3, we are sure of the 4, but the 7 is estimated, so it also contains some uncertainty. Because each digit reported in these measurements gives us some information about the accuracy of the measurements, they are all called *significant digits.* In this case, the mass measurement contains four significant digits, and the volume measurement contains two significant digits.

Uncertainties in measurements affect any calculations you perform using those measurements. If you calculate the density of the pebble by dividing 12.36 g by 4.7 cm^3 on a calculator, the answer that the calculator displays is 2.629787234. But do all those digits mean that we know the density of the pebble to the nearest billionth (0.000000001) of a gram per cubic centimeter? Even a calculator cannot produce numbers that are more accurate than the measurements used in the calculations!

For division and multiplication, it is good to remember a simple rule of thumb: The result of a calculation should have only as many significant digits as the measured value with the fewest significant digits. The density of the pebble is

$$\frac{12.36 \text{ g}}{4.7 \text{ cm}^3} = 2.6 \text{ g/cm}^3.$$

For the pebble, 12.36 g has four significant digits while 4.7 cm^3 has only two. This means that our density calculation is limited to just two significant digits.

Even though the numbers of significant digits in our measurements limit how many digits we can keep in a calculated answer, it is always

> When measured numbers are multiplied or divided, what determines the number of significant digits that should be kept in the answer?

advisable to calculate one additional digit and then round off. Of all the digits in the quotient provided by the calculator, only the 2 and the 6 have any meaning. The remaining digits displayed by a calculator are not significant and should be eliminated by rounding.

Why are the additional digits provided by a calculator not significant?

If we calculate the volume of an object from its dimensions, the same rules apply. Suppose the measured dimensions of a rectangular solid are 4.82 cm, 11.05 cm, and 1.28 cm. Then the volume of the solid is correctly reported as

$$4.82 \text{ cm} \times 11.05 \text{ cm} \times 1.28 \text{ cm} = 68.2 \text{ cm}^3.$$

The volume should *not* be reported as 68.174080 cm³!

Zeros present a special problem—sometimes they are significant and sometimes they are not. Zeros are only significant if they tell us something about the accuracy of a measurement.

Consider a measurement whose last digit is a zero, such as 4.20 cm. (Section 1.3 contains an explanation of why the zero is written.) In cases such as this, the zero is significant because it provides information about the accuracy of the measurement. However, in measurements such as 0.86 cm and 0.045 g, the zeros are not significant. These zeros act only as placeholders, helping to place the decimal point. As a result, both of these measurements have just two significant digits.

How many significant digits are there in each of the measured dimensions of the rectangular solid discussed above? Is the zero significant? Why or why not?

If a zero is in the middle of a measurement such as 11.05 g in the volume measurement above, the zero is a significant digit. There is no uncertainty in its value.

9. How many significant digits are in each of the following measurements?

   a. 4.0 cm³   e. 0.033 m

   b. 78.21 g   f. 225 cm

   c. 7.05 cm   g. 0.01 g

   d. 5.40 g   h. 0.930 m

10. Suppose that each of the numbers given below represents a measurement. Do the calculations, and report each answer to the proper number of significant digits.

   a. $\dfrac{125}{23.7}$ b. $\dfrac{20.5}{51.0}$ c. $\dfrac{0.065}{32.5}$ d. $\dfrac{1.23}{0.72}$

   e. 4.72×0.52 f. 6.3×10.08

   g. $1.55 \times 2.61 \times 5.3$ h. $3.01 \times 5.00 \times 25.62$

11. Suppose the measured dimensions of a rectangle are 3.62 cm and 12.06 cm.

a. With a calculator, determine the area of the rectangle and report all the digits on the display.

b. Suppose each measurement could be off by ±0.02 cm. Report the smallest and greatest possible values for the area of the rectangle. Use a calculator and report all the digits.

c. Which of the digits reported in part (a) are the same as those reported in part (b)?

d. Why should you report your answer to part (a) using only three digits, as suggested by the rule of thumb on page 48?

12. Suppose a pebble has a mass of 12.36 g. The volume of the pebble is 4.7 cm^3.

a. With a calculator, determine the density of the substance the pebble is made of. Report all the digits on the display.

b. Suppose the measurements could be off by ±0.01 g and ±0.1 cm^3. Report the least and greatest possible values for the density of the pebble. Use a calculator and report all the digits.

c. Which of the digits reported in part (a) are the same as those reported in part (b)?

d. Why should you report your answer to part (a) using only two significant digits, as suggested by the rule of thumb on page 48?

EXPERIMENT

E

3.5 The Density of a Solid

Pick up the two cubes that look alike and that have the same volume. Can you decide simply by handling them whether they have the same or different masses?

Mass the cubes on your balance.

• Which of the cubes has the greater density?

Now, just by handling them, compare the mass of each of the cubes with the mass of the slab. The slab has a different volume than the cubes.

- Can you decide in this way if the density of the slab is the same as or different than the density of either of the cubes?

Measure the dimensions of each of the three objects as accurately as you can. Calculate the volume and then the density of each.

- Are you now able to decide whether the slab is made of a different substance than either of the two cubes? Explain.

---

13. A block of magnesium whose volume is 10.0 cm³ has a mass of 17.0 g. What is the density of magnesium?

14. a. A 10.0-cm³ block of silver has a mass of 105 g. What is the density of silver?

   b. A 5.0-cm³ block of rock salt has a mass of 10.7 g. What is the density of rock salt?

   c. A 0.50-cm³ sample of alcohol has a mass of 0.41 g. What is its density?

15. What measurements and what calculations would you make to find the density of the wood in a rectangular block?

16. A student announced that she had made a sample of a new material that had a density of 0.85 g/cm³. Can you tell how large a sample she had made? Explain.

17. Would a cone-shaped piece of limestone and a cube of limestone that have the same mass also have the same volume? Why?

EXPERIMENT

E

3.6 The Density of a Liquid

Examine the two samples of liquid provided by your teacher. Smell them and shake them, but don't taste them. Can you tell whether they are the same or different? Finding their densities may help you answer this question. By massing a liquid on a balance and measuring its volume with a graduated cylinder, you can calculate its density.

- What are the densities of the two liquids?
- Are the two liquids the same or different?

18. Suppose you are given two clear, colorless liquids. You measure the densities of these liquids to see whether they are the same or different substances.

    a. What would you conclude if you found the densities to be 0.93 g/cm³ and 0.79 g/cm³?

    b. What would you conclude if you found the density of each liquid to be 0.81 g/cm³?

EXPERIMENT
E

3.7 The Density of a Gas

It is more difficult to measure the density of a gas than of a liquid or a solid. Gases are hard to handle, and most of them cannot even be seen. Because of this, early chemists neglected to take into account the mass of gases produced in experiments.

Mixing Alka-Seltzer tablets and water produces a large volume of gas. We can find the mass of the gas produced by massing the tablets and the water before and after they are mixed and calculating the difference. We can collect and measure the volume of the gas produced. Knowing the mass and volume of the gas allows us to calculate its density. You will recall that in Experiment 2.6, The Mass of a Gas, you measured the mass of some of this same gas, but you did not measure its volume.

Place two half-tablets of Alka-Seltzer and a test tube with about 5 cm³ of cold water on the pan of your balance as shown in Figure 3.2(a) or Figure 3.2(b). Find the total mass of these objects.

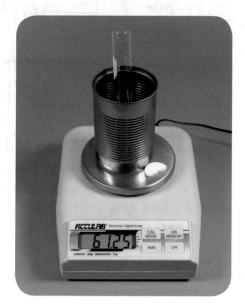

Figure 3.2(a)

A good way to support the test tube on an electronic balance.

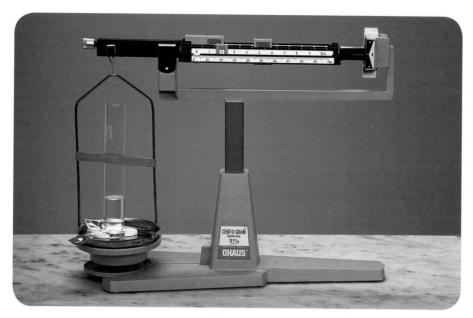

Figure 3.2(b)
A good way to support the test tube on a multibeam balance.

Arrange the apparatus as shown in Figure 3.3 so that you can collect the gas that will be produced. Be sure that the end of the rubber delivery tube is extended to the bottom of the inverted collecting bottle and that the whole length of the tube is clear and open.

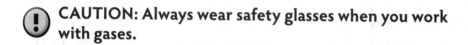

CAUTION: Always wear safety glasses when you work with gases.

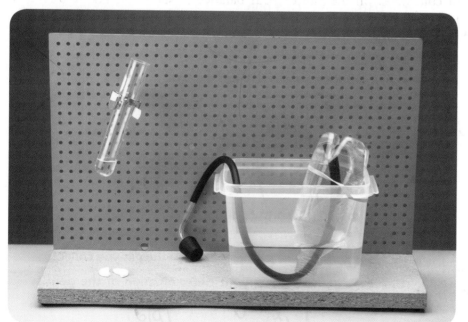

Figure 3.3
When the two half-tablets are added to the test tube, the gas generated is collected by displacing water from the inverted bottle on the right.

Drop the two half-tablets into the water, quickly insert the stopper into the test tube, and collect the gas produced. Practically all the gas will be produced in the first ten minutes of the reaction. At the end of this time, remove the delivery tube from the collecting bottle first, and then remove the stopper from the test tube.

- Why is it important to hold your hand over the mouth of the bottle while removing it from the water?

Turn the bottle upright, and find the volume of the water that has been displaced by gas.

- How is this volume related to the volume of the gas?
- How can you find the mass of the gas collected?
- What is the density of the gas?
- What assumptions have you made in using this method?

19. Does the density of a gas depend on how much gas is collected?

20. Which of the following is the approximate ratio of the density of the gas produced in Experiment 3.7 to the density of water (1.0 g/cm^3)?

    A. 1/1,000   E. 10

    B. 1/100   F. 100

    C. 1/10   G. 1,000

    D. About 1

21. Experiment 3.7, The Density of a Gas, is repeated with a sample of a different solid. Here are the data obtained:

Mass of solid, test tube, and water before reaction	35.40 g
Mass of test tube and contents after reaction	34.87 g
Volume of gas collected	480 cm^3

    Could this gas be the same as the one that you produced in Experiment 3.7?

22. The gas you collected in Experiment 3.7 dissolves slightly in water.

    a. How does this affect the volume of the gas you collect?

    b. How does this affect your determination of the density of the gas?

3.8 The Range of Densities

Table 3.1 lists the densities of various substances. Note that most solids and liquids have a density that is between 0.5 g/cm³ and about 20 g/cm³. The densities of gases are only about 1/1,000 of the densities of solids and liquids.

Is the density of a substance the same under all conditions? Samples of most substances expand when heated. That is, the volume increases, but the mass remains the same. Therefore, the sample's density decreases as the temperature rises. For liquids and solids, the expansion is very small and has little effect on the density.

The situation is quite different for gases, which expand greatly when heated. Moreover, unlike solids and liquids, gases are easily compressed, as you probably know from pumping up a bicycle tire. Therefore, when we measure the density of a gas, we have to know both the temperature and the pressure at which the density was measured.

Table 3.1 Densities of Some Solids, Liquids, and Gases (in g/cm³)			
Osmium	22.5	Oak	0.6–0.9
Platinum	21.4	Lithium	0.53
Gold	19.3	Liquid helium	
Mercury	13.6	(at −269°C)	0.15
Lead	11.3	Liquid hydrogen	
Copper	8.9	(at −252°C)	0.07
Iron	7.8	Carbon dioxide	1.8×10^{-3} *
Iodine	4.9	Oxygen	1.3×10^{-3}
Aluminum	2.7	Air	1.2×10^{-3}
Carbon tetrachloride	1.60	Nitrogen	1.2×10^{-3}
Water	1.00	Helium	1.7×10^{-4}
Ice	0.92	Hydrogen	8.4×10^{-5}
Methyl alcohol	0.79	Air (at 20 km elevation)	9×10^{-5}

At atmospheric pressure and room temperature

* Small numbers less than 1 can, like large numbers, be expressed in powers of 10. For example, we write 0.1 as 10^{-1}, 0.01 as 10^{-2}, 0.001 as 10^{-3}, and so on, using negative numbers as exponents.

If we have a decimal such as 0.002, we can write it first as 2×0.001, and then, in powers-of-10 notation, as 2×10^{-3}.

Another example: $0.00009 = 9 \times 0.00001 = 9 \times 10^{-5}$. The negative exponent tells how many places the decimal point must be moved to the left to give the correct value in ordinary notation.

Refer to Table 3.1 on page 55 to answer the following questions.

23. The densities in grams per cubic centimeter of various substances are listed below. For each density, tell whether the substance is most likely to be a gas, a liquid, or a solid.

    a. 0.0015   b. 10.0   c. 0.7   d. 1.1   e. 10^{-4}

24. Suppose you were given a kilogram of lead and a kilogram of oak. Which would have the greater volume? Which would have the greater mass?

25. Suppose you had 20 cm^3 of copper and 20 cm^3 of iron. Which would have the greater mass?

26. A small beaker contains 50 cm^3 of liquid.

    a. If the liquid is methyl alcohol, what is its mass?

    b. If the liquid is water, what is its mass?

27. Estimate the mass of air in an otherwise empty room that is the size of your classroom.

EXPERIMENT

(E)

3.9 Freezing and Melting

If you live in a part of the country where it snows in the winter, you know that a big pile of snow takes longer to melt than a small one. Does this mean that the big pile melts at a higher temperature? Is the temperature at which a sample of a substance melts or freezes really a characteristic property of the substance? To find out, we will measure the freezing temperatures of some substances using samples with different masses. For convenience, we will use substances that freeze above room temperature.

Your teacher will distribute test tubes containing different amounts of a solid substance. Use a similar empty test tube to determine the mass of your sample of the solid substance. Place the test tube containing the solid into a water bath, as shown in Figure 3.4. Heat the water until the solid in the test tube is completely melted.

(!) **CAUTION: Always wear safety glasses when you use a burner.**

Insert a thermometer into the molten substance. For comparison, it will be interesting to also know the temperature of the water bath. Measure the temperature of the water with a second thermometer. (See Figure 3.4.)

While the molten substance in the test tube cools, measure and record the temperatures of both the substance and the water bath every half-minute. Using the two thermometers, stir the water bath and the molten substance in the test tube to ensure that the temperatures will be the same throughout each substance.

Note and record the temperature of the molten substance just as it begins to solidify. Continue to take readings every half-minute until the temperature of the substance in the test tube drops to about 65°C.

You can stop stirring the substance in the test tube when the thermometer is no longer free to move.

 CAUTION: To prevent breakage, do not remove the thermometer from the solid substance in the test tube.

- What was the temperature at which the solid first appeared?
- What do you observe happening in the test tube and to the temperature soon after the solid first appears?
- In your table of temperatures and times, do you note any difference in the way the substance and the water cooled?

A better way to display your results is to plot the temperatures as a function of time on graph paper. Make a graph of the temperature of the substance and the temperature of the water using the same axes. (If you are unfamiliar with graphing, Section 3.10, Graphing, will be helpful.) Compare your graph of the temperature of the substance with those of your classmates.

- Do all of the graphs have a flat section?
- Does the temperature of the flat section depend on the mass of the sample that was cooled?
- Do you think that all the samples used in the class were the same substance?

You have now determined the *freezing point* of a substance by noting the temperature of the *plateau* (flat section) in the cooling curve. The freezing point is the temperature at which the substance changes from liquid to solid without continuing to cool down.

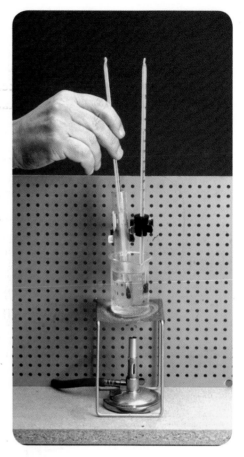

Figure 3.4

Apparatus used to obtain data for the cooling curve of a liquid as it cools and freezes. The thermometer in the test tube measures the temperature of the liquid; the one in the beaker measures the temperature of the water bath. Note that the level of the molten solid in the test tube is below the level of the water in the beaker.

Figure 3.5

The cooling curves of candle wax and of the water bath surrounding the test tube holding the wax. The absence of a plateau in the curve for the wax means that candle wax has no freezing point.

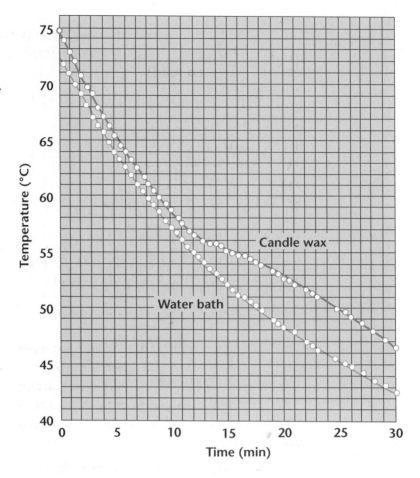

For some substances the plateau is more obvious than it is for others. Some cooling curves, however, may not have a flat section at all. For example, look at the cooling curve of candle wax shown in Figure 3.5. The data for this curve were obtained in the same way as in your experiment. The fact that no part of the curve is flat means that candle wax has no freezing point. Similarly, as you warm a piece of candle wax in your hand, it becomes softer and softer. However, there is no temperature at which it changes from hard solid to liquid without continuing to warm up; it has no *melting point.*

It is harder to measure the melting point of a substance than to measure the freezing point. Since we cannot stir a solid, it is necessary to heat it very slowly and evenly until it melts. If we do so, we find that we get a curve with the flat portion at exactly the freezing temperature. A solid melts at the same temperature that the liquid form of the same substance freezes. Thus the melting point and the freezing point of a substance are identical.

28. The graph in Figure A represents data from an experiment on the cooling of TOP. During which time intervals is there only liquid? Only solid? Both liquid and solid?

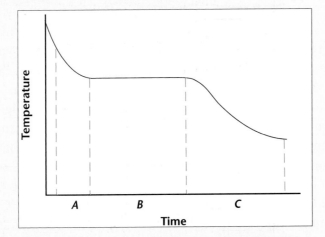

Figure A
For Problem 28

29. Water freezes at 0°C. Sketch a temperature-time graph for a container of water that is initially at 20°C and is placed in a freezer whose temperature is −10°C. Show the temperatures +20°C, 0°C, and −10°C on the vertical axis. Continue the graph until practically no further change will take place in the temperature of the ice.

30. A student uses a home freezer in an experiment to find the freezing point of rubbing alcohol. The temperature reaches a plateau at −10°C but the alcohol does not freeze. How can you explain this result?

3.10 Graphing

Several considerations enter into constructing a useful graph. Whether you draw the graph yourself or use a computer to do it, you must still make the crucial decisions.

The first step in drawing a graph is to determine which quantity to place on the horizontal axis and which on the vertical axis. In Experiment 3.9, Freezing and Melting, you controlled the time at which you read the temperature. This makes time the *independent variable*. The independent variable is placed on the horizontal axis. The temperature depended on the time, so it is the *dependent variable*. The dependent variable is on the vertical axis. A graph made this way is a graph of temperature *as a function of* time. The quantity preceding the words "as a function of" is always the dependent variable. The quantity following "as a function of" is always the independent variable.

The next step is to set suitable scales for the axes. Let us begin with the horizontal axis. Suppose that in Experiment 3.9 you took readings for 32 minutes. So the scale on the horizontal axis must extend from zero to at least 32 minutes. If you stop at 30 minutes, you will lose some data. Extending the axis to 35 minutes will make it easier to label the horizontal axis so that half-minutes can be read better.

Now consider the vertical axis. Suppose that the highest temperature in your data table is 96°C, and the lowest is 52°C. Assume that a piece of graph paper has 25 divisions along the vertical axis. Starting the vertical axis at 52°C and ending it at 96°C would spread 44°C over 25 divisions, that is 44/25, or 1.76°C per division. This would make it very difficult to plot and read the graph. Extending the scale from 50°C to 100°C makes it much simpler, since it allows us to spread 50°C over 25 divisions using 2°C per division.

To sum up, the following guidelines will help you choose suitable scales for your graphs:

(1) The scales must cover the entire range of your data points.

(2) There is no need to begin the scale at the least value and end it at the greatest value.

(3) Be sure that each division corresponds to a unit that makes plotting and reading easy.

Once all the points have been plotted, you can draw a smooth curve that passes through, or close to, the points. The curve does not have to pass through all the points. A curve drawn through all the points would contain many little wiggles resulting, in all likelihood, from uncertainties in your measurements. Therefore, a smooth curve that is close to most points and shows the general trend is a better picture of the results than a curve that passes through all the points. In some cases, the curve that best fits the data may not pass through any of the data points.

---

31. Suppose a substance was cooled from 83°C to 22°C. Which of the following pairs of temperatures, in Celsius degrees, should you choose for your lowest and highest values on the vertical axis of a graph of the cooling curve?

    A. 0, 100   B. 20, 90   C. 22, 83   D. 30, 80

32. a. What values correspond to points *A* through *D* on Scale I of Figure B?

    b. What values correspond to points *E* and *F* on Scale II?

    c. Which scale is easier to read and why?

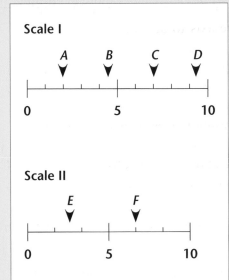

Figure B

For Problem 32

33. Which of the scales shown in Figure C would you choose to plot each of the following sets of numbers? In each case, explain the reason for your choice.

    a. 9.0, 17.5, 29.5, 36.0

    b. 17, 23, 55, 62

    c. 23.5, 31.2, 34.8, 39.0

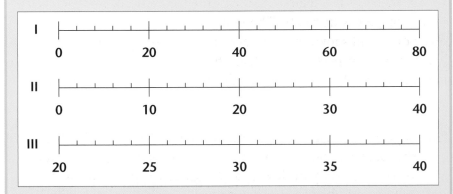

Figure C

For Problem 33

3.11 Boiling Point

Everybody knows that it takes longer to bring a full pan of water to a boil than a half-filled one. Does this mean that the full pan boils at a higher temperature? To help answer this question, you will be given either 10 cm^3 or 20 cm^3 of a liquid to heat using the apparatus shown in Figure 3.6. Before beginning, record the volume you are given. To prevent uneven boiling, add a few boiling chips—small pieces of porcelain—to the liquid. The vapors from the boiling liquid will condense in the cooled test tube in the water bath.

! CAUTION: Always wear safety glasses when you use a burner.

Some of the liquids you will be using may be flammable. To guarantee gentle heating, use the burner stand as shown in Figure 3.6.

Read and record the temperature of the liquid every half-minute until the liquid has been boiling for about five minutes. Then plot a graph with the temperature of the liquid as a function of time. Compare your results with those of other students in your class.

- Do all graphs look alike at the beginning?
- Do all of the graphs have a plateau?

A plateau occurs on the graph when the liquid is changing from liquid to gas without increasing in temperature. The temperature at this plateau is the *boiling point* of the liquid.

- Does the boiling point of a liquid depend on the amount of liquid?
- What does a difference in boiling point reveal?
- Is boiling point a characteristic property?

Figure 3.6

A thermometer supported by a rubber stopper in a test tube measures the temperature of a liquid as it is heated to its boiling point. To prevent uneven boiling, a few boiling chips are placed in the liquid. The water in the water bath should be cold.

---

34. The boiling points of two liquids are measured. Liquid A is found to have a higher boiling point than Liquid B. Using the same set of axes, sketch and label the temperature-time graph for each of these liquids without using any details as to the exact temperatures or times.

3.12 Boiling Point and Air Pressure

Suppose your class measured the boiling points of some liquids very carefully and compared the results with those of *IPS* students in other schools across the country. You would find that the results of some of the other schools differed slightly from yours. The differences would be greater if the other schools were at different elevations. The boiling point of a liquid depends on air pressure, which in turn depends on elevation and the weather.

You have changed air pressure many times. Think about a straw in a glass of water. The level of the water inside the straw is the same as the level outside the straw because the air pressure is the same in both places. When you drink through a straw, you remove some of the air from the straw by drawing it into your mouth. In this way, you reduce the air pressure inside the straw. The higher pressure on the water in the glass causes the water inside the straw to rise.

How high can water rise inside a straw or some other tube? With a long enough tube and a pump to remove the air, the water will rise to a height of about 10 m at sea level. If we replace the water with mercury, the mercury will rise to about 0.760 m or 760 mm (Figure 3.7). This is a much more convenient height to measure.

When the top of an evacuated tube containing mercury is sealed and a metric scale is placed next to it, we have a *barometer* (Figure 3.8). Depending on the weather, the height of the mercury column shows variations. A higher column indicates that air is pushing harder on the surface of the mercury. The height of the column does not depend on the diameter of the tube. This is why the height of the mercury column is used as a measure for the air pressure

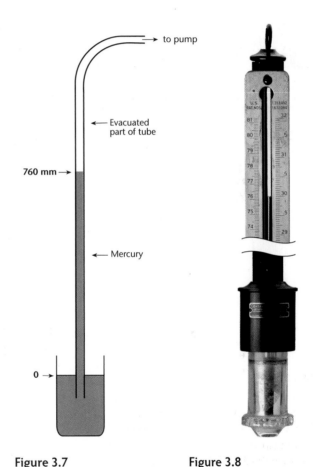

Figure 3.7

A glass tube in a cup containing mercury. As the air from the top of the tube is pumped out, the mercury rises in the tube.

Figure 3.8

The upper and lower parts of a mercury barometer. The long middle section is not shown. The scale on the upper part is in both millimeters and inches. Note that the mercury container at the bottom is much wider than the long tube.

generated by the atmosphere. This pressure is called *barometric pressure*. In weather reports, barometric pressure is often expressed in inches of mercury.

When the barometric pressure is higher, the boiling point of a liquid is higher; when the pressure is lower, the boiling point is lower. The variations in barometric pressure at any one location are rather small. The highest and lowest pressures recorded in Boston, Massachusetts, during one year were 780 mm and 730 mm, respectively. At these extreme conditions, the boiling point of water varies by only about 2°C.

The differences in barometric pressure at different elevations can be considerable, resulting in significantly different boiling points. The boiling points of water at various elevations are shown in Figure 3.9.

> On any given day, the barometric pressure at the top of Mt. McKinley (6,194 m) in Alaska is much lower than the barometric pressure in Miami, Florida (4 m). At which of these locations would water boil at a higher temperature?

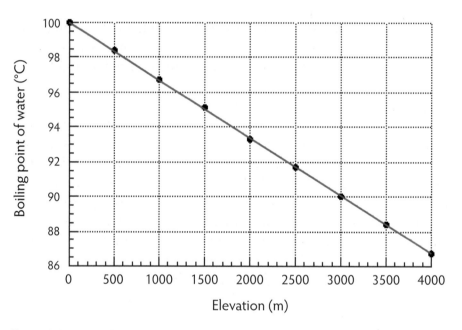

Figure 3.9

A graph of the boiling point of water as a function of elevation above sea level.

---

35. The highest capital city in the world is La Paz, Bolivia, with an elevation of about 3,600 m. What is the boiling point of water in La Paz?

36. Why would hard-boiled eggs need to be cooked longer in La Paz, Bolivia, than in Boston, Massachusetts?

37. The elevations of Memphis, Tennessee; Boulder, Colorado; and Los Alamos, New Mexico, are 80 m, 1,630 m, and 2,280 m, respectively. What is the boiling point of water in each of these cities?

38. Figure 3.9 shows how the boiling point of water depends on elevation. Under what conditions is it possible for the boiling point of water to exceed 100°C?

3.13 Distinguishing Substances

We have looked for properties that can help us distinguish between substances that appear to be the same. So far, we have found three properties that do not depend on how much we have of a substance or on its shape. These characteristic properties are density, melting point, and boiling point.

Suppose you measured the melting points of two samples of matter and found them to be the same. If you then measured their boiling points and found that these were also the same, you might suspect that you had two samples of the same substance. You might expect their densities and all other properties to be the same as well. But, as Table 3.2 shows, we cannot depend on only two properties to distinguish between substances, particularly if the measurements are not highly accurate.

In Group 1 of the table, the substances have the same boiling point and nearly the same melting point. It would be hard to measure these two properties carefully enough to see that they are different substances. However, a measurement of their densities would prove without question that they are different.

In Group 2 the substances have the same density and nearly the same boiling point, but they can be distinguished by their quite different melting points.

If you compared only the densities of the substances in Group 3, you might conclude that the three substances are the same. If you also measured their melting points, you would probably decide that the second and third substances in this group are the same. If you compared only their densities and boiling points but not their melting points, which substances would you conclude are the same? In fact, all three substances in Group 3 are different. That is why they were given different names when first discovered.

Table 3.2 Some Substances with Similar Properties			
	Density (g/cm³)	Melting point (°C)	Boiling point (°C)
Group 1			
Methyl acetate	0.93	–98	57
Acetone	0.79	–95	57
Group 2			
Isopropanol	0.79	–89	82
t-Butanol	0.79	26	83
Group 3			
Cycloheptane	0.81	–12	118
n-Butanol	0.81	–90	118
s-Butanol	0.81	–89	100

> How many characteristic properties must be the same in order for you to be confident that two samples are the same substance?

The names of the substances in this table are not important now, and you do not need to remember them. They are good examples of substances that we cannot tell apart unless we measure all three properties: density, melting point, and boiling point.

There are not many examples of substances that are nearly the same in two of these three properties and yet differ in the third. It would be even harder to find two substances that have the same density, melting point, and boiling point but differ in some other property. If we can determine density, melting point, and boiling point, we can distinguish among almost all substances.

In many cases, the melting point and the boiling point of a sample of matter can be measured easily in the laboratory. However, some substances have boiling points so high that it is difficult to make them hot enough to boil. For example, table salt boils at 1,413°C. Other substances have boiling points so low that it is difficult even to make them cold enough to become liquid. The same experimental difficulties come up when we try to determine the melting points of some substances. For example, grain alcohol melts at –117°C.

Suppose you have a sample of a newly made substance. You wish to find out whether it is truly a new substance, different from all others, or a substance already known but made in a new way. If its boiling and melting points are too high or too low to measure easily, you must look for other characteristic properties that might help to distinguish it from similar substances.

39. Which of the substances listed in Table 3.2 are solids, which are liquids, and which are gases at

    a. room temperature (20°C)?

    b. 50°C?

    c. 100°C?

40. Suppose you use the thermometers in your laboratory to measure the boiling points of two liquids. How far apart must the two measurements be for you to be confident that the two liquids are different?

FOR REVIEW, APPLICATIONS, AND EXTENSIONS

41. Object A has a mass of 500 g and a density of 5.0 g/cm^3; object B has a mass of 650 g and a density of 6.5 g/cm^3.

    a. Which object will displace the most liquid?

    b. Could object A and object B be made of the same substance?

42. A student uses water displacement to measure the volume of a small aluminum ball and then masses it on a balance. He finds that the sphere displaces 4.5 cm^3 of water and that the mass of the sphere is 6.5 g.

    a. What value does the student obtain for the density of aluminum?

    b. How can you use this information to decide whether the sphere is solid or hollow?

43. How can you distinguish between unlabeled pint cartons of milk and of cream without breaking the seals?

44. A student has several different-size samples of substances I and II. She measures the masses and volumes of these samples and plots the graphs shown in Figure D. Which substance has the greater density? How do you know?

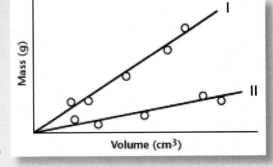

Figure D
For Problem 44

45. How can you determine the density of ice? Can you determine the volume of the ice by melting it and measuring the volume of the resulting water? Explain.

46. It is likely that the temperature readings on several thermometers will be different even when their bulbs are close together in a well-stirred beaker of water. What can you do so that data taken with the different thermometers can be accurately compared?

47. a. Would adding more ice to an insulated cooler filled with canned drinks make the drinks colder?

    b. If not, how would adding more ice affect the drinks?

    c. Describe an experiment to test your answer to part (b).

48. The melting point of a few tiny crystals of BHT can be measured by placing the crystals in a small capillary tube held next to the bulb of a thermometer in a water bath (see Figure E). When the melting point is found by this method, the result agrees with the freezing point you found in Experiment 3.9, Freezing and Melting, using about 10 cm^3 of the substance.

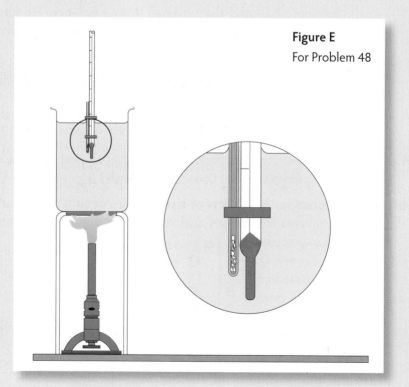

Figure E
For Problem 48

a. Use Figure E to estimate the volume of BHT used in the experiment. The inner diameter of the capillary tube is about 0.5 mm.

b. By what factor is the volume of BHT used in this experiment smaller than that used in Experiment 3.9?

49. Figure F shows a diagram of a double boiler. Why is a double boiler used to cook food that is easily scorched?

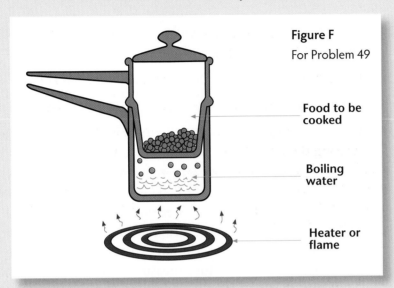

Figure F
For Problem 49

Food to be cooked

Boiling water

Heater or flame

50. In Table 3.1, why are the pressure and temperature stated for the densities of gases but not stated for the densities of solids and liquids?

51. A cylinder is closed with a tight-fitting piston 30 cm from the end wall (Figure G). The cylinder contains a gas with a density of 1.2×10^{-3} g/cm³. The piston is pushed in until it is 10 cm from the end wall. If no gas escapes, what is the density of the compressed gas? What is your reasoning?

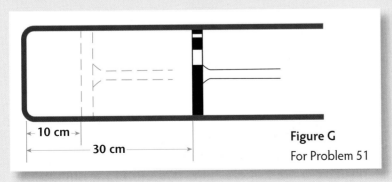

← 10 cm →

30 cm

Figure G
For Problem 51

52. Does the density of air change when it is heated

    a. in an open bottle?

    b. in a tightly stoppered bottle?

THEMES FOR SHORT ESSAYS

1. Ice floats on water. Suppose it did not. What would happen to life in lakes and rivers? Write a short science fiction story on this subject.

2. Write a short mystery story in which a criminal tries to pass off a small statue of gold-plated lead as solid gold. Have the detective uncover the plot without damaging the statue.

3. You learned about the sensitivity of your laboratory balances in Experiment 1.8, The Sensitivity of a Balance. What about your thermometers? Do they all display the same temperature when they are at the same temperature? Describe an experiment to show the difference in temperature measurements displayed by different thermometers in your class when all are at the same temperature.

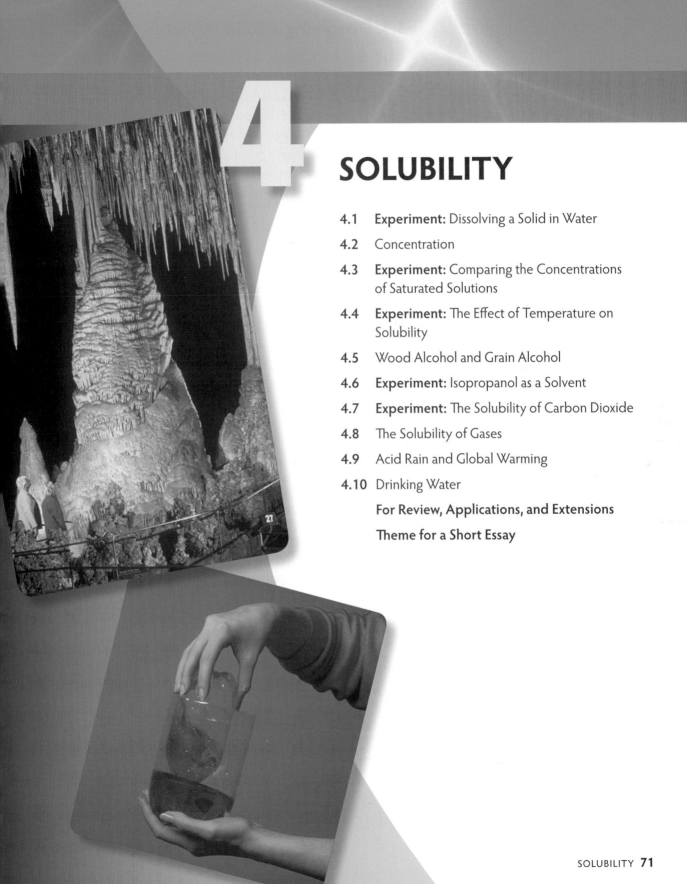

4 SOLUBILITY

4.1 Dissolving a Solid in Water

You know from daily experience that sand and chalk do not dissolve in water, but that sugar and table salt do. These are only *qualitative* observations—that is, observations that do not involve measurement. Are you sure that not even a tiny amount of chalk or sand dissolves in a gallon of water? Can you dissolve as much salt or sugar as you wish in a glass of water?

Whenever one substance, such as salt, dissolves in another substance, such as water, the result is called a *solution*. Many solutions, like those mentioned above, are colorless—there is nothing to be seen once the solid has dissolved. In this experiment we will begin our *quantitative* study of solutions. Quantitative observations are those that involve measurements. To make things visible, we will use solutions that have color.

Place 5.0 cm³ of water in one test tube and 20.0 cm³ of water in another. Add 0.30 g of an orange solid (or 0.15 g of blue solid) to each tube, then stopper and shake thoroughly.

> **What is the difference between qualitative and quantitative observations?**

> ! **CAUTION: Be careful not to get any solution on your hands. If some spills, wash thoroughly with water.**

- Did all of the solid dissolve in both test tubes?
- Do you think that each cubic centimeter of solution in one test tube contains the same amount of dissolved material?
- Both tubes contain the same amount of dissolved material, but is the shade of the color the same in both tubes?

Add another 0.30 g of the orange solid (or 0.15 g of the blue solid) to each tube. The solutions may cool as the solid dissolves. If so, keep the temperature fairly constant by warming the test tube with your hand.

- Did 0.60 g of the orange solid (or 0.30 g of the blue solid) dissolve as well in 20.0 cm³ as in 5.0 cm³ of water?
- Is the color uniform throughout the solution in each test tube?
- Is the shade of the color the same in the first and second solutions?

Add still another 0.30 g of the orange solid (or 0.15 g of the blue solid) to each solution.

- What is the total mass of orange or blue solid now in each test tube?
- What do you observe?
- How many grams of orange (or blue) solid do you think would have to be added to the 20.0 cm³ of water before the solid stopped dissolving? Test your prediction.

A solution in which no more orange (or blue) solid can be dissolved is called a *saturated solution* of the orange (or blue) solid.

- Do you have a saturated solution in either of your test tubes? What is your evidence?

> 1. Some people say that sugar "melts" when it is added to water. How would you describe the difference between melting and dissolving?

4.2 Concentration

In the last experiment, the color of the solution became more intense as you added more solid, and the color remained uniform throughout each test tube. This uniformity of color suggests that the solid dissolved evenly throughout the solution. That is, any cubic centimeter of a given solution contained the same mass of orange (or blue) material as any other cubic centimeter of that solution. For example, if you used the orange solid, at the beginning of the experiment one test tube contained

$$\frac{0.30 \text{ g}}{5.0 \text{ cm}^3} = 0.060 \text{ g/cm}^3$$

of material and the other test tube contained

$$\frac{0.30 \text{ g}}{20.0 \text{ cm}^3} = 0.015 \text{ g/cm}^3.$$

The mass of solid dissolved per cubic centimeter of liquid is called the *concentration* of the solution. The unit of concentration is the same as that of density, g/cm^3. However, in the case of density, the mass and the volume refer to the same substance. In the case of concentration, the mass refers to the dissolved solid (called the *solute*) and the volume refers to the liquid (called the *solvent*).

To avoid confusion and for convenience, concentrations are often given in $g/100 \text{ cm}^3$. For example, a concentration of 0.015 g/cm^3 means that 0.015 g of solute is dissolved in 1 cm^3 of water. Therefore, a volume of 100 cm^3 of water will contain

$$100 \times 0.015 \text{ g} = 1.5 \text{ g}$$

> Density and concentration are given in g/cm^3. To which quantity does the unit of volume refer in each case?

> When sugar is dissolved in water, which is the solvent and which is the solute?

of solute. So the concentration of the solution given in g/100 cm^3 is 1.5 g/100 cm^3. To express the concentration of a solution in g/100 cm^3, multiply the concentration in g/cm^3 by 100.

2. If you dissolve 25.0 g of sugar in 150 cm^3 of water, what is the concentration in

    a. g/cm^3?

    b. g/10 cm^3?

    c. g/100 cm^3?

3. Which solution is more concentrated, 2.5 g/cm^3 or 2.6 g/10 cm^3?

4. Which of the following steps will increase the concentration of a solution of salt and water?

    A. Allowing some of the water to evaporate

    B. Adding water to the solution

    C. Adding salt to the solution

    D. Pouring out some of the solution

5. For Experiment 4.1, Dissolving a Solid in Water, calculate the concentration of the solutions in g/cm^3 and in g/100 cm^3 after the addition of each sample of solid.

6. What was the greatest concentration you were able to achieve in Experiment 4.1, Dissolving a Solid in Water?

EXPERIMENT E   4.3 Comparing the Concentrations of Saturated Solutions

From the results of dissolving the orange or blue solid (Experiment 4.1, Dissolving a Solid in Water), you know that there is a point where no more solute will dissolve in the solvent. The solution then has the largest possible concentration and is called a saturated solution, as stated in Section 4.1.

To find the concentration of a saturated solution, you could add the solid a tiny amount at a time and see whether it dissolves. A better method is to first saturate a solution by adding a large mass of solid to a solvent and shaking the container until no more solid will dissolve. By pouring off some of the clear liquid, you can find the mass of a sample of the solution. You can then evaporate the solution to dryness and mass the dry solid left behind.

Subtracting the mass of the remaining dry solid from the mass of the solution will give you the mass of the water in your sample. Then, using the density of water you can calculate the volume of the solvent. This will give you the data you need to calculate the concentration of the saturated solution.

Add 5 g of two solids in separate test tubes, each containing 5 cm³ of water. Stopper the test tubes, and shake them vigorously for several minutes until the solution is saturated. If the tube cools during the process, keep it warm with your hand.

- How do you know if either solution is saturated?
- Does one sample of solid appear to be more soluble in water than the other? Which one?

Do the following for each of the solutions.

Mass the evaporating dish and then pour almost all of the saturated solution into it. Be careful not to pour out so much solution that undissolved solid is added to the evaporating dish.

After finding the total mass of dish and solution, slowly evaporate the saturated solution to dryness over a flame, as shown in Figure 4.1, and then find the mass of the remaining solid.

Figure 4.1

Evaporating a solution in an evaporating dish heated over a microburner. If the liquid spatters, it should be heated more slowly by moving the burner to one side so that the flame heats only one edge of the dish.

 CAUTION: Always wear safety glasses when you use a burner.

Be careful to heat the solution very slowly so the solid does not spatter out of the dish. Keep watching the dish, and move the flame away whenever spattering begins.

- What is the mass of the solid remaining in the dish?
- What was the mass of the water it was dissolved in? (This is the water you evaporated.)
- What was the volume of the water?
- What is the concentration of each of the saturated solutions?
- How would the calculated concentration be affected if some of the undissolved solid had been added to the dish?
- How would the calculated concentration be affected if some of the solid had spattered out of the evaporating dish?
- Using the results of all lab groups, what does your class find for the concentration of each of the saturated solutions?

The concentration of a saturated solution is called the *solubility*. In this experiment you found the solubilities of two substances in the same solvent, water.

> If the solubility of a solid in water is 130 g/100 cm³, how much of the solid must be dissolved in 100 cm³ of water to create a saturated solution?

Solubility does not depend on how much sample you started with. It is a characteristic property of both the solute and the solvent. If we were to use a liquid other than water, the solubility of the solute would be different.

7. Suppose you dissolve 0.60 g of a powder in 20.0 cm³ of water. The solution is not saturated. Which of the following outcomes might be observed if the solution was left in an open dish for several days?

   A. Some water evaporated and there is no solid at the bottom of the dish.

   B. Some water evaporated and there is some solid at the bottom of the dish.

   C. Only solid remains in the dish.

8. A student poured 60 g of sodium nitrate into 100 cm³ of water and observed that all of the solid dissolved. Which of the following can she conclude about the solubility of sodium nitrate in water?

   A. It is less than 60 g/100 cm³.

   B. It is 60 g/100 cm³.

   C. It is greater than 60 g/100 cm³.

9. A solid is placed in a container with water and stirred thoroughly. Some solid dissolves and some remains at the bottom of the container.

   a. Will adding more water and stirring cause more of the solid to dissolve?

   b. Does adding more water increase the solubility of the solid?

10. Mario wishes to construct a table that lists the solubility of several substances in water. From various sources, he finds the following data for solubilities at 0°C.

    a. Boric acid   0.20 g in 10 cm³ of water

    b. Bromine   25 g in 600 cm³ of water

    c. Washing soda   220 g in 1,000 cm³ of water

    d. Baking soda   24 g in 350 cm³ of water

    Find the solubility of each substance in g/100 cm³ of water.

11. From your answers to Question 10, find the largest mass of each substance that will dissolve in 60 cm³ of water.

12. Suppose that 200 cm³ of a saturated solution of potassium nitrate were left standing in an open beaker on your laboratory desk for three weeks. During this time most of the water evaporated.

    a. Would the mass of potassium nitrate dissolved in the solution change?

    b. Would the concentration of the potassium nitrate solution change during the three weeks?

4.4 The Effect of Temperature on Solubility

In the last experiment, you tried to keep the temperature of the solution constant by warming the test tube with your hand if it cooled. How are the solubilities of different substances affected by the temperature of the liquid? Remember that solubility is the maximum mass of a solid that will dissolve in a given volume of liquid. In other words, it is the concentration of a saturated solution.

To find out if the solubilities of different substances are affected by temperature, add 10 g of two solids to two test tubes, each of which contains 10 cm³ of water. Place both test tubes in a large beaker of room-temperature water, and stir the solutions for several minutes until they are saturated.

• How do the solubilities of the two substances compare at room temperature?

Now heat the beaker, stirring both solutions constantly, until the water in the beaker is near boiling.

CAUTION: Always wear safety glasses when you use a burner.

• What do you observe?
• Do the solubilities of the substances appear to change equally or differently as the temperature of the water is increased?
• What do you predict will happen if you remove the burner and cool both test tubes together in a beaker of cold water? Try it.

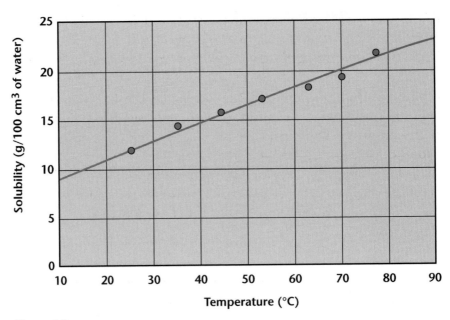

Figure 4.2

A graph of the solubility of potassium sulfate as a function of temperature. Note that the line does not extend through all the points (Section 3.10).

Figure 4.2 shows the result of an experiment with potassium sulfate. The solubility at different temperatures was measured by the same method you used in Experiment 4.3, Comparing the Concentrations of Saturated Solutions. The solubility is expressed as the mass in grams of the substance that is dissolved in 100 cm³ of water to make a saturated solution or, to put it another way, the maximum mass of the substance that can be dissolved in 100 cm³ of water.

Suppose we first dissolve 20 g of potassium sulfate in 100 cm³ of water at 80°C, and then cool the solution to room temperature (20°C). Figure 4.2 shows that at 80°C the potassium sulfate is completely dissolved. As the temperature is lowered to about 70°C, the solution becomes saturated. We know this because the graph shows that, at 70°C, 100 cm³ of water will dissolve only 20 g of the solute. At this temperature small crystals of solid potassium sulfate begin to appear in the solution. As cooling continues, more crystals are produced in the solution, and they sink to the bottom. Figure 4.2 shows that when the solution cools to 20°C, only 12 g of the potassium sulfate can be dissolved; the remaining solid has crystallized.

When a solid crystallizes out of a saturated solution in this manner, we say that it *precipitates* out of solution, and we call the solid a *precipitate*.

In this case, the mass of potassium sulfate that will precipitate out of solution and collect at the bottom will be 20 g – 12 g = 8 g.

Figure 4.3 shows solubility as a function of temperature for three common substances, all plotted together on the same graph. The solubility of each substance increases with an increase in temperature, but each curve is distinct. Therefore, we conclude that the way the solubility of a substance changes with temperature is a characteristic property that can help to distinguish among various substances.

You can see from the graph, for example, that the solubilities of potassium nitrate and sodium chloride (ordinary table salt) are very nearly the same at room temperature (about 20°C) but are very different at higher and lower temperatures.

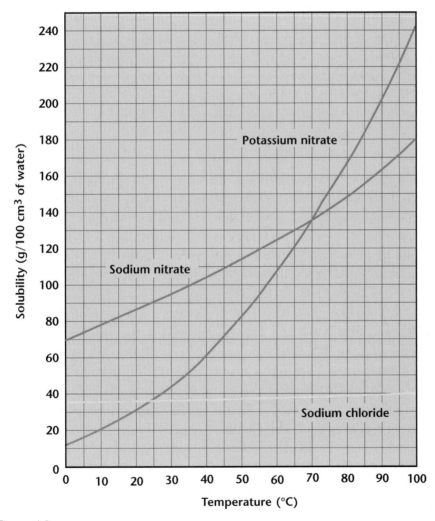

Figure 4.3
Solubility curves of different substances in water as a function of temperature.

13. Examine Figure 4.3. At what temperature are the solubilities of potassium nitrate and sodium nitrate equal?

14. What mass of sodium chloride (in grams) can be dissolved in 100 cm³ of water at 20°C? at 100°C?

15. Suppose you have a saturated solution of potassium sulfate at room temperature. From Figure 4.2, what do you predict will happen if you

    a. heat the solution?

    b. cool the solution?

16. If you plotted the data from Figure 4.2 on Figure 4.3, where would the curve be found?

17. Give a reason for heating the solutions in Experiment 4.4, The Effect of Temperature on Solubility, by immersing the test tubes in a beaker of hot water rather than heating the test tubes directly over a burner flame.

18. What temperature is required to dissolve 110 g of sodium nitrate in 100 cm³ of water?

19. a. If 20 g of sodium chloride is dissolved in 100 cm³ of water at 20°C, is the solution saturated?

    b. How can you determine whether a solution is saturated?

20. A mass of 30 g of potassium nitrate is dissolved in 100 cm³ of water at 20°C. The solution is heated to 100°C. How many more grams of potassium nitrate must be added to saturate the solution?

21. A mass of 10 g of sodium nitrate is dissolved in 10 cm³ of water at 80°C. As the solution is cooled, at what temperature will a precipitate first appear?

4.5 Wood Alcohol and Grain Alcohol

Most rocks and metals, and many other materials, have such a low solubility in water that we cannot measure the very small amounts that dissolve. Water, however, is not the only liquid. Perhaps some substances that hardly dissolve at all in water will dissolve easily in other liquids. If so, we can use the different solubilities of substances in these liquids to distinguish among them, as we did with materials soluble in water. Wood alcohol and grain alcohol are two common liquids, in addition to water, that can be used as solvents.

Wood alcohol, as its name implies, was first made from wood. The ancient Syrians heated wood to obtain the liquids and tars that resulted. These watery liquids (including the alcohol) were used as solvents and as fuel for lamps. The tars were used to fill the seams in boats, to preserve wood against rot, and as mortar for bricks.

The method used by the Syrians in making these substances was quite crude. Lengths of wood were stacked closely in a dish-like depression in a mound of earth. A drain ran from the middle of the depression to a collection pit. After the wood was covered with green branches and wet leaves, a fire was started inside the pile. As this fire smoldered, watery liquids and tars drained off from the pile and collected in the pit. Later it was discovered that the watery liquids could be separated. One of these liquids was wood alcohol.

Grain alcohol can be made by fermenting grains such as corn, barley, and rye and by fermenting grapes and other fruits. Fermentation is the process that goes on naturally when fruit juice or damp grain is stored with little exposure to air. Gas bubbles out of the liquid, and the liquid that remains boils at a temperature lower than the boiling point of water. As had been discovered long before the beginning of recorded history, this liquid contains a new substance, different from water, which was used as a beverage and as a medicine.

By the twelfth century, people had boiled the wine from fermented grapes, collected the vapor, and allowed the vapor to cool. The condensed liquid was described as the "water that burns." It was named *alcohol vini*, or "essence of wine," and later came to be called grain alcohol.

If you measure the densities of the alcohols from various grains and fruits, you find no difference among them. These alcohols also have the same boiling point and melting (or freezing) point. In fact, they are all the same substance. Similarly, the alcohols (or essences) produced from different kinds of wood are all the same: all have the same density, boiling point, and melting point. Since the liquids obtained from wood and fermented grain are both called alcohol, you might think they are the same substance. But from an examination of Table 4.1, you see that they are indeed different. Though their densities are nearly the same, their melting points and boiling points differ enough so that there can be no possibility that they are the same substance. Today, wood alcohol is called *methanol*, and grain alcohol is called *ethanol*.

Table 4.1 Some Characteristic Properties of the Most Common Alcohols			
	Density (g/cm³)	Melting point (°C)	Boiling point (°C)
Wood alcohol (methanol)	0.79	–94	65
Grain alcohol (ethanol)	0.79	–117	79

> Why is it dangerous to drink burner fuel, even though one of its ingredients is commonly found in alcoholic beverages?

Ethanol is the important ingredient in alcoholic beverages and is the main ingredient in burner fuel. Methanol, on the other hand, is very poisonous. To make burner fuel undrinkable, some methanol or other poison is usually added to it. Ethanol treated this way is said to be *denatured*. Ethanol is now also added to gasoline in some parts of the United States to reduce the consumption of gasoline.

Both of these alcohols will dissolve many substances that are insoluble in water, and both have been used for centuries as solvents. During the nineteenth century, substances with properties similar to those of methanol and ethanol were made in the laboratory. They were also called alcohols. A common alcohol is isopropyl alcohol or *isopropanol*, also known as rubbing alcohol. Isopropanol also dissolves many substances that are insoluble in water. You will use isopropanol in the next experiment.

EXPERIMENT E

4.6 Isopropanol as a Solvent

Sugar and citric acid look the same. They are both white. Their densities are so close that you could not distinguish between them with the equipment used in this course. Their solubility in water is also not much help in distinguishing between them, because both substances are very soluble in water.

Suggest a way to distinguish between these two substances by using their solubilities in isopropanol. Have your teacher approve your plan before you begin.

 **CAUTION: Do not inhale isopropanol vapor.**

- How do the solubilities of sugar and citric acid in isopropanol help to distinguish between these substances?

You can also test the solubilities of other substances, such as TOP and baking soda.

- Does TOP dissolve in water? In isopropanol?
- Does baking soda dissolve in water? In isopropanol?

You can see how valuable solubility in different solvents is for distinguishing between substances. Suppose you have samples of two solids that look alike and dissolve about equally well in one solvent but very differently in a second solvent. You can be certain that the two solids are different substances. You saw an example of this when you compared the solubility of sugar and citric acid in isopropanol.

Likewise, you can distinguish between two similar liquids if a single substance is much more soluble in one liquid than in the other. You saw examples of this when you compared the solubilities of TOP and sugar in water and isopropanol.

Solubility is another characteristic property of a substance, a tool that you can add to your list of ways to distinguish between substances. With the addition of solubility, you do not always have to measure the density, melting point, or boiling point to distinguish between substances. The more tools you have for distinguishing between substances, the easier your job becomes.

22. a. Which of the substances in the table below are the same? Explain your reasoning.

   b. How might you test them further to make sure?

Substance	Density (g/cm^3)	Melting point (°C)	Boiling point (°C)	Solubility in water at 20°C (g/100 cm^3)	Solubility in methanol at 20°C
X	1.63	80	327	20	Insoluble
Y	1.63	81	326	19	Insoluble
Z	1.62	60	310	156	Insoluble

4.7 The Solubility of Carbon Dioxide

EXPERIMENT
E

The gas you produced by heating baking soda in Experiment 1.1, and whose density you measured in Experiment 3.7, is called *carbon dioxide*. You increase the amount of carbon dioxide in the air with every breath you exhale.

Carbon dioxide is produced by a variety of substances when they burn, including wood and gasoline. Since carbon dioxide does not burn, it makes a good fire extinguisher. With a density greater than that of air, it simply smothers the fire like a blanket.

What is the solubility of carbon dioxide in water? Figure 4.4 shows the equipment you will use to generate carbon dioxide gas and to collect it by water displacement and determine its solubility.

! CAUTION: Always wear safety glasses when you work with gases.

Before you begin to generate the gas, you need to prepare a known volume of water in which you will dissolve the gas. An easy way to determine the volume of water is to completely fill the collecting bottle with

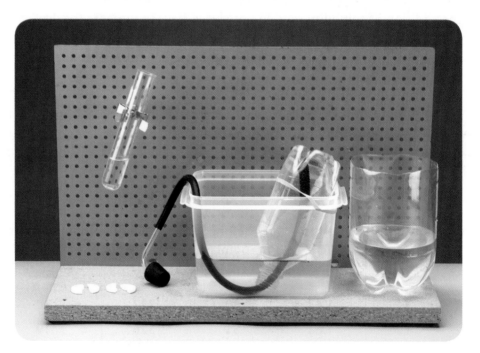

Figure 4.4

Equipment used to collect a full bottle of carbon dioxide and to measure its solubility. The large test tube contains 10 cm³ of water and the inverted collecting bottle is filled with water. The volume of water in the container on the right is the same as the volume of the collecting bottle.

cold tap water and then pour the water into a graduated beaker. After recording the volume, pour the water into the container in which you will later invert the collecting bottle. This container is shown on the right in Figure 4.4.

- What is the volume of the collecting bottle?

Now refill the collecting bottle with water in preparation for collecting the carbon dioxide. Two Alka-Seltzer tablets (four halves) placed in the test tube will generate enough gas to fill the collecting bottle. Add the tablets and quickly put the rubber stopper in place. Allow the carbon dioxide to force air out of the test tube and the rubber delivery tube for just a couple of seconds so that the air will not be collected. Then carefully insert the delivery tube all the way up to the bottom of the inverted collecting bottle.

- How will you know when you have collected a full bottle of carbon dioxide?

When the collecting bottle is completely filled with gas, invert it in the container having the same volume of water (Figure 4.5). Be sure not to lose any gas in the process.

Gases, like most substances, do not dissolve rapidly. Try moving the inverted plastic bottle back and forth in the larger container to cause a little water to enter its mouth. Be careful to keep the mouth of the bottle against the bottom of the container so that no bubbles of carbon dioxide escape. As more gas dissolves and water rises into the collecting bottle, you can shake it back and forth more and more vigorously. The shaking also mixes the water inside and outside the collecting bottle, ensuring that the gas is dissolved in all of the water. Eventually, all of the water, both inside and outside of the collecting bottle, will be saturated with carbon dioxide.

- After 10 to 15 minutes of shaking, does the carbon dioxide continue to dissolve?
- How will you know when the water has become saturated with carbon dioxide?

To measure the volume of gas that dissolved, you must turn the bottle upright without losing

Figure 4.5

A bottle full of gas ready to be placed in the container of water. To prevent the gas from escaping, be sure to hold your hand over the mouth of the bottle until it is under water. (Blue coloring was added to the water for contrast.)

Figure 4.6

A bottle full of gas placed in the container of water. Shake the inverted bottle back and forth vigorously so that the gas and water mix well. Hold the mouth of the bottle firmly against the bottom of the plastic container to prevent any gas from escaping. (Blue color was added to the water for contrast.)

any saturated solution from inside it. This can be done by quickly inverting the entire assembly shown in Figure 4.6 over a large sink. Only the solution from the container outside the bottle will spill into the sink.

- What is the volume of carbon dioxide that dissolved in the water?
- Use the class data of Experiment 3.7, The Density of a Gas, or Table 3.1 to find the mass of carbon dioxide that dissolved in the saturated solution.
- What is the volume of water of the saturated solution?
- What is the solubility of carbon dioxide in g/100 cm^3 of water?

23. When conducting Experiment 4.7, a student stopped shaking the inverted bottle before all the carbon dioxide had completely dissolved. How did this affect the calculated solubility of the gas?

24. Suppose the water rose to completely fill the inverted collecting bottle used in Experiment 4.7. How would this affect the calculated solubility of carbon dioxide? Explain your reasoning.

25. Suppose Experiment 3.7, The Density of a Gas, was done twice with the same amount of Alka-Seltzer and water in each case. In the first trial, the rubber tube was placed as shown in Figure 3.3, and 435 cm^3 of gas was collected. In the second trial, the tube reached only slightly beyond the mouth of the bottle, and only 370 cm^3 of gas was collected. The change in mass of the reactants was the same in both cases.

    a. What volume of gas dissolved in the water?

    b. Use the class data from Experiment 3.7 to find what mass of gas dissolved in the water.

4.8 The Solubility of Gases

Table 4.2 shows the solubilities of several gases in water. It is clear from the table that the solubilities of gases vary greatly. Gases of low solubility can be collected by water displacement. Gases with high solubility, such as hydrogen chloride, cannot be collected over water. These gases dissolve in the water instead of displacing it. Hydrogen chloride was prepared more than two hundred years ago by the French chemist Antoine Lavoisier by reacting sulfuric acid with table salt. He collected the gas by displacement of mercury—a substance that does not dissolve hydrogen chloride.

> Why was Lavoisier able to collect hydrogen chloride by mercury displacement but not by water displacement?

Table 4.2 The Solubility of Gases in Water at Various Temperatures (in g/100 cm³)						
Temperature (°C)	Nitrogen	Oxygen	Carbon dioxide	Sulfur dioxide	Hydrogen chloride	Ammonia
0	2.4×10^{-3}	7.0×10^{-3}	0.34	23	82	90
20	1.9×10^{-3}	4.4×10^{-3}	0.17	11	72	53
40	1.4×10^{-3}	3.3×10^{-3}	0.10	5.5	63	32
60	1.1×10^{-3}	2.8×10^{-3}	0.07	3.3	56	14

You can see in Table 4.2 that the solubility of nitrogen is small compared with the solubility of hydrogen chloride or ammonia, which are two of the most soluble gases known. The solubility of each of the gases in Table 4.2 decreases as the temperature increases. This behavior is different from that of solids, which you observed in Experiment 4.4, The Effect of Temperature on Solubility, and in Figures 4.2 and 4.3. As temperature increases, the solubility of most solids increases, and the solubility of most gases decreases.

26. The data in Table 4.2 for the solubilities of six gases at four temperatures are not plotted on a graph like the one in Figure 4.3. Even so, to be able to compare data in a table without the aid of a graph is a valuable skill. Examine Table 4.2.

  a. Which gas has the greatest solubility at 0°C?

  b. Which gas has the smallest solubility at 20°C?

  c. Which gas has the greatest solubility at 20°C?

  d. How many of the gases have solubilities that increase and how many have solubilities that decrease as the temperature increases?

e. Which gas has the greatest decrease in solubility in grams per 100 cm³ of water when the temperature increases from 0°C to 60°C?

27. Why were you instructed in both Experiment 1.1, Heating Baking Soda, and Experiment 4.7, The Solubility of Carbon Dioxide, to insert the gas delivery tube "all the way up to the bottom" of the inverted collection bottle (Figure 4.4)?

28. From the data in Table 4.2, draw a graph of the solubilities of hydrogen chloride and ammonia versus temperature. At what temperature do the two gases have the same solubility in water?

29. Fish prefer to live in cool water that has splashed over rocks rather than in warm water that is stagnant. Based on information in Table 4.2, present an explanation for this observation.

30. A collection bottle contains 500 cm³ of ammonia.

    a. The density of ammonia is 7.7×10^{-4} g/100 cm³ at atmospheric pressure and room temperature. What is the mass of ammonia in the bottle?

    b. What do you expect to happen when the bottle is inverted and placed in a container that contains 1,000 cm³ of water?

31. Glass bottles of carbonated soft drinks can be transported in the sun and stored at room temperature. If they are opened when they are cool, they fizz, showing that the solution is saturated in carbon dioxide.

    a. What do you think happens to the carbon dioxide in the water when the bottles are in the sun?

    b. Why do glass bottles containing carbonated drinks sometimes explode when left in the sun for too long?

    c. What happens to the carbon dioxide when the bottles cool down again?

4.9 Acid Rain and Global Warming

When some gases, such as carbon dioxide, sulfur dioxide, and hydrogen chloride, are dissolved in water, the properties of the solution are very different from the properties of water alone. These solutions have a sour taste and are able to dissolve minerals and metals to a much greater extent than water. They are called *acidic solutions.*

Raindrops dissolve carbon dioxide as they pass through the atmosphere, forming an acidic solution known as *carbonic acid.* Limestone and chalk are much more soluble in carbonic acid than in water. When rains seep through the soil over a long time, a very large volume of acidic water can come into contact with limestone rock below the surface. This large volume of water can dissolve a large amount of limestone, leaving an empty space beneath the soil's surface. When the soil above this empty space can no longer support itself, it collapses, as shown in Figure 4.7.

Carbon dioxide is produced and added to the atmosphere when coal, oil, wood, and gasoline are burned. Consumption of these fuels is increasing worldwide. Thus, the concentration of carbon dioxide in the atmosphere is increasing. This increase in carbon dioxide in the atmosphere is closely related to an increase in the average temperature near the surface of the earth. This increase in average temperature is called *global warming.*

Much of the coal we burn as fuel contains sulfur. When sulfur is burned, sulfur dioxide is produced. As you can see in Table 4.2, sulfur

> How does carbonic acid cause sinkholes?

> What effect does the burning of gasoline and coal have on the environment?

Figure 4.7

A "sinkhole" in central Florida. The surface collapsed after limestone below the top layer was dissolved over a long period of time by water containing carbon dioxide. *(AP/Wide World Photos)*

Figure 4.8

A statue of Civil-War General William F. Draper in Milford, Massachusetts. The statue, made in 1912 and photographed in 1987, has been damaged by acid rain. *(Courtesy, Center for Conservation and Technical Studies, Harvard University Art Museums)*

Figure 4.9

Spruce trees on White Face Mountain in New York that have been killed by acid rain. *(USDA Forest Service)*

dioxide has a higher solubility in water than does carbon dioxide. Water falling to the earth that contains dissolved sulfur dioxide is called *acid rain*.

Acid rain dissolves the surface of stone used in buildings and statues, as shown in Figure 4.8. It can also damage or kill plants, as Figure 4.9 shows. In addition, if enough acid rain or snow accumulates in lakes and ponds, it harms the animals living there.

4.10 Drinking Water

Most people get their drinking water from wells, rivers, or lakes. This water was once rain or snow that traveled great distances through the air, over rocks and land, and through soil, dissolving many substances along the way. In addition to dissolved minerals from rocks and soil, drinking water may also have dissolved fertilizers, herbicides, pesticides, and other substances made by people.

The concentrations of substances dissolved in drinking water are very low. If they were not, the water might be harmful or have a strange taste. For example, the concentration of table salt in your water is probably less than 0.005 g/100 cm^3. The concentrations of several substances in the drinking water of three cities are listed in Table 4.3.

The concentrations listed in Table 4.3 are very low compared with the solubilities that you measured and observed in earlier sections. Also, the concentrations listed vary from substance to substance and city to city.

Sodium chloride, iron chloride, and calcium carbonate are examples of substances that are not very toxic but affect the taste of water. Water that contains too much iron has a strange taste and leaves a rust-colored stain in containers. Water containing excessive amounts of calcium carbonate is said to be *hard water*. This water has a mineral-like taste and soaps do not lather or clean effectively in it.

Other substances are important because small concentrations of them in drinking water can be dangerous to people's health. Substances that contain arsenic, lead, and mercury are toxic substances that are harmful if present in too high a concentration in drinking water.

If too much acid rain becomes a part of the water supply, drinking water will dissolve metals. When acidic drinking

Table 4.3 Analysis of City Water Supplies

Substance	Concentration (g/100 cm³)		
	Belmont, MA	Denver, CO	Memphis, TN
Arsenic chloride	$< 2.4 \times 10^{-6}$	$< 2.4 \times 10^{-6}$	$< 1.2 \times 10^{-6}$
Calcium carbonate	1.2×10^{-3}	2.2×10^{-3}	1.2×10^{-3}
Iron chloride	1.4×10^{-6}	1.4×10^{-5}	9.6×10^{-5}
Lead nitrate	$< 2.8 \times 10^{-7}$	$< 2.8 \times 10^{-7}$	1.4×10^{-7}
Mercury chloride	$< 2.7 \times 10^{-8}$	$< 1.4 \times 10^{-8}$	$< 2.7 \times 10^{-8}$
Sodium chloride	2.0×10^{-3}	5.1×10^{-3}	2.5×10^{-3}
Potassium nitrate	2.6×10^{-4}	1.8×10^{-4}	1.8×10^{-4}

water passes through lead pipes or pipes having joints sealed with lead solder, some of this lead dissolves in the drinking water.

Drinking water with a high enough concentration of lead can cause damage to the brain and other parts of the nervous system. Lead seems to affect young children more than adults. Perhaps this is because lead is not eliminated from the body quickly, as many other toxic substances are. Instead, it accumulates in the body, so that its concentration increases as time passes.

Why is lead solder no longer used in water supply systems?

32. Which city listed in Table 4.3 has the hardest water?

33. A typical person drinks about two liters (2,000 cm³) of water a day. How much sodium chloride would a person in Memphis take in from drinking water each day? How much in a year?

34. Why would it be unwise to pass a law stating that if any toxic substances were shown to be in a municipality's drinking water, the water could not be distributed and used by its citizens?

35. Large deposits of sodium chloride or potassium nitrate near the surface of the earth are found mostly in deserts. Why?

36. Each of four test tubes contains 10 cm³ of water at 25°C. The following masses of an unknown solid are placed in the test tubes: 4 g in the first, 8 g in the second, 12 g in the third, and 16 g in the fourth. After the tubes are shaken, all of the solid has dissolved in the first two tubes, but some undissolved solid remains in the other two tubes.

    a. What is the concentration of the solid in each of the first two tubes?

    b. What can you say about the concentration of the solid in the last two tubes?

37. a. Which of the substances shown in Figure 4.3 could be the unknown solid of Question 36?

    b. If the unknown is the substance you named in (a), what will happen if the solution in each test tube is cooled to 10°C?

38. The solubility of the orange solid that you dissolved in water in Experiment 4.1 is shown below for various temperatures. What would you expect the solubility to be at 15°C? at 40°C? Explain.

Temperature (°C)	Solubility (g/100 cm³)
10	6.6
20	12.2
30	18.0

39. In many localities, after a kettle has been used for some time for boiling water, a flaky solid appears on the inside-bottom and on the sides of the kettle that have been in contact with the water. How do you account for the presence of this "boiler scale"?

40. There are two kinds of felt-tip (magic-marker) pens. Some are labeled "permanent" and some are labeled "water color."

    a. What does the label tell you about the solubility in water of the dye in the two inks?

    b. Do you think the liquid in both inks is water?

41. In dry cleaning, a garment is sprayed with liquids that dissolve various stains. Often a brightly colored cotton shirt carries a label: "Dry clean only—colors may bleed when washed."

    a. What does such a label tell you about the solubility of the dye in hot water containing a detergent or soap?

    b. Do you think the dye dissolves in cold tap water?

42. An Alka-Seltzer tablet is dissolved in 10 cm^3 of water, and the gas is collected as in Experiment 3.7, The Density of a Gas. The volume of gas collected is 450 cm^3. When 50 cm^3 of water is used, the volume of gas collected is 400 cm^3. The tube was all the way up in the bottle in both cases.

    a. Why do you think less gas is collected when more water is used to dissolve the tablet?

    b. Would this make a difference in the density calculation?

43. If you have a certain amount of a solid to dissolve in water, you usually can speed up the process in various ways. Why do you think each of the following steps is effective in making the solid dissolve faster?

    a. Stirring the water

    b. Crushing the solid into smaller particles

    c. Heating the water

44. In Experiment 3.7, The Density of a Gas, you were directed to insert the rubber delivery tube all the way up to the bottom of the inverted collection bottle before collecting any gas. In Experiment 4.7, you began to generate carbon dioxide gas before inserting the delivery tube into the collection bottle. Why was it unnecessary to push the delivery tube up to the bottom of the inverted collection bottle? Explain the significance of the variations between the two procedures.

45. Water analysis reports usually give the concentrations of dissolved substances in parts (of solute) per million (parts of solution), or ppm. If the concentration of sodium chloride in drinking water was listed as 14 ppm, what would its concentration be in g/100 cm^3?

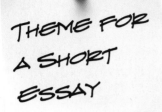

THEME FOR A SHORT ESSAY

Write an episode for a mystery centered on the possibility of selectively dissolving some substances mixed in with others. For example, a secret message written in ink may be covered by a painting. Describe real (not fictitious) substances.

5

THE SEPARATION OF MIXTURES

In this chapter we will use the characteristic properties studied so far to work out a variety of methods for separating mixtures. These mixtures may involve gases, liquids, or solids. We will begin with a method to separate a mixture of liquids. The characteristic property that we will use is boiling point.

5.1 Fractional Distillation

Part A

Your teacher provided you with a sample of a mixture of liquids. Before attempting to separate this liquid into different substances, it is wise to know some of the liquid's properties.

- Can you tell just by looking at the liquid whether it is a single substance or a mixture of more than one substance?
- Does the liquid have an odor?

Dip a small piece of paper in the liquid, and use a match to try lighting the liquid on the paper.

> **CAUTION: Always wear safety glasses when you work with a flame. Put a bucket of water on your table in case the paper burns.**

- Does the liquid burn?
- What is its density?
- Does sugar dissolve in the liquid?

Part B

Use the apparatus shown in Figure 5.1 to boil 5 cm³ of the mixture almost to dryness. Use a single test tube to collect the condensed liquid. Heat the liquid just enough to keep it boiling. Record the temperature of the vapor from the boiling liquid every half-minute while it boils. Make a graph of the temperature of the vapor as a function of time.

Note that the thermometer bulb is close to the top of the test tube so that it measures the temperature of the vapor that condenses in the outlet tube. If there is more than one liquid in the mixture, most of the high-boiling-point liquids will condense and flow back down the test-tube walls before they reach the upper part of the test tube.

- What do you conclude from your graph about the number of substances with different boiling points that make up the mixture?

Why is the thermometer bulb placed close to the top of the test tube?

Figure 5.1

Apparatus for the fractional distillation of a liquid. The thermometer in this apparatus is used to measure the temperature of the vapor at the top of the test tube, not the boiling temperature of the liquid. As the vapor entering the plastic tubing cools, it condenses and collects in the test tube held in cold water.

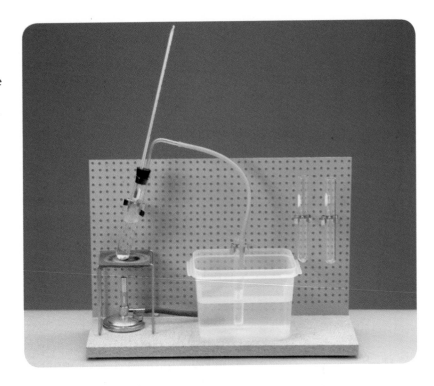

• Suppose you want to collect the separate substances while the mixture is boiling. At what temperatures should you shift from one collecting tube to another?

On your graph, indicate the temperatures at which you decided to change collecting tubes to collect the different fractions of the original mixture. What you will be doing is called *fractional distillation.*

Part C

Now fractionally distill about 25 cm³ of the liquid. Label the test tubes containing the fractions as "Fraction 1," "Fraction 2," and so on. This will allow you to keep track of them throughout the rest of the experiment. Test each of the fractions for odor and flammability.

Part D

• What is the density of Fraction 1?
• Does sugar dissolve in Fraction 1?

Distill Fraction 1 into a single test tube, recording the temperature of the vapor every half-minute until the fraction has nearly boiled away. Draw a graph that shows the temperature of the vapor as a function of time for Fraction 1.

Part E

Repeat Part D for each of the other fractions.

Part F

Summarize your findings, and compare the odor, flammability, density, ability to dissolve sugar, and boiling point of each of the fractions and of the original mixture.

- What do you conclude about the composition of the fractions?
- Can you identify the substances in the original mixture? (See Table 3.2 on page 66.)
- What other tests might you run to help identify these substances?
- What do you think would happen if you were to fractionally distill each of the fractions separately?

1. What characteristic property of two liquids must differ if a mixture of them is to be separated by fractional distillation?

2. In the fractional distillation of liquids, which fraction has the highest boiling point? Which has the lowest boiling point?

3. The temperature-time graph shown in Figure A was made during the fractional distillation of a mixture of two liquids, *E* and *F*. Fractions were collected during the time intervals I, II, III, and IV. Liquid *E* has a higher boiling point than Liquid *F*. What liquid or liquids were collected during each of the time intervals?

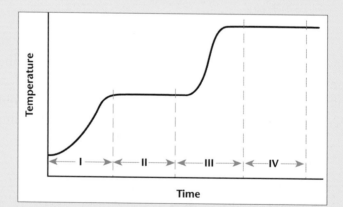

Figure A
For Problem 3

4. Suppose that when conducting Experiment 5.1, a student collected two fractions, changing test tubes at the end of the first plateau. How would this have affected the composition of the two fractions?

5.2 Petroleum

It is not always easy to separate a mixture of liquids into pure substances by fractional distillation. If the boiling points of the substances in a mixture are nearly the same, they will all boil off together. In a liquid mixture containing many substances, some are sure to have boiling points close together. When we distill such a mixture, each fraction may be made up of several different substances whose boiling points are close together. The first part to condense in one fraction may contain some of the substances that condensed in the last part of the prior fraction. However, the fractions that have the more widely separated boiling range are less likely to contain the same substances. Petroleum is an example of such a mixture. The compositions of typical fractions distilled from petroleum are shown in Table 5.1. The fractions correspond to some of the common products of petroleum that you may be familiar with.

When you fractionally distill a mixture of liquids, the fractions may still contain two or more different liquids. Why?

Table 5.1 A Few of the Substances Found in Petroleum						
Substance	Density at 0°C (g/cm³)	Freezing point (°C)	Boiling point (°C)	fuel gas	Common products of petroleum gasoline	kerosene
Methane	7.16×10^{-4}	−182.5	−161	X		
Ethane	1.35×10^{-3}	−183	−88	X		
Propane	2.02×10^{-3}	−190	−43	X		
Butane	2.68×10^{-3}	−138	−0.5	X		
Pentane	0.626	−129	36			
Hexane	0.660	−94	69		X	
Heptane	0.684	−90	98		X	
Octane	0.703	−57	125		X	
Nonane	0.722	−51	151		X	X
Decane	0.730	−30	174		X	X
Undecane	0.741	−26	196			X
Dodecane	0.750	−10	216			X
Tridecane	0.755	−5.5	236			X
Tetradecane	0.765	5.5	254			X
Pentadecane	0.776	10	271			X
Hexadecane	0.773	18	287			X

There are many more substances in the above products and in the higher-boiling-point fractions not listed in the table. Among the products not listed here are fuel oils, lubricating oils, waxes, asphalt, and coke (mostly carbon).

Figure 5.2

A cross section of the earth's crust, showing how oil and natural gas are trapped in a porous rock layer by nonporous rock layers above and below. Note that Well A produces only water, and Well C produces only natural gas.

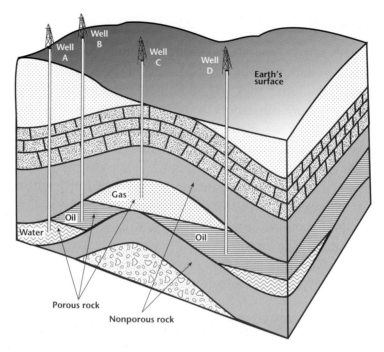

Petroleum is produced naturally from vegetable and animal matter at the bottoms of shallow seas and swamps. When tiny plants and animals die in the sea, they settle slowly to the bottom, where they become trapped in mud and sand. This sediment of mud, sand, and dead organisms slowly thickens. In a million years, it may become hundreds of meters deep. Such layers of sediment are very heavy, and the lower layers are compressed so much that they turn into rock layers. During this time, some of the body tissue of the entrapped organisms changes into a viscous, sticky liquid that is a mixture of many thousands of different substances. This liquid is called *petroleum* or *crude oil*. It is slowly squeezed out of the sediment in which it forms and eventually spreads through porous rock layers like water through a sponge.

In the course of more millions of years, the ever-changing crust of the earth—buckling in some places, rising in others, and sinking in still others—slowly moves and compresses the rock layers that were on the ocean bottom. Sometimes the porous oil-bearing rock is covered by a layer of hard, nonporous rock that has been bent into a dome or arch, as shown in Figure 5.2. Then the oil is trapped and cannot by itself squeeze to the surface. If it were not trapped, much of it would wash away and be lost.

Most of the petroleum in the earth's crust is stored by nature under formations of nonporous rock that trap the liquids below them. As Figure 5.2 shows, natural gas (the low-boiling-point substances in petroleum) and saltwater from the sea are often trapped along with the oil. The nonporous "cap rock" may be hundreds of meters thick. It is

What was the original source of the substances that eventually formed petroleum?

What is the importance of the nonporous cap rock?

expensive and difficult to drill through all this rock to get to the petroleum below, and it is not easy to predict where oil is trapped. Deep and expensive wells often fail to reach oil or gas. Some wells produce nothing but salt water, whereas others remain dry.

Petroleum was first discovered where it seeped to the surface in shallow pools. Once exposed to the air, some of the lower-boiling-point substances slowly evaporated, leaving behind tarry, almost solid asphalt. These tars, as well as the liquid petroleum, were used in the ancient world as mortar and embalming material.

One of the ancient methods used to distill crude oil consisted of heating the oil in a copper urn with a wool "sponge" at the narrow mouth of the vessel. The vapors condensed in the sponge, which was squeezed out into containers from time to time. A variation of this method made use of a heavy wick of wool that led from the mouth of the urn into a collecting vessel. Such a wick was a crude form of condenser.

The widespread use of kerosene lamps more than 100 years ago—and the more recent use of gasoline engines—created a new demand for petroleum. This led to improved methods of locating oil and drilling wells. Better equipment was also developed for fractionally distilling petroleum on a large scale (Figure 5.3).

A simplified diagram of this equipment, called a *fractionating column*, is shown in Figure 5.4. Heated crude oil enters the column near the bottom. The column contains a series of horizontal trays. As vapors from the heated liquid pass up through the column, the high-boiling-point substances condense in the lower, hotter trays.

Figure 5.3
A fractionating column at a refinery.

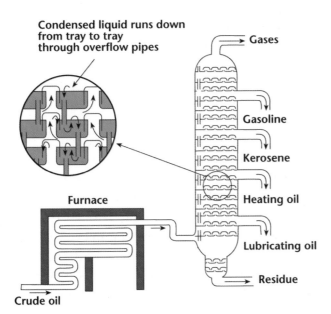

Figure 5.4
A simplified diagram of a fractionating column used in the fractional distillation of petroleum.

As the vapors move upward, they bubble through the liquid in the trays. In each tray, the condensing vapors increase the concentration of the substances whose boiling points are higher than the temperature of the tray. The rising vapors therefore become richer in the low-boiling-point substances. Some of the liquid that condenses in each tray overflows into the tray below, where it becomes heated again and re-distills. Each tray thus boils a particular mixture at a particular temperature. The temperatures of the trays and the boiling points of the substances in them decrease as one goes higher up the column.

Different fractions leave the column at different heights (Figure 5.4). In the case of a fractionating column, the fractions are not single substances but a mixture of several substances. Products with which you may be familiar are gasoline, kerosene, diesel fuel, heating and lubricating oils, paraffin, and asphalt. Some of these are indicated in the last three columns of Table 5.1.

> How is the change in temperature within a fractionating column related to the separation of petroleum into different fractions?

5. Examine Table 5.1. What relationship can you identify between the densities of these substances and their freezing points? Between densities and boiling points? Between freezing points and boiling points?

6. a. In Table 5.1, which substances would be liquid at room temperature (20°C)? Which would be solids? Which would be gases?

   b. You can see from the table that pentane is not an ingredient in any of the common products listed. What do you think accounts for this?

7. A sample of crude oil is boiled for several minutes. How does the density of the crude oil change during this time? (See Table 5.1.)

5.3 The Separation of Insoluble Solids

Solids with a density greater than that of water sink in water, and those with a density less than water float, if they are insoluble. We can use this fact to separate a mixture of sawdust and sand. After stirring the mixture in water, we can skim off the floating sawdust. Then we can pour off the water and dry the sand.

This method is called *separation by flotation* and is widely used in industry to concentrate ores. For example, a common copper ore, copper sulfide, is usually found mixed with large amounts of worthless rock. The ore and rock are crushed and then mixed with water and other substances that produce a heavy foam when the mixture is agitated violently with air. The copper sulfide is contained in the floating foam; the crushed rock settles. The foam is removed, and the copper sulfide is recovered.

> Is the foam more or less dense than water? How do you know?

8. Sawdust and sand can be separated by flotation in water. Could sawdust from two different woods that had densities of 0.6 and 0.9 g/cm³ be separated by flotation in water? By flotation in decane (see Table 5.1)?

9. The example in Section 5.3 of separating sand and sawdust requires that the substances have different densities. What needs to be true about their solubilities for this process to work?

EXPERIMENT E

5.4 The Separation of a Mixture of Solids

Examine the mixture of two solids supplied by your teacher. If one of the solids in the mixture is soluble in water and the other is not, you can separate them easily by dissolving one and separating it from the other by filtering. You can do this in the following way: Put about 1.5 g of the mixture into a test tube, and add 5 cm³ of water. Stopper the test tube, and shake it for several minutes.

- Do you think either substance dissolved?

To find out, filter out the undissolved solid, as shown in Figure 5.5. Wash the precipitate on the filter paper by pouring an additional 10 cm³ of water into the funnel. You can now put about 5 cm³ of the clear liquid that passes through the filter paper—the *filtrate*—into an evaporating dish and boil it to dryness. Be careful to heat the liquid slowly so that the solid does not spatter out of the dish.

- Have the two substances been separated?

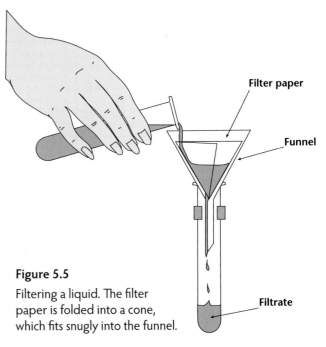

Figure 5.5
Filtering a liquid. The filter paper is folded into a cone, which fits snugly into the funnel.

Filter paper

Funnel

Filtrate

10. In what characteristic property must two solids differ if they are to be separated by the method used in this experiment?

11. Much salt is obtained from salt mines in which great masses of salt occur mixed with insoluble earthy impurities. What steps can be taken to purify the salt?

12. How can drinking water be obtained from seawater?

5.5 The Separation of a Mixture of Soluble Solids

In the previous experiment, you were able to separate two solids because one of them was soluble in water and the other was not. How can a mixture of two soluble solids be separated? To illustrate the method of separation, consider a mixture of 8.0 g of sodium chloride and 5.0 g of potassium nitrate. At room temperature these two substances have nearly the same solubility (Figure 5.6), but at higher temperature the solubilities are quite different. We will use this difference in solubilities to separate the substances.

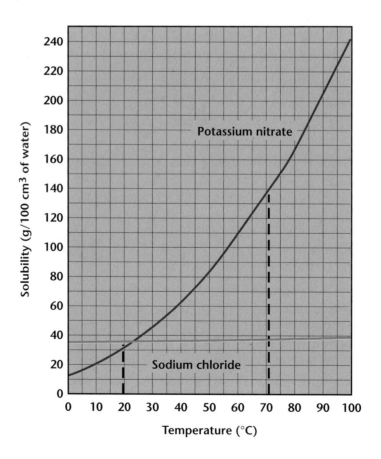

Figure 5.6

Solubility curves of sodium chloride and potassium nitrate.

Suppose we dissolve the mixture in water at 70°C. From Figure 5.6 we can see that at this temperature, the solubility of potassium nitrate is much greater than that of sodium chloride. If we use just enough water to dissolve the potassium nitrate at 70°C, most of the sodium chloride will remain undissolved and can be filtered out.

After filtering, the filtrate contains all of the potassium nitrate but only a small amount of dissolved sodium chloride. We now let the solution cool down to room temperature—about 20°C. Almost all the sodium chloride will remain in solution, because its solubility hardly changes with temperature. However, the solubility of potassium nitrate is much lower at room temperature than at 70°C. Therefore, as the solution cools, potassium nitrate will precipitate out of the solution and can be filtered out. This process, called *fractional crystallization*, is summarized in Figure 5.7. By repeated fractional crystallizations, even solids whose solubilities are very close to each other at room temperature can be separated.

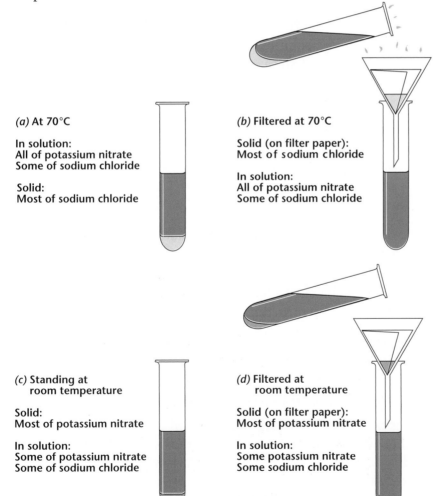

(a) At 70°C

In solution:
All of potassium nitrate
Some of sodium chloride

Solid:
Most of sodium chloride

(b) Filtered at 70°C

Solid (on filter paper):
Most of sodium chloride

In solution:
All of potassium nitrate
Some of sodium chloride

(c) Standing at
      room temperature

Solid:
Most of potassium nitrate

In solution:
Some of potassium nitrate
Some of sodium chloride

(d) Filtered at
      room temperature

Solid (on filter paper):
Most of potassium nitrate

In solution:
Some potassium nitrate
Some sodium chloride

Figure 5.7

A diagram of the series of steps for separating a mixture of sodium chloride and potassium nitrate.

To achieve a better understanding of the process, we shall review it using solubility values from Figure 5.6. At 70°C, the solubility of potassium nitrate is 138 g/100 cm³. That is, 100 cm³ of water will dissolve 138 g of potassium nitrate. To dissolve 5.0 g of potassium nitrate will require

Why is 100 cm³ multiplied by the fraction 5.0/138?

$$100 \text{ cm}^3 \cdot \frac{5.0 \text{ g}}{138 \text{ g}} = 3.6 \text{ cm}^3.$$

of water.

The 5.0 g of potassium nitrate is mixed with 8.0 g of sodium chloride. How much sodium chloride will dissolve in 3.6 cm³ of water? Figure 5.6 tells us that to dissolve 38 g of sodium chloride at 70°C requires 100 cm³ of water. Therefore, in 3.6 cm³ of water only

Why is 38 g multiplied by the fraction 3.6/100?

$$38 \text{ cm}^3 \cdot \frac{3.6 \text{ cm}^3}{100 \text{ cm}^3} = 1.4 \text{ g}$$

of sodium chloride will dissolve with the potassium nitrate. The remaining 6.6 g of sodium chloride in the original mixture can be filtered out.

When the filtered solution is cooled down to room temperature, almost all the 1.4 g of sodium chloride will remain dissolved. How much of the 5.0 g of potassium nitrate will precipitate? At 22°C the solubility of potassium nitrate is 37 g/100 cm³. (Again, see Figure 5.6.) The 3.6 cm³ of water in which the 5.0 g of potassium nitrate was originally dissolved at 70°C will now dissolve only

Why is 37 g multiplied by the fraction 3.6/100?

$$37 \text{ g} \cdot \frac{3.6 \text{ cm}^3}{100 \text{ cm}^3} = 1.3 \text{ g}$$

of potassium nitrate, so 3.7 g will precipitate and can be filtered out. Thus, 6.6 g of sodium chloride and 3.7 g of potassium nitrate have been separated from the mixture. Only 1.4 g of sodium chloride and 1.3 g of potassium nitrate remain in the solution. By repeated fractional crystallizations, the two substances can be separated further.

13. Suppose two substances have the same solubility in water at all temperatures. Can they be separated by fractional crystallization? Why or why not?

14. Suppose you wish to separate more of the two solids, sodium chloride and potassium nitrate, remaining in solution, as described at the end of Section 5.5. How should you proceed to do this?

15. Suppose that you planned to separate a solution of 8 g of sodium chloride and 5 g of potassium nitrate that was originally at 80°C rather than 70°C. How would this higher temperature affect the separation of the two solids in this mixture?

16. What temperature should you choose to precipitate potassium nitrate from a saturated solution of sodium chloride when the two are present in equal amounts in a mixture? Explain.

17. Would being able to control the temperature of the funnel used to separate a mixture of soluble solids by fractional crystallization help you to better separate the solids? Why or why not?

5.6 Paper Chromatography

So far you have learned how differences in density, boiling point, and solubility can be used to separate substances. In this experiment you will investigate a method that works even when the substances in the mixture are present in extremely small amounts.

In a plastic bottle containing water, hang a strip of filter paper streaked with ink from a water-soluble pen, as shown in Figure 5.8. When the color has risen up the paper to about 2 or 3 cm below the top, remove the paper and hang it up to dry.

Figure 5.8

One method of making a paper chromatograph. The point of the filter-paper strip extends into the water so that the ink streak is about 1 cm above the water. The strip is held in place by a stopper.

- How many different substances can you identify?

Is it possible to put the substance back together to make green ink? To find out, cut out each of the colored sections, and put each one in a separate test tube. Add between 0.5 cm^3 and 1 cm^3 of water to each tube.

- Do the colored substances dissolve?

Pour the liquids from both test tubes into a single test tube.

- What color is produced?

5.7 Mixtures Involving Gases

So far in this chapter you have learned how to separate mixtures of liquids, mixtures of solids and liquids, and mixtures of solids. We have not yet considered the separation of mixtures of gases or a mixture of a gas and a liquid. If a gas is dissolved in a liquid, all we have to do is heat the mixture. Because the solubility of gases decreases with an increase in temperature (Table 4.2, page 87), dissolved gas will leave the solution as the liquid is heated.

For example, when a beaker of cold water is heated, air bubbles appear and some rise to the top long before the water reaches its boiling point. Collecting the air would require additional equipment.

Separating mixtures of gases alone, however, requires different methods from those used so far. There are several ways to do the separation. One that is widely used is to cool the mixture until it condenses to form a liquid. Then we can make use of the different boiling points of the various liquids in the mixture to fractionally distill the cold liquid. The gases are collected one by one as the boiling temperature levels off at new plateaus.

Air that is liquefied and fractionally distilled in this way separates mainly into two fractions. If you light a wooden splint and blow it out so that it is just glowing, it will burst into flames when placed in one of the gases. If a splint that is burning brightly is placed in the other gas, it goes out. The gas that causes the glowing splint to burst into flame is oxygen, and the one that extinguishes the flaming splint is nitrogen. These two gases together make up about 99 percent of the gases in air. Nitrogen makes up about 78 percent of the atmosphere, and oxygen about 21 percent. The densities, melting points, and boiling points of nitrogen and oxygen are given in Table 5.2.

The cheapest way of obtaining oxygen and nitrogen is to condense air into a liquid and then fractionally distill it. Most of the oxygen and nitrogen commercially manufactured is produced by this method.

How would you eliminate the carbon dioxide that may be dissolved in a sample of water?

How can you distinguish between nitrogen and oxygen using a glowing splint?

In addition to nitrogen and oxygen, air also contains carbon dioxide and various other gases. Approximately what percent of air is made up of gases other than nitrogen and oxygen?

Table 5.2			
Gas	Density (g/cm³)	Melting point (°C)	Boiling point (°C)
Nitrogen	1.2×10^{-3}	−210	−196
Oxygen	1.3×10^{-3}	−218	−183
Hydrogen	8.4×10^{-5}	−259	−253

The densities are given for atmospheric pressure and room temperature.

18. To what temperature should a mixture of nitrogen and oxygen be cooled in order to separate them using fractional distillation?

19. Could nitrogen, oxygen, and hydrogen occur together in a mixture of liquids?

20. How can you separate propane gas from air?

5.8 Mixtures and Pure Substances

In this chapter we have found ways to separate different substances from each other by using characteristic properties. A difference in density can be used to separate two solids; solids can also be separated by differences in solubility. A difference in the boiling points of different liquids enables us to separate them by fractional distillation.

Suppose we experiment with a piece of solid material to see if we can separate it into two or more substances. First we grind it up and mix it with water, stirring it thoroughly. We observe that some particles of a yellowish solid float on the surface, while particles of a gray solid sink to the bottom. We skim off the floating material, whose density is obviously less than that of water. We dry it, label it "Fraction 1," and set it aside. Then we filter the water together with the denser solid that is in the bottom of the test tube. This solid, which remains on the filter paper, we dry, label "Fraction 2," and set aside also. We know that these two solids, Fractions 1 and 2, are different substances, because they have different densities.

We now test the filtrate to see if any material has dissolved in the water. When we evaporate the water, we find a small amount of white solid. This substance, which is different from both Fractions 1 and 2 because it is soluble in water, we call Fraction 3. The whole process of

What property allows us to separate out the solid that we call Fraction 2? Is Fraction 2 more or less dense than water?

Which is more soluble in water—Fraction 2 or Fraction 3?

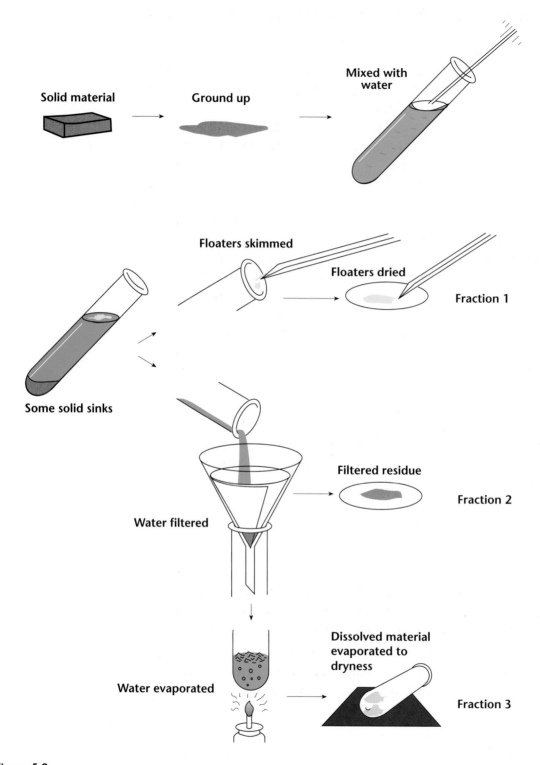

Figure 5.9

A diagram of an example of the series of steps for separating three fractions obtained from a ground-up solid.

the separation of the three fractions from a piece of solid material is diagrammed in Figure 5.9.

We now have separated our original material into three different fractions, but perhaps each of these can be further separated. To find out, we use other separation methods. We may, for example, try to melt and even fractionally distill each of the fractions, or we may try dissolving them in different liquids. Suppose that boiling, melting, and mixing with alcohol and other liquids do not produce anything with characteristic properties different from those of the three original fractions. By using all these various tools of separation again and again, we find that the characteristic properties of our three fractions remain unaltered. We call such substances whose properties are not changed by repeating any of these procedures *pure substances*.

Suppose we mix together all the pure substances that we obtain in this way. If the resulting material has the same characteristic properties as the original sample, we can say that the original sample was a mixture of the pure substances. For example, if you mixed all the fractions you separated in Experiment 5.1, Fractional Distillation, you would end up with a substance that has the same properties as the original liquid that you started with. Similarly, mixing together the various fractions obtained from the distillation of liquid air would yield a gas with exactly the same properties as ordinary air. Therefore, air is a mixture.

Note that many properties of a mixture are intermediate between the properties of the pure substances that form the mixture. For example, the density of air is between the density of nitrogen and that of oxygen. A mixture of alcohol and water may smell faintly of alcohol, but it does not have as strong an odor as pure alcohol, nor is it odorless like water. Similarly, since alcohol is flammable but water is not, the mixture may or may not burn. It will burn only if it contains enough alcohol.

---

21. Suppose a mixture is separated and found to contain iron filings, salt, and sulfur. If the same amounts of these three substances are mixed together again, will the new mixture have the same properties as the original mixture?

22. Consider two mixtures of nitrogen and oxygen; one is 5 percent nitrogen and the other is 50 percent nitrogen. Do the two mixtures have identical characteristic properties?

23. Suppose you mixed together all the fractions from the fractional distillation of the liquid in Experiment 5.1, Fractional Distillation. What do you think would be the properties of this liquid?

24. A sample of a liquid was boiled for 12 minutes. During that time, the boiling point remained constant and the sample boiled down to half of its original volume. Is the liquid a pure substance?

25. In earlier times, people searched out sandy streambeds where small particles of gold were mixed with the sand. They separated this gold from the sand by "panning." Find out how this was done. What characteristic property of the substances made panning possible?

26. Figure 5.2 shows natural gas, oil, and water trapped below a nonporous rock layer. Why is the layer of water below the oil and the layer of gas above the oil?

27. Figure 5.2 shows four oil wells drilled into oil-bearing porous rock. Can you suggest some method, other than drilling deeper, for getting more oil from Well D after the oil level drops below the end of the well?

28. Using the data in Table 5.1 (page 99), draw and label a possible distillation curve for a mixture of hexane, nonane, and tetradecane.

29. Oil and vinegar are often served as salad dressing. They can be poured into the pitcher shown in Figure B. The pitcher has a spout on each side. Yet oil comes out on one side and vinegar on the other. How do you think the pitcher works?

Figure B
For Problem 29

30. a. If a solution containing 40 g of potassium nitrate in 100 cm^3 of water at 100°C is cooled to 25°C, how much potassium nitrate will precipitate out of solution? (See Figure 5.6.)

b. Suppose that the 40 g of potassium nitrate is dissolved in only 50 cm^3 of water at 100°C. How much potassium nitrate will precipitate out if the solution is cooled to 25°C?

31. Suppose you dissolve 30 g of sodium chloride in 100 cm^3 of water at 100°C and boil away 50 cm^3 of the water.

   a. How many grams of sodium chloride will remain in solution?

   b. How many grams will precipitate out of solution?

32. Suppose you dissolve 40 g of potassium nitrate in 100 cm^3 of water at 100°C.

   a. If half the solution is poured out, how many grams of potassium nitrate will the remaining solution contain?

   b. Now, instead of pouring out part of the solution, you boil away 50 cm^3 of water. How many grams of potassium nitrate will remain in solution at 100°C?

   c. If the solution remaining in (b) were cooled to 25°C, how much potassium nitrate would precipitate out of solution?

33. When ethanol is to be used for industrial or commercial purposes other than as a beverage, it is customarily denatured. What, in general, do you think some of the properties of the added substance might be?

34. How would you separate a mixture of powdered sugar and powdered citric acid?

35. The mineral called gaylussite appears to be a pure substance, but it is actually a mixture composed of calcium carbonate (limestone), sodium carbonate (soda ash), and water. Describe how you could go about separating these three substances from the rock. Some of the properties of calcium carbonate and sodium carbonate are listed in the following table.

Property	Calcium carbonate	Sodium carbonate
Melting point	Decomposes at 825°C	851°C
Solubility in alcohol	Insoluble	Insoluble
Solubility in hydrochloric acid	Soluble	Soluble
Solubility in water	Insoluble	7 g/100 cm^3 at 0°C; 45 g/100 cm^3 at 100°C

36. You can use paper chromatography to separate the components in many common substances. Try this technique with any of the following items you can find at home: tomato paste; different colors and brands of ink; the coloring in leaves, flower petals, or vegetables (grind the item first and mix it with alcohol).

37. Chlorophyll can be extracted from leaves by grinding them with alcohol to give a dark-green solution. After careful application of paper chromatography, bands of yellow and red color, as well as green bands, can be detected. What other reason do you have to suspect the presence of substances producing these colors in leaves? Why do you ordinarily not see them?

38. As liquid air boils away, the remaining liquid becomes richer in one of the two gases—nitrogen or oxygen. Which one is it? How do you know?

39. What should you do to separate

    a. alcohol from water?

    b. sodium chloride from sodium nitrate?

    c. nitrogen from oxygen?

THEME FOR A SHORT ESSAY

You devoted several hours to the "sludge test." Do you think this test is a good way to assess your progress in this course? Why, or why not? Include enough information about the test so that a friend who has never heard about the sludge test will be able to understand your reasoning.

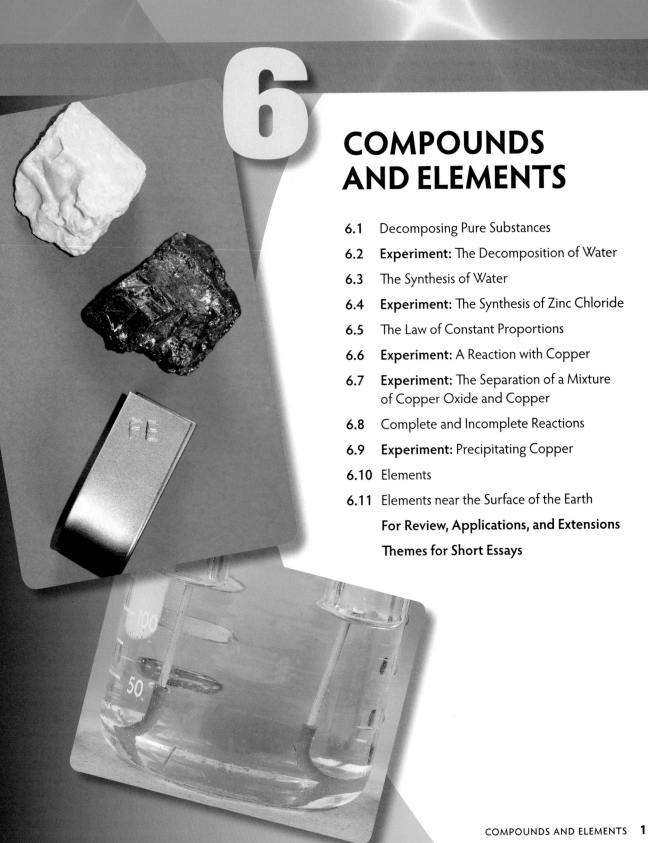

6

COMPOUNDS AND ELEMENTS

6.1 Decomposing Pure Substances

In the previous chapter we investigated several methods for separating pure substances from mixtures. In addition, we found that the original mixtures could be restored simply by mixing the pure substances back together again. Can pure substances also be broken down into even simpler substances? If so, will mixing the simpler substances back together restore the original pure substance?

Consider the case of mercuric oxide, a pure substance that is an orange powder. When heated in a test tube, it gives off a gas. Testing the gas shows that it is oxygen. Furthermore, some droplets of liquid mercury appear in the test tube. Mixing the oxygen and the mercury together, however, will not restore the mercuric oxide. Once it has been *decomposed* (or broken down) by heating, it cannot be put back together simply by mixing. The two substances, a gas and a silvery liquid, remain separated.

Similarly, baking soda, which you heated in Chapter 1, is a pure substance. It decomposed into a solid, a liquid, and a gas. If you had tested these new substances, you would have found that they were also pure substances. But mixing them will not bring back the baking soda.

Heating is not the only method for decomposing a pure substance. In the next experiment, you will use a different method.

> 1. A solution of table salt in water can be separated by boiling the solution to dryness and condensing the water vapor. What are the main similarities and differences between this separation and the two separations described in this section?

6.2 The Decomposition of Water

EXPERIMENT E

Water is one of the substances you have separated out of many mixtures. But water itself cannot be separated into other substances by the methods used in Chapter 5. After heating, distilling, and freezing water, we still always end up with plain water. Therefore, we know it is a pure substance. To decompose water into simpler substances, we need a new method, different from any used so far. Such a method, developed at the beginning of the nineteenth century, relies on electricity and is called *electrolysis*.

 **CAUTION: Be sure to wear safety glasses.**

Figure 6.1 (a)

Apparatus for decomposing water. The electrodes are attached alongside the inverted test tubes. Although the test tubes have been left empty here to increase visibility in the photograph, they should be filled with water before being inverted in the beaker. When you are ready to perform the experiment, connect the black wire to the negative (–) terminal of the battery. Any gas that forms on either of the stainless-steel electrode tips will be collected when it rises and displaces water from its test tube.

Figure 6.1 (b)

A close-up showing the positions of the electrodes centered below the openings of the test tubes.

Set up the apparatus shown in Figure 6.1a. Note the location of the J-shaped electrodes shown in Figure 6.1b. Connect the wires to start the electrolysis.

Since this reaction is very slow when pure water is used, something must be added to speed up the process. Add between 10 and 30 cm^3 of sodium carbonate solution to the water in an amount directed by your teacher. Record the amount you added.

Disconnect the battery when one of the test tubes is nearly full of gas. Before removing the tubes from the water, mark the volume of gas in each tube with a grease pencil or rubber band.

Remove the test tubes from the water in such a way that you do not lose any gas. Your instructor may suggest a method to do this.

You have probably heard that water is made up of hydrogen and oxygen. Recall that a glowing splint bursts into a bright flame when placed in oxygen (Section 5.7). On the other hand, hydrogen burns (or pops) in the presence of a flaming splint. Test the gases with either a flaming or glowing splint to determine which test tube contains which gas.

Using the marks or rubber bands that you placed on the test tubes, measure the volumes of the gases that were collected in the test tubes. To compare these two volumes, divide the volume of the hydrogen by the volume of the oxygen. This gives you the ratio of the volume of hydrogen to the volume of oxygen.

Compare your ratio of volumes with the ratios obtained by students who added different amounts of sodium carbonate solution to the water.

- Does the amount of sodium carbonate solution added to the water affect the volume ratio?
- Using Table 3.1, what is the ratio of the mass of hydrogen to the mass of oxygen? What does your class find for the mass ratio of hydrogen to oxygen?

A pure substance that can be decomposed into two or more pure substances is called a *compound*. The characteristic properties of a compound are quite different from those of its components.

2. Suppose that during Experiment 6.2, some oxygen gas was inadvertently bubbled outside of the test tube. How would this affect the calculated volume ratio of hydrogen to oxygen?

3. Suppose that when conducting Experiment 6.2, a student allowed the hydrogen gas to completely fill the test tube until it began to overflow. How does this error affect the volume ratio of hydrogen to oxygen that the student determines?

4. Does the volume of hydrogen plus the volume of oxygen collected in Experiment 6.2 equal the volume of water decomposed?

5. a. What is the combined mass of oxygen and hydrogen that can be produced when 180 g of water is decomposed by electrolysis?

   b. If all the hydrogen produced in part (a) were burned in air to form water, what mass of water would result?

6. Suppose in decomposing water you had filled so many test tubes with gas that much of the water disappeared from the beaker. Suppose you refilled the beaker without adding more sodium carbonate. You would have found that the ratio of hydrogen to oxygen produced remained constant. What does this tell you about the source of the gases? About the role of the sodium carbonate?

7. What would be the ratio of the volumes of gas in the two test tubes if you had switched the connections to the terminals of the battery halfway through the experiment?

6.3 The Synthesis of Water

In the last experiment, you could have mixed oxygen and hydrogen gas together in a test tube. Nothing would have happened unless you had ignited the mixture. Then a violent reaction would have occurred. As a result of the ignition, the two gases would have combined to form a compound—water vapor. The combining of substances to form a compound is called *synthesis*. This process is the opposite of decomposition.

When you electrolyzed water, you found the ratio of the volume of hydrogen to the volume of oxygen produced. No matter how much water you decomposed, the ratio remained the same. This is not surprising, since all the water you used came from the same source. But can hydrogen and oxygen combine in different proportions, or will they combine only in the same ratio of volumes?

To answer this question, we did an experiment. We first filled a special shock-resistant glass tube with water and inverted it in a tray of water. We then added different volumes of hydrogen to a fixed volume of oxygen, as shown by the photo sequences in Figure 6.2 (on page 120). (The water levels are marked by rubber bands.) Each mixture was ignited, and the volume of any gas that remained uncombined was measured.

> How does synthesis differ from decomposition?

⚠ **CAUTION: This is not an experiment that you or your teacher should do. It requires special glassware and safety procedures not available in classrooms.**

In Figure 6.2(a), a volume V of oxygen was bubbled into the water-filled tube (left photo). We then added an equal volume V of hydrogen to the same tube (center photo). Next, we ignited the mixture of gases by sending an electric spark through it. After ignition, we measured the volume of gas that remained unreacted (right photo). In this case, after ignition, a volume of gas equal to $\frac{1}{2}V$ did not react.

In Figure 6.2(b), the volume of hydrogen used was $2V$, or twice the volume of oxygen. This time practically all of the mixture reacted. The volume of any small bubble that may remain is within the uncertainties of the measurements of the volumes of hydrogen and oxygen that were originally added to the tube.

In Figure 6.2(c), the volume of hydrogen added before ignition was $3V$. A volume equal to $1V$ of gas did not react.

> In which trial(s) did some gas remain unreacted?

Figure 6.2

In each of the three parts of this figure, (a), (b), and (c), the tube on the left was first full of water (not shown). The open (lower) end of each tube was submerged in water. Then, a volume V of oxygen was bubbled into the bottom of the tube.

(a) Trial 1: An equal volume, V, of hydrogen was added to the oxygen already in the tube, and the mixture was ignited by an electric spark. Note that about $\frac{1}{2}V$ of gas remained unreacted.

(b) Trial 2: A volume $2V$ of hydrogen was added to the oxygen. When ignited, all the gas reacted.

(c) Trial 3: A volume $3V$ of hydrogen was added to the oxygen. Now a volume equal to $1V$ remained unreacted.

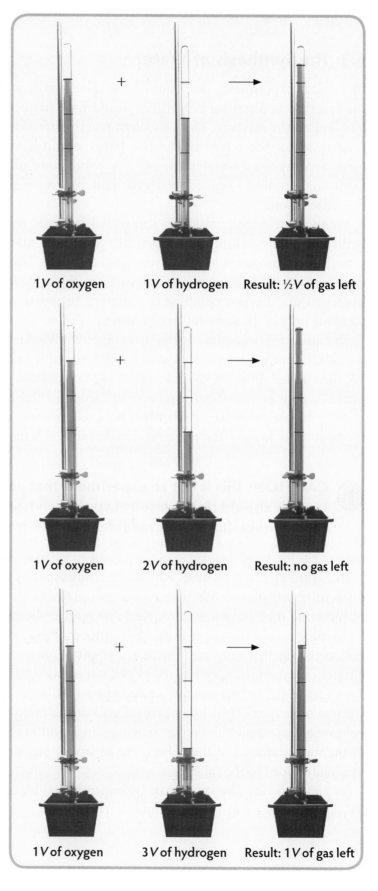

1V of oxygen   1V of hydrogen   Result: $\frac{1}{2}V$ of gas left

1V of oxygen   2V of hydrogen   Result: no gas left

1V of oxygen   3V of hydrogen   Result: 1V of gas left

From Figure 6.2, you can see that the ratios of the volumes of hydrogen to oxygen before ignition in (a), (b), and (c) were 1/1, 2/1, and 3/1, respectively. When tested after ignition, the gas remaining in (a) was oxygen and that in (c) was hydrogen. In (b), any bubble remaining is so small that it is within the experimental uncertainty. The increased amount of water in the tubes came from the tray of water. The actual amount of water produced in the reactions amounted to only a few drops.

Table 6.1					
Tube	Initial volume of oxygen (cm^3)	Initial volume of hydrogen (cm^3)	Final volume of gas (cm^3)	Volume of oxygen that combined (cm^3)	Volume of hydrogen that combined (cm^3)	Ratio of hydrogen to oxygen
1	25.0	25.0	12.4 oxygen	12.6	25.0	1.98
2	25.0	50.0	0.8 hydrogen*	25.0	49.2*	1.97
3	25.0	75.0	24.6 hydrogen	25.0	50.4	2.02

For the purpose of calculation, we assume the remaining bubble to be hydrogen. In all likelihood, it is a mixture of hydrogen and oxygen.

The results of this experiment are summarized in Table 6.1. As you can see, the ratio of the volume of hydrogen to the volume of oxygen that combined to form water was practically the same in each case. The value remained the same regardless of the ratio of the volumes of the two gases in the mixture before they were ignited by an electric spark.

The ratio of the volume of hydrogen gas to oxygen gas (2.0) observed in the synthesis of water is the same ratio obtained by the electrolysis of water in Experiment 6.2, The Decomposition of Water. In Experiment 6.2, you calculated the ratio of the mass of hydrogen to the mass of oxygen and found it to be 0.13. Since the volume ratios of hydrogen and oxygen are the same in decomposition and synthesis, this must hold also for the mass ratios. Hydrogen and oxygen will combine in a mass ratio of 0.13 to form water.

The experiment in Figure 6.2 shows what happens to any excess gas. Over the range of volumes used, if the volume of either gas was greater than the volume needed for a hydrogen-to-oxygen ratio of 2:1, only part of the gas reacted. The excess gas remained uncombined.

Examine Table 6.1. In each setup, is the ratio of the gases before ignition the same as the ratio of gases that reacted to form water?

8. Suppose four tubes are filled with a mixture of hydrogen and oxygen in a manner similar to that used in Figure 6.2. The tubes contain the volumes of hydrogen and oxygen shown in the table below:

Tube	Volume of oxygen (cm³)	Volume of hydrogen (cm³)
I	25	75
II	50	50
III	25	50
IV	100	150

After the mixture in each tube has been ignited, which of the following represents the volume and the identity of the unreacted gases in Tube I? In Tube II? In Tube III? In Tube IV?

A. 25 cm³ of oxygen

B. 50 cm³ of hydrogen

C. 25 cm³ of hydrogen

D. No unreacted gas

9. If 18 g of water is decomposed into hydrogen and oxygen by electrolysis, 16 g of oxygen and 2 g of hydrogen are produced. Using the densities in Table 3.1 (page 55), find (a) the volume of water decomposed and (b) the volume of hydrogen produced.

10. Suppose you were not told the identity of the gases that remained unreacted in the experiment shown in Figure 6.2. Suggest a line of reasoning that would lead to the conclusion that the remaining gas in part (a) is oxygen and in part (c) is hydrogen.

11. Suppose you mixed 100 cm³ of oxygen with 200 cm³ of hydrogen. The volumes of both gases are measured at atmospheric pressure and 20°C.

    a. Calculate the mass of oxygen and the mass of hydrogen used.

    b. If you ignited the mixture, what mass of water would result from the reaction?

    c. What volume of water would be produced?

12. If in Question 11 you had used 100 cm³ of oxygen and 50 cm³ of hydrogen, what mass of water would have resulted?

6.4 The Synthesis of Zinc Chloride

You have learned that hydrogen and oxygen combine in a definite ratio of masses to form water, no matter how much of each mix together and ignite. That reaction involves two gases. You will now investigate the reaction of a metal with an acid: in this case, zinc with hydrochloric acid.

Hydrochloric acid is a solution of hydrogen chloride, which is a compound of hydrogen and chlorine in water. When zinc is placed in hydrochloric acid, a gas is released and a solid residue is found when the remaining liquid is evaporated. This solid, called zinc chloride, is a compound formed from the chlorine in the acid and the zinc.

Will the ratio of the mass of zinc reacted to the mass of chlorine reacted remain constant regardless of how much zinc is added to the hydrochloric acid?

Everyone in your class will use the same amount of hydrochloric acid, but different groups will add different amounts of zinc. Your teacher will tell you how many pieces of zinc to use.

Mass the zinc you will be using. (It should be between 0.5 g and 4.0 g.) Place the zinc in a test tube and add 10.0 cm³ of hydrochloric acid.

The reaction between the zinc and the acid will produce a considerable amount of heat. To keep the mixture cool, you can perform the reaction in a large test tube placed in a beaker of cool water (Figure 6.3).

Figure 6.3

Zinc is placed in 10.0 cm³ of hydrochloric acid in a test tube, which is placed in a beaker of cool water to keep the solution from becoming too hot.

CAUTION: Always wear safety glasses when you work with acids. Be careful not to spill any of the solution on your books or clothes. If some acid spills on your hands, wash them thoroughly with water.

• What is the gas given off in the reaction?

The reaction at first is quite vigorous. However, to make sure that it is complete, allow the mixture of zinc and acid to stand overnight.

Next day, mass an evaporating dish and then pour the liquid from the test tube into it. If there is still zinc left over from the reaction, be sure the solid stays in the test tube when you pour off the solution. Wash the test tube, and any zinc remaining, with 5 cm³ of water, and add the wash water to the evaporating dish.

• Why should you add the wash water to the evaporating dish?

Dry the leftover zinc, and mass it.

• How much zinc reacted with the hydrochloric acid?

The evaporating dish can be placed on a burner stand and heated, as shown in Figure 6.4. If the solution begins to spatter, immediately move the flame to the side so that it heats only one side of the dish.

Heat the material until it appears to be dry. Continue heating until the solid begins to melt and a tiny pool of liquid forms in the bottom of the evaporating dish. You can mass the dish and its contents as soon as they have cooled.

• What is the mass of zinc chloride formed?

The reaction

$$\text{Zinc} + \text{chlorine} \longrightarrow \text{zinc chloride}$$

is, like all other reactions, governed by the law of conservation of mass:

Mass of zinc reacted + mass of chlorine reacted = mass of zinc chloride

So, knowing the mass of zinc that reacted and the mass of zinc chloride that was produced, you can use subtraction to find the mass of chlorine that reacted.

• What is the mass of chlorine that reacted?
• What is the ratio of the mass of zinc that reacted to the mass of chlorine that reacted?

Figure 6.4

Evaporating a solution in an evaporating dish. The dish can be heated more slowly by moving the burner to one side so that the flame heats only one side of the dish.

- If the zinc chloride were not completely dry when massed, how would this affect your ratio?
- Compare your results with those of your classmates. Did an excess of unreacted zinc or hydrochloric acid affect the mass ratio?

13. Suppose that there are 25 students in a class. Ten of them are boys.
    a. What is the number of girls in the class?
    b. What is the ratio of boys to girls in the class?
    c. What would be the ratio of boys to girls if the class were three times larger but the ratio of boys to the total number of students were the same?

14. Suppose that some zinc chloride solution was left in the test tube when the solution was poured into the evaporating dish. How would this affect your calculation for the ratio of the mass of zinc reacted to the mass of chlorine reacted?

15. a. How much chlorine will react with 5.00 g of zinc to form zinc chloride?

    b. How much zinc chloride will be produced?

16. When various amounts of zinc react with hydrochloric acid, zinc chloride and hydrogen are produced. Which of the following ratios of masses of the various products and reacting substances are constant regardless of the amounts of zinc and acid mixed together?

a. $\dfrac{\text{Zinc added}}{\text{Zinc chloride produced}}$ b. $\dfrac{\text{Zinc reacted}}{\text{Hydrochloric acid reacted}}$

c. $\dfrac{\text{Zinc reacted}}{\text{Hydrogen produced}}$ d. $\dfrac{\text{Zinc reacted}}{\text{Zinc chloride produced}}$

e. $\dfrac{\text{Zinc added}}{\text{Hydrochloric acid added}}$ f. $\dfrac{\text{Zinc chloride produced}}{\text{Zinc reacted}}$

g. $\dfrac{\text{Zinc reacted}}{\text{Chlorine reacted}}$

6.5 The Law of Constant Proportions

In the previous two sections, you studied the synthesis of two compounds: water from oxygen and hydrogen, and zinc chloride from zinc and hydrochloric acid. You found that hydrogen and oxygen combine only in the definite mass ratio of 0.13. It does not matter in what proportion these gases are mixed. When they are ignited, the hydrogen and oxygen that react do so in a definite proportion to produce water.

In Experiment 6.4, zinc chloride was produced when zinc combined with the chlorine in the hydrochloric acid. The ratio of the mass of zinc that reacted to the mass of chlorine was constant. It was independent of whether there was an excess either of hydrochloric acid or of zinc.

We consider both water and zinc chloride to be compounds, and not mixtures, because their characteristic properties are quite different from those of the substances that react to produce them. Do all pure substances combine in a constant proportion when they form compounds?

The early chemists strongly disagreed about the ratio of masses of substances that react to form compounds. On one side of the controversy was a distinguished French chemist, Claude Louis Berthollet (1748–1822). On the basis of his experiments, he claimed that a pair of substances can combine over a range of ratios to form a compound. On the other side was another distinguished French chemist, Joseph Louis Proust (1754–1826). He based his answer on evidence obtained from experiments that showed constant proportion, like the synthesis of water and of zinc chloride.

Proust suggested a new law of nature, *the law of constant proportions*, which he stated in 1799:

> We must recognize an invisible hand which holds the balance in the formation of compounds. A compound is a substance to which Nature assigns fixed ratios; it is, in short, a being which Nature never creates other than balance in hand.

In plainer language, the law that Proust formulated can be stated as follows: When two substances combine to form a compound, they always combine in a constant proportion. The ratio of the masses that react remains constant, no matter how much of the substances are mixed. If there is too much of one of the substances in the mixture, some of it just will not react.

When the law of constant proportions was formulated, the evidence in its favor was much weaker than the evidence you gathered for the law of conservation of mass in Chapter 2. Proust's law of constant proportions fits what you have learned from your experiments. It was not a

> Does the law of constant proportions refer to the ratio of masses that are mixed before a reaction takes place, or does it refer to the ratio of masses that react to form a compound?

matter of Proust being a better chemist than Berthollet. Both men based their conclusions on data collected from experiments. We have seen two reactions, the synthesis of water and the synthesis of zinc chloride, that support Proust's position. In the next section we will examine an experiment that seems to support Berthollet's position.

6.6 A Reaction with Copper

Some substances react very quickly. As you learned in Section 6.3, when a test tube of hydrogen and oxygen is ignited, the reaction is extremely rapid. Indeed, it is explosive and ends in a fraction of a second. Solids usually do not react as fast as gases. In this experiment, you will investigate the reaction of finely ground copper with oxygen in the air.

Mass a dry crucible and add about 1 g of copper dust. Now find, as accurately as possible, the total mass of the copper and the crucible.

Heat the copper gently, as shown in Figure 6.5, for 6 minutes. While heating, watch the copper carefully.

CAUTION: Always wear safety glasses when you use a burner.

• Does a reaction take place?

When the crucible is cool, mass it and its contents.

• Did the crucible and its contents gain or lose mass?
• Is your answer to the previous question further evidence that a reaction has taken place?

Assume that in the reaction, oxygen and copper produced copper oxide.

• What mass of oxygen combined with the mass of copper?

Break up the contents of the crucible with a scoopula and examine the pieces.

• Do you think that all the copper has reacted?

NOTE: Do not discard the black solid in your crucible. After labeling a test tube with your name, pour the pieces of solid into the test tube and save them for use in the next experiment.

Figure 6.5

Powdered copper in a crucible supported by a triangle over a microburner. The wires of the triangle are bent so that they can be hooked into holes in the pegboard for rigid support.

EXPERIMENT
E

6.7 The Separation of a Mixture of Copper Oxide and Copper

Suppose all the copper that you started with in the preceding experiment had reacted with oxygen. In that case, the black solid in the crucible at the end of the experiment would be the pure substance copper oxide. If, however, not all the copper reacted, then the black solid would be a mixture of copper and copper oxide. To determine whether the black solid is a mixture, you will attempt to separate it in a way similar to that used in Section 5.4, The Separation of a Mixture of Solids.

A good way to separate a mixture like copper oxide and copper is to place the mixture in a solvent that will dissolve one of the components but not the other. Copper will not easily dissolve in hydrochloric acid, as your teacher can show you. Copper oxide, on the other hand, is soluble in hydrochloric acid.

Retrieve the test tube containing the black solid you obtained in the previous experiment. Add 5 cm³ of hydrochloric acid and stir gently with a glass stirring rod for 5 to 10 minutes.

CAUTION: Always wear safety glasses when you work with acids. Be careful not to get any hydrochloric acid on yourself, your books, or your clothes. If some acid spills on your hands, wash them thoroughly with water.

After letting the solid settle to the bottom, slowly pour off the liquid into another test tube.

NOTE: Do not discard the acid solution. You will need it for the next experiment.

Now wash the remaining solid several times with water and discard the wash water.

- What does the remaining solid look like?
- Was the black solid obtained in the last experiment a mixture? Why or why not?

> 17. Compare the method of separating the black solid mixture in this experiment and the method of separating a mixture of solids in Experiment 5.4. How are they similar? How are they different?

6.8 Complete and Incomplete Reactions

Many reactions, like the reaction of copper with oxygen, are slow. It is difficult in such cases to tell when one of the reacting substances has been completely used up. Because the copper in your crucible changed to a black solid, you may have assumed that all the copper had reacted. This would have been an incorrect assumption, as the presence of copper in the black solid has indicated.

Reactions such as the one between copper and oxygen are called *incomplete reactions*. In incomplete reactions, neither one of the reacting substances—in this case copper or oxygen—is completely used up. Other reactions, such as the one between zinc and hydrochloric acid that you studied in Section 6.4, are *complete reactions*. Zinc will continue to react with hydrochloric acid until either the zinc or hydrochloric acid has been completely used up.

Recall the controversy that existed among early chemists about the validity of the law of constant proportions (Section 6.5). At least part of the controversy was due to the mistaken assumption that certain incomplete reactions were complete. As a result, they often mistook the masses they mixed for the masses that reacted. As your own experience in Experiment 6.6 shows, this mistake is easy to make.

> What distinguishes a complete reaction from an incomplete reaction?

18. If two substances react to form a compound, and only one of them remains when the reaction is over, is the reaction complete or incomplete?

19. A complete reaction takes place between Substance A and Substance B. What will remain after the reaction? (Select all the possible correct answers.)

    A. Substance A and the product of the reaction only

    B. Substance B and the product of the reaction only

    C. Both Substance A and Substance B, along with the product of the reaction

    D. Neither Substance A nor Substance B; all that will be left is the product of the reaction

20. An incomplete reaction takes place between Substance A and Substance B. What will remain after the reaction? (Select all the possible correct answers.)

    A. Substance A and the product of the reaction only

B. Substance B and the product of the reaction only

C. Both Substance A and Substance B, along with the product of the reaction

D. Neither Substance A nor Substance B; all that will be left is the product of the reaction

21. When there is an incomplete reaction, will some of each reacting substance always remain?

6.9 Precipitating Copper

When you heated a sample of fine copper powder in Experiment 6.6, A Reaction with Copper, you observed an increase in mass. This indicated that something was being added to the copper. A new substance, copper oxide, was formed. In Experiment 6.7, The Separation of a Mixture of Copper Oxide and Copper, you dissolved the copper oxide in hydrochloric acid, and from the black solid you produced a colored solution.

What happened to the copper in all these reactions? Did it disappear forever, or is it still in the solution in some form? Putting a piece of zinc in the solution will provide you with an answer. As you already know, zinc in hydrochloric acid will generate considerable heat. Because there is still acid in the colored solution, follow the safety precautions given here!

CAUTION: Always wear safety glasses when you work with acids. Put the test tube containing the solution in a beaker half-filled with cool water.

Put a piece of zinc in the solution you saved from Experiment 6.7, and observe the reaction. While the reaction is going on, break up the solid from time to time with a glass stirring rod.

After the zinc has finished reacting, pour off the solution from the remaining solid and wash the solid several times with water to clean off the acid. Remove the washed solid from the test tube and dry it quickly by pressing it between two layers of paper towel.

Press a scoopula firmly against the paper towel and move it across the dry solid.

• Can you identify the solid?

- Using either a labeled diagram or a paragraph, trace what happened to the copper, starting with Experiment 6.6 and going through Experiments 6.7 and 6.9.

22. **What would happen if you heated the solid that you recovered in this experiment?**

23. **How do you expect the total mass of solid recovered in Experiments 6.7 and 6.9 to compare with the initial mass of copper you heated in Experiment 6.6?**

6.10 Elements

Heating copper in air is only one of many possible reactions of copper and other substances. There are many other reactions, and they all have one feature in common: The product of the reaction always has a larger mass than the mass of the original sample of copper. Neither heating nor electrolysis will change copper into something that has a smaller mass than the copper with which we started. Copper cannot be decomposed.

Contrast this behavior of copper with that of mercuric oxide (Section 6.1). When mercuric oxide is heated, oxygen is given off, and the resulting mercury has a smaller mass than the original quantity of mercuric oxide. We observe that mercuric oxide decomposes into two simpler substances, mercury and oxygen.

In Experiment 6.2, The Decomposition of Water, you electrolyzed water, causing it to decompose into two pure substances, hydrogen and oxygen. In the same way, molten sodium chloride can be decomposed by electrolysis into chlorine and sodium. The mass of either the chlorine alone or the sodium alone is less than the mass of the sodium chloride from which they were produced. Thus, sodium and chlorine must be simpler substances than sodium chloride. However, just as with copper, none of the methods that can be used to decompose other substances work for either sodium or chlorine. Pure substances that do not break up by heating, electrolysis, reacting with acids, or similar methods are called *elements*.

What elements have you worked with in this chapter?

Because elements do not decompose they seem to be permanent; they cannot be destroyed. The copper in Experiment 6.6 appeared to no longer be present when the black solid formed. But this was not the case. As you saw in Experiments 6.7 and 6.9, the copper was still there. Some of it was recovered when the copper oxide was separated from the copper by dissolving it in hydrochloric acid. The remaining copper precipitated when zinc was added to the solution of copper oxide in hydrochloric acid. The copper was always there in one form or another even if it could not always be seen, supporting the idea that it and other elements are permanent.

It is not necessary, of course, to try to break up the many thousands of pure substances to find out which of them are elements and which are compounds. In many cases, we know substances are compounds simply because they can be made by combining other substances. For example, we can "burn" sodium in an atmosphere of chlorine gas. The resulting white solid has the characteristic properties of table salt. Thus, table salt is not an element. It is the compound sodium chloride.

Using this reasoning, early chemists were able to identify a relatively small number of pure substances as possible elements. One such list of elements, proposed by the French chemist Antoine Lavoisier in 1789, was accompanied by the following explanation:

> Since we have not hitherto discovered the means of separating them, they act with regard to us as simple substances, and we ought never to suppose them compounded until experiment and observation have proved them to be so.

Lavoisier's list of elements included several well-known substances that are also found on today's list of elements. Among them are iron, copper, silver, gold, hydrogen, oxygen, and carbon. From a historical point of view, two substances are of special interest. One was on Lavoisier's list and one was not.

The first substance is lime, which can be produced by strongly heating limestone. Lime was known to the Romans as early as 200 B.C.E. Many attempts were made over the years to decompose lime: It was heated in air, heated in a vacuum, and heated with carbon. Every attempt failed, and most people agreed that lime must be an element. However, there were a few doubters, who thought that lime was probably a compound formed by a metal reacting with oxygen—a metal oxide—a compound too difficult to decompose at that time.

As so often happens, a new discovery had to wait for a new experimental method. In this case, the electric battery, invented by Alessandro Volta in 1800, was the necessary tool. In 1807, the English chemist Humphry Davy used an electric battery to decompose metal oxides. He had already used a battery to decompose molten potash and molten soda to obtain the new elements potassium and sodium. A similar procedure failed to work with lime because lime could not be melted. After much experimentation, however, Davy finally succeeded. He was able,

Is lime an element or a compound? How do you know?

by carefully electrolyzing moist lime, to produce tiny amounts of a new element he called calcium.

Missing from Lavoisier's list was a very reactive gas, slightly green in color. It was discovered in 1774 as a by-product of some experiments with muriatic acid. (Muriatic acid is now called hydrochloric acid.) Various people experimented with the new gas and found it similar in many ways to the gases from other strong acids. In those days, acids were considered to be substances that were strongly corrosive and had a sour taste. Since oxygen was believed to be the active ingredient in all acids, this new substance was named "oxymuriatic acid gas."

This name stuck for more than thirty years, mainly because it had been suggested by some very important and respected chemists. Several people tried, unsuccessfully, to decompose the gas. They always blamed their failures on poor methods and poor tools. In 1810 Humphry Davy, after working with his usual patience and brilliance for a full two years, finally announced the results of his long series of experiments. These experiments, Davy wrote,

> incline me to believe that the body improperly called oxymuriatic acid gas has not as yet been decompounded; but that it is a peculiar substance, elementary as far as our knowledge extends, and similar in many of its properties to oxygen gas.

So people would no longer be misled into thinking it a compound, he suggested a new name "based upon one of its obvious and characteristic properties—its color." He called it chlorine, from the Greek word meaning "greenish-yellow." Davy's conclusion—that chlorine is an element and not a compound—has stood the tests both of time and of new techniques. Therefore, chlorine is included in the present-day list of elements.

Why did Humphry Davy conclude that chlorine is an element?

24. **Which of the following can you use to justify the statement that the iron found in a sample of iron oxide is an element and not a compound?**

   A. The mass of the iron oxide is greater than the mass of the iron alone.

   B. Iron is shiny while iron oxide is not.

   C. Iron cannot be broken down into simpler substances.

25. **How do you know that water, zinc chloride, and baking soda are not elements?**

26. Hydrogen chloride—a gaseous, pure substance—can be decomposed into two different gases, each of which acts like a pure substance. On the basis of this evidence alone:

   a. Can hydrogen chloride be an element?

   b. Can either of the other two gases be an element?

   c. Can you be sure that any of the pure substances mentioned is an element?

27. While on a class field trip, a student found a shiny rock that appeared to be a metal. When she returned to the classroom, she heated the rock for a while and found that it lost mass. Further heating did not affect the mass. Could this rock be an element? Explain your answer.

28. Explain in your own words how you would decide that a pure substance is an element and not a compound.

6.11 Elements near the Surface of the Earth

Of the 92 elements that occur naturally on earth, only about 50 are commonly used today. These elements are listed in Table 6.2. The elements on the left side of the table are listed in decreasing order of abundance near the surface of the earth. The elements on the right side of the table are listed alphabetically; their abundance, which is less than that of argon, is not listed.

The part of the earth that was used to calculate abundance includes the atmosphere, the oceans, and the ground to a depth of one kilometer below the surface (including that below the oceans). The data used in the calculations are based on the analysis of thousands of samples of soil, seawater, and air collected at many locations.

Note how few elements account for most of the mass around us. The first five elements (oxygen to iron) in the left-hand column of Table 6.2 account for almost 92 percent of the total mass of the elements found near the surface of the earth. Oxygen, the most abundant element, occurs in the atmosphere, as well as in many compounds found in the ground. Ordinary sand, for example, contains mostly silicon dioxide, a compound of oxygen and silicon. Silicon dioxide is also the main ingredient of glass. Hydrogen, the third element in Table 6.2, is found primarily in the water of the oceans. The other 42 naturally occurring elements that are not listed in the table together account for less than 0.001 percent of the mass near the earth's surface.

Table 6.2 Elements Found near the Surface of the Earth				
Name	Symbol	Abundance (in % by mass)	Name	Symbol
Oxygen	O	65.5	Arsenic	As
Silicon	Si	13.7	Boron	B
Hydrogen	H	5.4	Bromine	Br
Aluminum	Al	4.2	Cadmium	Cd
Iron	Fe	3.1	Cesium	Cs
Calcium	Ca	2.4	Cobalt	Co
Sodium	Na	1.7	Germanium	Ge
Magnesium	Mg	1.5	Gold	Au
Chlorine	Cl	0.95	Helium	He
Potassium	K	0.94	Iodine	I
Titanium	Ti	0.32	Krypton	Kr
Nitrogen	N	0.14	Lead	Pb
Sulfur	S	0.061	Lithium	Li
Phosphorus	P	0.060	Mercury	Hg
Manganese	Mn	0.053	Neon	Ne
Fluorine	F	0.028	Osmium	Os
Barium	Ba	0.020	Platinum	Pt
Strontium	Sr	0.019	Polonium	Po
Carbon	C	0.010	Radium	Ra
Vanadium	V	0.0067	Radon	Rn
Chromium	Cr	0.0060	Silver	Ag
Nickel	Ni	0.0050	Tin	Sn
Zinc	Zn	0.0039	Tungsten	W
Copper	Cu	0.0034	Uranium	U
Argon	Ar	0.0023	Xenon	Xe

29. Oxygen makes up only about 20 percent of air by mass. How can you account for the fact that oxygen makes up 65.5 percent of the mass near the surface of the earth (Table 6.2)?

30. How many elements collectively compose 99 percent of the mass near the surface of the earth?

31. The total mass of the one-kilometer layer of ground, the oceans, and the atmosphere is 2.8×10^{21} kg. What is the mass of (a) iron, (b) sulfur, and (c) copper in this layer?

32. Data for elements present in living matter were not used to calculate the abundances of the elements listed in Table 6.2. Even so, the data in Table 6.2 are correct. How do you think that this can be so?

33. Which of the elements listed in Table 6.2 have you actually held or seen?

FOR REVIEW, APPLICATIONS, AND EXTENSIONS

34. When doing Experiment 6.2, The Decomposition of Water, a student began with 100 cm^3 of water in the apparatus. The student collected 57 cm^3 of hydrogen and 28 cm^3 of oxygen. What fraction of the total volume of water was decomposed?

35. For each particular color of paint, a paint manufacturer takes great care to make sure that the same ingredients are always mixed in exactly the same relative amounts. Although the composition of a particular paint does not change, why is the paint not a compound?

36. Is the melting point of zinc chloride lower than the temperature of your burner flame? How do you know?

37. When you make a solution of salt and water, over what range of values can you vary the mass ratio of salt to water at a given temperature?

38. When two pieces of magnesium are placed in a test tube containing a fixed amount of hydrochloric acid, all the magnesium dissolves and a gas is given off. When six pieces are used, some magnesium is left over, even when the acid is left overnight.

a. In which case or cases was the reaction complete?

b. Why was it advisable to leave the test tube overnight?

39. Discuss the process of boiling an egg in terms of complete and incomplete reactions. What may affect the time required for a complete reaction?

40. What evidence do you have for each of the following statements?

a. Zinc chloride is a pure substance and not a mixture.

b. Water is a pure substance.

41. A student heated a crucible containing 2.15 g of powdered copper until the mass of the contents of the crucible became 2.42 g. The black solid in the crucible was then placed in hydrochloric acid, and 1.08 g of copper remained undissolved in the acid. What is the ratio of the mass of oxygen reacted to the mass of copper reacted?

42. Hydrochloric acid is a water solution of the compound hydrogen chloride. Suppose there were two bottles containing hydrochloric acid in your lab. How could you determine whether the concentration of hydrogen chloride in each bottle is the same?

43. a. If you heat a piece of blue vitriol (a blue solid), its mass decreases and the solid changes to a white powder. Which of the two substances might be an element?

b. If you dissolve the white powder in water and place an iron nail (iron is an element) in the solution, the nail will become coated with a thin layer of copper. What can you now conclude about the two substances in part (a)? Is either of them an element?

44. The two primary elements in air, nitrogen and oxygen, can be separated by fractional distillation as described in Section 5.7.

a. Now that you have heated copper in air, can you suggest another way to separate nitrogen from oxygen in an air sample?

b. How could you tell that oxygen was being removed from the air sample?

c. How would you test the gas sample to determine that oxygen had been removed?

45. Silicon is one of the most abundant elements near the surface of the earth. However, few people have seen or could recognize a sample of silicon. Why do you think this is so?

THEMES FOR SHORT ESSAYS

1. "Seeing is believing" is a common saying. But does "not seeing" imply "not believing"? Neither hydrogen nor oxygen is visible in Figure 6.2 or in the laboratory. Is there, perhaps, a form of indirect seeing? Express your thoughts on this subject.

2. Express the main points of Section 6.5 as a debate between Berthollet and Proust.

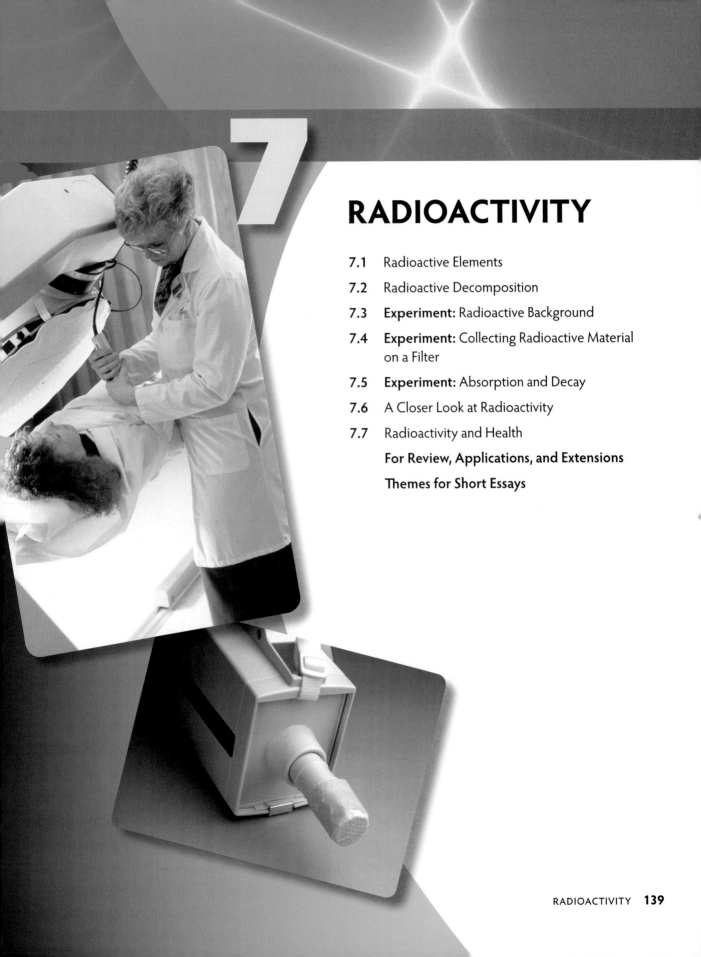

RADIOACTIVITY

7.1 Radioactive Elements

You have now reached an important point in your study of matter. Through simple experiments, you have traced the evidence leading to an understanding of how the material world is put together. To a great degree, your work has been similar to the impressive accomplishments of the past few centuries. The millions of mixtures around us are now known to be made up of tens of thousands of compounds, which in turn are composed of only about 90 elements. Compounds have characteristic properties that are different from those of the elements that combine to produce them. Yet the elements never really disappear. They can always be extracted from their compounds. Elements seem to be permanent.

In science, however, it often happens that a new observation is made just when we think that our understanding of a subject is complete. This observation forces us to admit that our picture is incomplete; some new features must be added.

In the case of elements, some substances that qualified as elements were found to be *not* permanent, but to change on their own into other elements. The groundbreaking experiment that led to this discovery was conducted by the French physicist Henri Becquerel in 1896. We will now describe a modern version of his experiment.

Six plastic boxes containing samples of different substances were placed on photographic film. The film was wrapped in black paper to shield it from light. After three days the film was developed. Figure 7.1 shows where the boxes were placed. Figure 7.2 shows three white squares on the developed film where Boxes A, C, and E were placed. Apparently, the material in these three boxes gave off something that was able to get through the black paper and affect the film in the same way as light.

Figure 7.1

Six different substances in small plastic boxes are placed on photographic film that has been enclosed in black paper. The boxes are left in position for three days before the film is developed and the photograph produced.

The elements contained in the boxes (all are in compounds except in box F, which contains an element alone) are listed in Table 7.1. Can we identify which elements affected the photographic film by examining the elements in each box? Boxes A and B had two elements in common: sulfur and oxygen. However, box A affected the film while Box B did not. This suggests that uranium was the element that emitted, or *radiated*, something. This conclusion is supported by the fact that Box C, which also contained uranium, left a mark on the photographic film.

A comparison of the contents of Boxes D and E suggests that the thorium in Box E is the cause of the mark on the film.

Photographic film is not the only tool that distinguishes Boxes A, C, and E from the others. If we place any one of these boxes near an instrument

Table 7.1	
Box	Elements
A	Uranium, sulfur, oxygen
B	Sodium, sulfur, oxygen
C	Uranium, nitrogen, oxygen
D	Sodium, nitrogen, oxygen
E	Thorium, nitrogen, oxygen
F	Sulfur

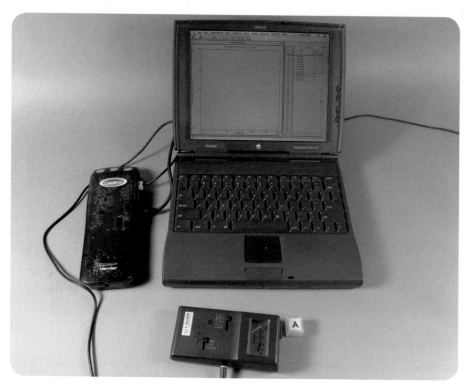

Figure 7.3

A Geiger counter used to detect radiation from radioactive substances. The detector, next to the yellow sample A, is connected to a computer that serves as a recorder.

How can radiation from radioactive elements be detected?

called a Geiger counter (Figure 7.3), the counter produces clicks that can be counted. Boxes B, D, and F do not affect the counter at all.

There are other elements found near the surface of the earth (listed in Table 6.2) that radiate something that affects photographic film and a Geiger counter. These elements are called *radioactive elements*.

1. Elements X, Y, and Z form compounds XY, XZ, and YZ. Compounds XY and YZ are radioactive but compound XZ is not. Which element is radioactive?

2. Is the radiation emitted by uranium compounds due to elements other than uranium that are present in the compounds? What evidence do you have for your answer?

3. An experiment similar to the one described in Figures 7.1 and 7.2 showed that a compound of polonium, sulfur, and oxygen is radioactive. Which of the three elements must be radioactive?

4. A piece of zinc placed in hydrochloric acid causes hydrogen to be released. Evaporation of the resulting solution leaves behind a white solid. A similar reaction occurs when a piece of uranium is placed in hydrochloric acid: A different white solid is left behind when the solution is evaporated. Do you expect this white solid to be radioactive?

7.2 Radioactive Decomposition

What happens to a radioactive element when it radiates?

To answer this question, radioactive elements have been studied using a variety of methods. One method, spectral analysis, will be discussed in Chapter 8. When polonium emits radiation, spectral analysis shows that the polonium changes into lead and helium. Spectral analysis shows that other radioactive elements also change into different elements. In many cases, helium is one of the elements that is produced. The process in which a radioactive element emits radiation and changes into one or more new elements is called *radioactive decomposition* or *radioactive decay*.

Is radioactive decomposition different from the decomposition of water or other compounds? You saw that the elements produced from the decomposition of water could be recombined to form water. The same holds true even for compounds that are difficult to decompose. Recall that lime, which Lavoisier thought was an element, was decomposed by Humphrey Davy into calcium and oxygen by electrolysis. Yet calcium and oxygen easily recombine to form lime. In all cases, it has been possible to recombine the elements that have been obtained from the decomposition of compounds. However, methods that were successful in recombining elements in these previous cases have never worked for those trying to recombine the products of radioactive decomposition.

How are the products of radioactive decomposition different from the products obtained from the decomposition of compounds?

In many of the experiments you have done and read about in this course, temperature has had a big effect on what happened and how fast it happened. Baking soda emitted a gas only when you heated it. Hydrogen does not burn by itself in air, but when it is heated with a burning splint, it catches fire very easily—sometimes explosively. What happens to a radioactive element when it is heated? Does temperature change the rate at which it emits radiation?

The effect of temperature on the rate at which radiation is emitted by radioactive substances has been studied. Samples of the substances were heated to very high temperatures and cooled to very low temperatures. Temperature had no effect on the rate of radiation from a radioactive substance.

To sum up, radioactive elements have all the properties of elements that you studied in the preceding chapters. They form compounds in constant proportions, and they have characteristic densities, melting points, and boiling points. They cannot be decomposed by ordinary heat, electricity, or reaction with acids. They differ from nonradioactive elements in that they affect photographic film and decompose into other elements. The rate at which they decompose cannot be changed by any of the means that affect the rate at which compounds decompose. In addition, the products of decay cannot be recombined to form the original element. That is why these substances are called elements; but to set them apart, we call them radioactive elements.

> How will the rate of radiation for a sample of uranium be affected if the sample is cooled?

> Other than radioactivity, what characteristic properties do radioactive active elements have that nonradioactive elements do not?

5. Suppose the boxes shown in Figure 7.1 had been cooled below the freezing point of water. How would this have affected the appearance of the photographic film shown in Figure 7.2?

6. A radioactive sample at 20°C is placed near a Geiger counter. The average counting rate is found to be 1.0×10^2 counts per minute. The temperature of the sample is then raised to 100°C. What will the new average counting rate be?

7. What are the two most important differences between the following reactions?

    a. Water decomposes into hydrogen and oxygen.

    b. Polonium decomposes into lead and helium.

EXPERIMENT E

7.3 Radioactive Background

When a Geiger counter is placed near a radioactive substance, it counts the decays of radioactive elements. What do you expect a counter to read if there is no known radioactive substance nearby?

When there is only one Geiger counter per class, each of you may be assigned different tasks in this class experiment. Set up a Geiger counter in your classroom and let it count for 1.0 minute. Reset the counter and take two or three additional readings for one minute each.

- What was the number of counts in each reading? Were the readings all the same?

Let the counter run for 30 minutes.

- What was the average number of counts per minute over the 30-minute interval?

The average number of counts per minute registered by a counter when no obvious radioactive source is present is called the *radioactive background*, or *background* for short.

Does the background depend on location? Repeat the background measurement in the basement or another room chosen by your teacher.

- What was the background in the basement or other room? How does it compare to the count in the classroom?

8. In an experiment to determine the radioactive background, a Geiger counter detected 940 counts during 60.0 minutes. Which of the following should you report for the radioactive background?

   A. 15.7 counts/min

   B. 940 counts/min

   C. 56,400 counts/min

9. A student measured the radioactive background in two locations. At location A, she observed 50 counts in 2.0 minutes. At location B, she observed 150 counts in 10.0 minutes. Which location had the higher background?

10. Six readings of a Geiger counter were taken over 1-minute intervals. The numbers of counts per minute were 12, 14, 15, 9, 7, and 18. What do you think the result of the next reading would have been? Why?

EXPERIMENT
E

7.4 Collecting Radioactive Material on a Filter

You should be able to tell whether the background in the basement is significantly higher than in your classroom. You also can find out if the background radiation in the basement comes from the same source as the background radiation upstairs. Radiation can come down from the sky, it can come up from inside the earth, or it can come from radioactive material floating in the air.

How might you tell whether the radiation comes from the earth, air, or space?

Suppose the source is dust in the air. We can test this possibility by catching some of this dust in both your classroom and the basement by passing a large volume of air through a filter. You can do this by fastening a piece of paper towel around the end of the tube of a vacuum cleaner (Figure 7.4). After the air has flowed through the filter for an amount of time specified by your teacher, turn off the vacuum cleaner and place the Geiger counter in front of the filter for 3 or 4 minutes (Figure 7.5). Dividing the number of counts by the time during which they were recorded gives the *counting rate*.

- How does the counting rate observed when classroom air is passed through the filter compare with the background in the classroom?

The counting rate that you have measured so far includes the background. To find the counting rate due to just the radioactive material, subtract the background from the measured counting rate. The difference is called the *net counting rate*.

Net counting rate = measured counting rate – background

Whenever the measured counting rate is much greater than the background, the net counting rate is close to the measured counting rate. However, when the measured counting rate is close to the background, the net counting rate is close to zero.

- What is the difference in the net counting rates from the filter in the classroom and the filter in the basement?
- What do you conclude about the source of the extra counts?

Figure 7.4

The end of a tube of a vacuum cleaner covered with a piece of paper towel serving as a filter.

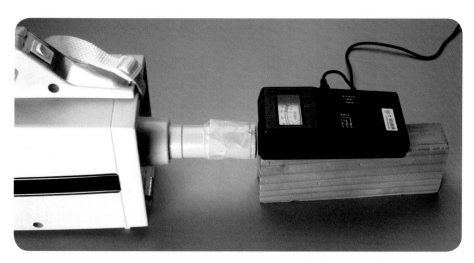

Figure 7.5
The loaded filter and the Geiger counter.

11. The counting rate near a radioactive source was 49 counts/min. When the source was removed, the counting rate dropped to 21 counts/min. Which of the following was the net counting rate of the source in counts/min?

    A. 21   B. 28   C. 49   D. 70

12. A laboratory group found the background in a basement to be 15 counts/min and the counting rate for basement air passed through a filter to be 176 counts/min. What should the group report for the net counting rate on the filter?

13. A class had the following results when collecting radioactive material on a filter: in a closed basement closet, 412 counts in 2.00 minutes; on an open terrace, 36 counts in 2.00 minutes. A background of 19 counts/min was found from an earlier run that lasted 30.0 minutes.

    a. What were the two measured counting rates in counts per minute?

    b. What were the two net counting rates?

    c. If one of the net counting rates were negative, how would you explain such a result?

14. Suppose the net counting rate observed when basement air passed through a filter was close to zero. What would you expect to find for the net counting rate if you repeated the experiment outside or in the classroom? Give your reasoning.

7.5 Absorption and Decay

Note: For reasons that will become clear very shortly, these measurements are best done very quickly, one right after the other.

Keep the filter and the counter in fixed positions. Hold one, two, and more pieces of paper between them, and notice the absorption of the radiation by the paper by listening to the counting rate. Continue to add more sheets of paper until the counting rate is noticeably reduced. Then use a piece of aluminum or a similar metal that is one or two millimeters thick.

- Does the paper affect the net counting rate? If so, how?
- Which has the greater effect on the net counting rate—several pieces of paper or a sheet of aluminum or other metal?

We learned in Section 7.2 that temperature does not affect the rate at which radiation is emitted. We might ask an additional question: As a radioactive element decays, does the rate at which radiation is emitted remain constant over time?

To find out, your teacher will set up your counter, interface, and computer to count the decay of the radioactive substance on your filter every minute for about two hours. If an interface is not available, your teacher will record the net counting rate every five minutes for the two-hour period. In either case, your teacher will provide you with a plot of data for the net counting rate as a function of time.

Your data may look somewhat like those in Figure 7.6. The counting rate decreases with time, but apparently in an irregular way. Should we represent such data by a smooth curve?

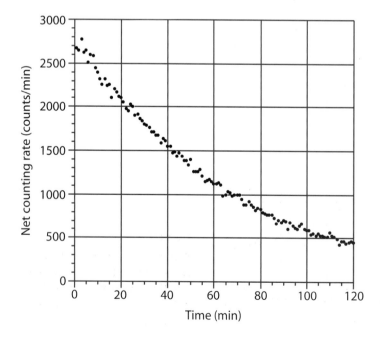

Figure 7.6

Actual class data for the net counting rate for radioactive material collected on a paper filter.

There is a difference between the results of radioactivity measurements and, for example, the results of mass measurements. Massing a test tube several times will give the same results within the sensitivity of the balance. For example, the results may vary between 23.24 g and 23.26 g. However, a mass of 15.85 g would clearly indicate an error in reading or a malfunction of the balance. The results of counting-rate measurements are quite different. Background measurements over short time intervals vary considerably. The same is true for the net counting rate of a radioactive substance. Another run under the same conditions would produce different numbers showing only the same general trend.

Therefore, it does not make sense to try to draw a curve that passes through every data point. Rather, the practice is to draw a smooth curve that has about the same number of data points on each side. Such a curve is likely to fit different sets of data from other identical experiments. Figure 7.7 shows such a curve. Other curves close to the one in Figure 7.7 would also be acceptable.

Draw a smooth curve for your net counting rate as a function of time.

> What is the procedure for drawing a smooth curve through a collection of data points?

- How long did it take for the net counting rate to decrease to half its original value? From half to one quarter of the original value?
- Do you see any relation between these two time intervals?
- What net counting rate do you expect to find after one 24-hour day?

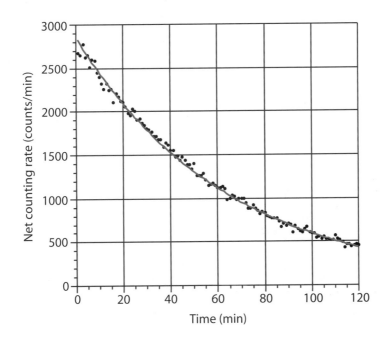

Figure 7.7

A smooth line has been drawn close to the data points in Figure 7.6. The fact that the first and last points are closest to the curve is accidental.

15. Why is it important to perform the paper and aluminum foil measurements quickly?

16. In Figure 7.7, how long did it take for the net counting rate to decrease to half its original value? From half the original value to one quarter?

17. Figure A is a graph of the net counting rate as a function of time for a sample of polonium.

   a. How long did it take for the counting rate to decrease to half its original value? From half the original value to one quarter?

   b. How are these two time intervals related?

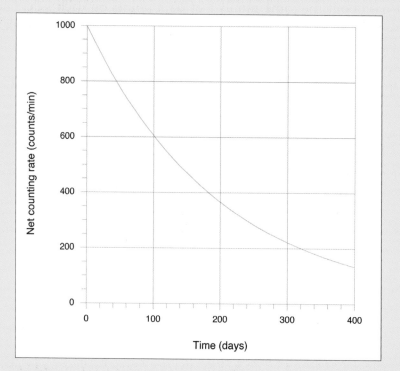

Figure A
For Problem 17

18. Suppose a filter used to collect radioactive dust is made of two layers of paper towel. The two pieces of paper are placed in front of identical Geiger counters for the same length of time. Which layer, the outer or the inner, will produce the greater number of counts? Explain your reasoning.

7.6 A Closer Look at Radioactivity

So far we have observed some general features of radioactive decay. Now we will take a closer look at how it happens. We begin with the effect of radiation from a radioactive element on photographic film. Look again at Figure 7.2 on page 141. The two white squares and the gray square appear uniform.

A similar experiment was done using a very small sample of polonium. Using the apparatus shown in Figure 7.8, we exposed three sheets of photographic film to radiation emitted by the polonium. Each film was exposed for a different amount of time. The first film was exposed for 66 hours, the second for 94 hours, and the third for 144 hours. When the films were developed, the first one showed a uniform very light gray area. The second also was a uniform gray, but the gray shade was darker. The third film was a uniform gray but even darker than the second.

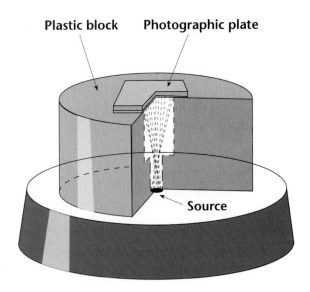

Plastic block · **Photographic plate** · **Source**

Figure 7.8

A photographic film exposed to a tiny amount of polonium.

When the center of each of the areas was photographed through a high-powered microscope with a magnification of about 1000x, none of the areas appeared to be a uniform shade. Rather, they seem to be composed of individual dots (Figure 7.9). In all the photographs, the dots are about equal in size and blackness, and they form no particular pattern. They appear to be distributed without any regular order or pattern in a *random* way. As the time that the photographic films were exposed to the radiation increases, so does the number of dots in each circle and, on the average, in each small square.

Two photographic plates are exposed to the same radioactive source—one for twice as long as the other. Which plate will show the greater "density" of dots?

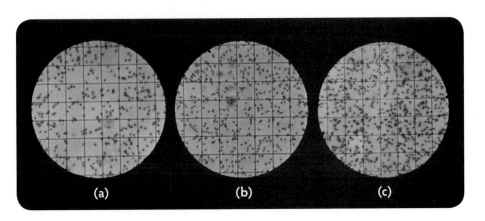

(a)   (b)   (c)

Figure 7.9

Three photographic negatives obtained with the apparatus shown in Figure 7.8. The three pictures show very small, equal-sized areas of the negatives, magnified a thousand times. Negative (a) was exposed for 66 hours, (b) for 94 hours, and (c) for 144 hours.

Figure 7.10

A simple cloud chamber. The chamber itself is a cylindrical plastic box resting on a block of dry ice. A felt band soaked in isopropanol encircles the inside of the top of the chamber. The bottom of the chamber is painted black so that the white fog track will be clearly visible from above. The chamber is illuminated from the side. The radioactive source is on the tip of the needle.

Figure 7.11

Fog tracks produced in a cloud chamber by polonium. The preparation of the cloud chamber and the formation of the tracks are shown in the *IPS* video "Radioactive Substances II."

When a Geiger counter is close to a radioactive sample, you hear distinct clicks. The clicks occur at random. Even after listening for hours, you would not be able to predict when the next click would come. We can be confident about only the average number of clicks in any given time interval.

A more vivid picture of radioactive decay is provided by a device called a *cloud chamber* (Figure 7.10). Figure 7.11 shows a photograph of a cloud chamber that contains a sample of polonium. You can see individual tracks originating from the sample. As far as one can tell just by looking, the tracks are formed instantaneously. Nevertheless, it seems reasonable that they are formed by particles flying off very quickly from the radioactive source.

When you watch a cloud chamber in operation, you will notice that the tracks shoot off in an irregular or random way. Just as with the black dots on the film and the clicks of the counter, you will not be able to predict when the next track will appear or in what direction it will go. Only the average number of tracks produced in a long time interval can be predicted from past observations.

This kind of behavior is characteristic of events that happen by chance. For example, suppose you throw 10 dice many times. In each throw of 10 dice, you are likely to find one or two sixes. In some cases, you will find three or more sixes—or none at all. You have no way of telling what the next throw will produce. However, the average number of sixes in many throws of 10 dice can be predicted to be 1/6 of 10, or 10/6. In the same way, you can only predict the average number of cloud chamber tracks produced during a time interval. You cannot predict exactly when a track will appear or exactly how many will appear in a given interval.

The manner in which film, Geiger counters, and especially cloud chambers record radioactive decomposition suggests that this process takes place in discrete, or countable, events. Each black dot, click, or track signals the arrival of a small particle emitted by the radioactive source. In many cases, this is a particle of the element helium. The fact that other elements such as lead are also produced during radioactive decomposition leads to a far-reaching assumption: Elements are made up of discrete units, or some sort of tiny particles, called *atoms*.

Historically, the idea that elements are made up of atoms preceded the discovery of radioactivity. We have chosen to introduce this idea through the topic of radioactivity because radioactivity enables us to count individual events in which elements are changed.

> If you toss one die, what is the likelihood that a one will appear on the side that is face-up?

19. Having observed a cloud chamber and a Geiger counter near a radioactive source, which of the following can you predict?

    A. The next track only

    B. The next click only

    C. Both of these events

    D. Neither of these events

20. Can you tell whether the tracks in Figure 7.11 are slanting upward, are slanting downward, or are horizontal? What assumption are you making in arriving at your answer?

21. Summarize the similarities between radioactive decay as observed with a cloud chamber and with a Geiger counter.

22. State in your own words why radioactive decomposition suggests that elements are made of tiny particles.

7.7 Radioactivity and Health

When the radiation from radioactive substances hits photographic film, it makes some changes in the film. If it did not, the film could not serve as a detector. Radiation also causes changes to other materials when it hits them. If the radiation hits a human body, the changes can be harmful if the radiation is intense. What is the danger to the human body from radiation found in basements?

Recall that in Experiment 7.5, we found that several sheets of paper absorb a noticeable fraction of the radiation emitted from the vacuum filter or another source. This observation suggests that much of the radiation found in basements will be stopped by clothing and skin and can easily be washed off. However, when we inhale radioactive material, our lungs have no skin to protect them. They have a large surface area for the exchange of oxygen and carbon dioxide. As we breathe, radioactive material in the air can be deposited onto this lung surface.

In general, the concentration of radioactive material in the air of a basement is small. This is why we needed a vacuum cleaner to collect enough radioactive material from a large volume of air. However, if the concentration of radioactive material in the air is large enough and the air is breathed over a long enough time, the danger of lung cancer cannot be ignored.

Why is the danger mostly in basements? A radioactive gas called *radon* originates inside the earth. Radon, an element like helium and neon, does not readily react with other elements to form compounds. Therefore, as it comes to the surface of the earth, it enters the atmosphere instead of combining with other elements in the rocks. If it reaches a basement its concentration increases, because basements are not as well ventilated as upstairs rooms. When we enter the basement, we are likely to inhale some of the radioactive material.

The radiation emitted by radon is the kind that most Geiger counters cannot detect. What you observed in Experiments 7.4 and 7.5 was the radiation emitted by the decay of elements that themselves were produced by the decay of radon.

This discussion has dealt with radon found in some basements. However, some materials are so radioactive that, to protect human beings, they must be placed behind a thick wall that provides adequate absorption of the radiation.

Just as radiation from radioactive substances can be harmful to humans, it also destroys the bacteria that cause fruits to rot and milk to spoil. In recent years, irradiation—that is, the exposure of food to radiation—has increasingly been used to preserve food products. Food

> Why is radon in your lungs a more serious health threat than radon in the air around you?

> How does radiation help to preserve food?

Figure 7.12

A comparison between irradiated (right) and nonirradiated strawberries (left). Both samples were kept under refrigeration for two weeks beneath a plastic cover. *(Courtesy International Atomic Energy Agency)*

preserved in this way does not become radioactive and does not contain any chemical additives (Figure 7.12).

FOR REVIEW, APPLICATIONS, AND EXTENSIONS

23. A plant absorbs various substances through its roots. Different elements of these substances concentrate in different parts of the plant. Suppose one of these elements is radioactive. How would you determine in what parts of the plant it concentrates?

24. a. With a paper towel in place on a small vacuum cleaner, it took 32 seconds to fill a 160-liter plastic bag with air. How much air passed through the filter in 1 second? in 1 minute?

    b. Suppose you had used the vacuum cleaner from part (a) to perform Experiment 7.4. How much air would pass through the filter during the time you collected the radioactive material?

25. Which could you predict with more confidence?

    A. The time between two consecutive automobile collisions at a busy intersection.

    B. The total number of collisions per year at the same intersection.

26. a. Exhale normally into a small plastic bag and estimate the volume of air that you exhale in one breath.

b. Count how many times you exhale per minute (breathing normally).

c. What volume of air passes through your lungs each minute?

d. Suppose you stayed in the basement for as long as it took to collect the radioactive material in Experiment 7.4. How much air would have passed through your lungs?

e. Suppose that your lungs act like a combination of the filter and the counter used in Experiment 7.4. What would be the "counting rate" of your lungs due to breathing the basement air?

27. In the *IPS* video "Radioactive Substances I," the Geiger counter counted much faster when Box A was placed next to it than when Box E was. Is this what you would have expected on the basis of the brightness of the white squares in Figure 7.2? Why or why not?

28. The *IPS* video "Radioactive Substances II" shows tracks being produced in a cloud chamber. From what you see in the video, can you be sure that the tracks start at the source rather than end there? What does this tell you about the speed of the particles that cause the tracks?

THEMES FOR SHORT ESSAYS

1. The use of fluoride to reduce tooth decay was quite controversial in the past. Today, irradiating fruits and vegetables to reduce spoilage is controversial. Interview your teachers, parents, and friends to assess their feelings on this issue. Try to determine the basis for these feelings.

2. The "background" in "background radiation" is a metaphorical term borrowed from the arts, including theater and painting. Write your thoughts on how background radiation is both similar to and different from the background in a theatrical production or painting.

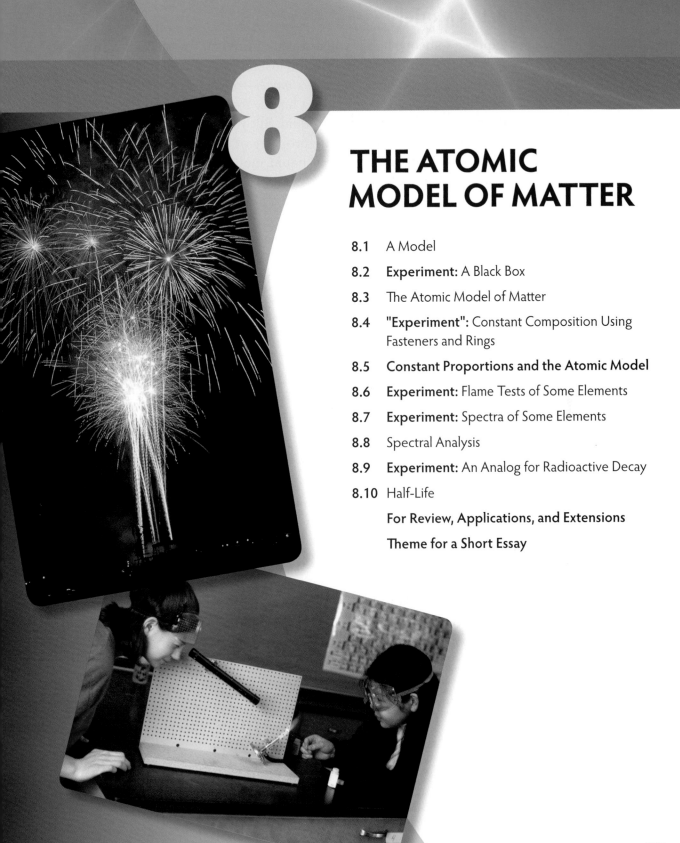

8

THE ATOMIC MODEL OF MATTER

8.1 A Model

Suppose someone hands you a sealed can. When you shake it, you hear and feel something sloshing around inside. From this simple experiment you can form a mental picture—a *model*—of what is inside the can. You conclude that the can contains a liquid. You have no knowledge about the color, taste, or odor of the liquid. But you are sure that the contents of the can has a characteristic property of liquids—it sloshes around when you shake the can. The "liquid model" of the can accounts for your observation.

However, for a model to be useful, it has to offer more than just a convenient way of accounting for known facts. A model must also enable us to make testable predictions. For example, from the liquid model of the can, we can make the following prediction: If you punch a small hole in the bottom of the can, liquid will drip out.

The simple model we have made for the behavior of the contents of the can was the result of just one experiment—shaking the can. It led to only one rather obvious prediction.

The experiments and observations with radioactivity in Chapter 7 suggested that elements are made up of particles we call atoms. Before we go on to more fully develop an atomic model of matter, you will do an experiment with a "black box." This experiment will give you an opportunity to develop a richer idea of a model than the one offered by the can. It will also make it easier for you to understand the atomic model of matter and how we can validate our model.

What was the "obvious" prediction?

Where did the idea for the model of elements as particles come from?

1. A good model enables us to summarize and account for the facts we learn from observation and experiment. What else should a good model do for us?

2. Suppose you have two eggs in a refrigerator. One is raw and the other is hard-boiled, but you do not know which is which. You spin each egg. One egg spins freely. The other egg comes to rest after very few rotations.

    a. Suggest a model that will account for the different behavior of the two eggs.

    b. Suppose the eggs were boiled for 10 minutes. On the basis of your model, what do you predict about how the two eggs will spin?

    c. Check your prediction at home.

8.2 A Black Box

The insides or contents of all the boxes you and your classmates will use in this experiment are the same (Figure 8.1). The first step is to find out as much as you can about these boxes without pulling out the rods and, of course, without opening the boxes. Look at one of them. Shake it lightly, tilt it back and forth in various directions, and listen carefully to the sounds. Writing down your observations will help you compare notes with your classmates. You will then be ready to arrive jointly at a model, use the model to make predictions, and test those predictions.

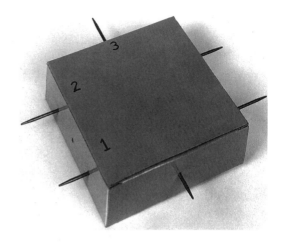

Figure 8.1
A black box.

Do all the experiments you can think of, short of pulling out the rods or opening the box. Try to imagine in a general way what is inside the box that could account for your observations. A diagram of what you think is inside would help. This will be your model for the box. Do not be distracted by details. Do not, for example, try to name the objects inside the box; only describe them using the properties that you have found in your experiments. If you hear something sliding on one of the rods, you might be tempted to name it as a washer or a ring. But the important point is that it is something with a hole through which the rod passes.

After you and your classmates have drawn models that account for your observations, predict what will happen when you pull out a particular rod. Also predict how this will affect the results of the tests you performed earlier. (Be sure to write down your predictions so that you can check them.)

Now you or one of your classmates may remove this rod from one of the boxes. Leave all the rods in place in the other boxes. If what happens confirms your prediction, you can use the same box to test predictions about what would happen if another rod were pulled. You also can use one of the other boxes to test predictions about what would happen if a different rod were pulled out first. If, however, your first prediction was not confirmed, modify your model before experimenting further. Continue this process until you have confidence in your model.

> Why should each prediction be tested by pulling a rod from just one box?

> 3. While doing Experiment 8.2, A Black Box, why were you not permitted to open the box and look inside?

4. a. While investigating the black box, you did certain things to it that you could undo. Give some examples.

   b. What did you do to the black box that you could not undo?

   c. Does dissolving zinc in hydrochloric acid resemble the kinds of tests you mentioned in part (a) or part (b)?

5. In what way is pulling a rod from a black box similar to heating baking soda in Experiment 1.1?

8.3 The Atomic Model of Matter

Let us now begin to build a model for matter by reviewing some of the common properties of elements, mixtures, and compounds that we have observed during this course. We will build the model by introducing a series of assumptions that will account for these properties. We will concentrate on stable, nonradioactive matter in all but the last two sections of this chapter.

First, we consider elements. We observed that different samples of an element have the same characteristic properties. To account for this, we will introduce our first assumption: that an element is made up of only one kind of particle. We have called these tiny particles atoms. We further assume that different elements are made up of different kinds of atoms. Atoms cannot be seen even with strong optical microscopes. So they must be very small, and there must be very many of them in any sample large enough for us to examine.

At this point, we do not know how atoms of different elements differ from each other. But we can use familiar objects to illustrate the idea that they are different. Figure 8.2 shows a group of paper fasteners and a

> What observation leads to the assumption that each element is made up of a different type of atom?

Figure 8.2

Paper fasteners representing atoms of "element" Fs, and rubber rings representing atoms of "element" R.

group of rubber rings. Think of a fastener as an atom of element Fs, and think of a ring as an atom of element R. Of course, nobody believes that an atom looks like a fastener or a ring. But this simple analogy illustrates the basic idea of the atomic model: All atoms of one element are alike, but they are different from the atoms of all other elements.

Second, let us consider the properties of mixtures. We know that mixtures of elements can be made in varying proportions. Furthermore, the characteristic properties of a mixture may vary widely as the proportions of the individual elements in the mixture are changed. At least some of the characteristic properties of the individual elements (for example, color and the ability to react with other substances) are usually present in a mixture.

We can account for the behavior of mixtures by assuming that in mixtures the atoms of the individual elements remain unchanged. The numbers and masses of the atoms remain the same after the elements are mixed. The atoms just get mixed like marbles of different colors. Note that with this assumption the model guarantees that mass is conserved when mixtures are made and then separated. Figure 8.3 uses fasteners and rings to illustrate two different mixtures of the same two elements.

Third, we consider compounds. When elements form a compound, they combine only in a definite ratio. You saw evidence for the law of constant proportions in the burning of hydrogen with oxygen (Section 6.3) and in the synthesis of zinc chloride (Experiment 6.4). Furthermore, the compound produced in each case had its own set of characteristic properties, which were usually quite different from those of the reacting elements. For example, the characteristic properties of water are entirely different from those of the hydrogen and oxygen that combine to make it.

To account for the law of constant proportions, we must add a new assumption to the atomic model. We assume that when a compound is formed, each atom of one element attaches to a fixed number of atoms of the other elements in a particular pattern. A simple illustration of

> What two ideas about atoms form the basis of the atomic model of matter?

> What observation leads to the assumption that in a mixture, the atoms of each element are unchanged?

> What observation leads to the assumption that the atoms of different elements attach to form a compound?

Figure 8.3

Two mixtures of the "elements" Fs and R in very different proportions.

Figure 8.4

The compound FsR made by attaching one "atom" of Fs to one "atom" of R. Note the excess of Fs.

compound formation is provided by the attachment or "reaction" of one "atom" of Fs to one "atom" of R (Figure 8.4). Note that the excess of Fs did not "react." Thus the idea of attachment leads directly to the law of constant proportions.

6. If several bins of different sizes were completely filled with the compound FsR, which of the following would be the same?

   A. The number of rings in each bin

   B. The number of rings and fasteners in each bin

   C. The percent by mass of rings in each bin

   D. The percent by mass of fasteners in each bin

7. Suppose that M atoms of mercury combine with N atoms of oxygen to form mercury oxide. Which of the following choices represents the total number of atoms in the mercury oxide produced?

   A. M C. $M + N$

   B. N D. $2M + N$

8. Suppose the mercury oxide produced in Problem 7 is then decomposed by heating to form gaseous mercury and oxygen. Which of the following choices represents the numbers of atoms of mercury and oxygen you would expect to find?

   A. M atoms of mercury and no atoms of oxygen

   B. No atoms of mercury and N atoms of oxygen

C. _M_ atoms of mercury and _N_ atoms of oxygen

D. 2_M_ atoms of mercury and _N_ atoms of oxygen

9. Would your answer to Problem 8 be different if you had condensed the gases to liquid mercury and liquid oxygen?

8.4 Constant Composition Using Fasteners and Rings

To illustrate how the attachment of elements in the atomic model leads to the formation of compounds in constant proportion, you will use the "elements" Fs and R introduced in the preceding section. When you fit or attach rings on fasteners as shown in Figure 8.4, the number of rings and the number of fasteners are the same both before and after they are attached. Hence the total mass does not change. The atomic model accounts for the conservation of mass.

Making a compound from fasteners and rings is similar to forming copper oxide from copper and oxygen (Experiment 6.6, A Reaction with Copper). In that experiment you worked with large numbers of invisible atoms. However, in this experiment you will illustrate the process by using a few visible "atoms" to form a sample of a compound.

- What is the mass of all the Fs that you have?

Make as much of the "compound" FsR as your supply of "atoms" allows by putting one ring on each fastener (Figure 8.4). When we write "FsR," we mean a compound made up of one "atom" of Fs for each "atom" of R.

- Did your reaction go to completion?
- What is the mass of the product you have synthesized?

If you have an excess of Fs, find its mass.

- What is the mass of Fs that reacted with R?
- Without further massing, what is the mass of R that reacted with Fs?
- What is the ratio of the mass of Fs to the mass of R in your sample of the "compound"?

Compare your results with those of your classmates.

- Does the ratio of the mass of Fs to the mass of R depend on how big a sample you make?

- Does the model, as illustrated by fasteners and rings, agree with the law of constant proportions?
- Would the ratio have been the same if you had used heavier rings?

Suppose you "decomposed" your "compound" into pure Fs and R by taking the rings off the fasteners. You would get back all the "atoms" you started with.

- If you then measured the masses of the "elements" Fs and R, would the model agree with the law of conservation of mass?

– – – – – – – – – –

Suppose the "atoms" of Fs and R combined in a ratio of one atom of Fs to two atoms of R. Such a "compound" would have the formula FsR_2 (Figure 8.5). The "$_2$" in the formula means that there are two atoms of R for every atom of Fs in the compound.

- If you decomposed this compound, would the mass ratio of Fs to R be constant regardless of the size of the sample or the excess of Fs or R you had when forming it?
- If so, would the constant be the same as the mass ratio of Fs to R in the compound FsR?

Figure 8.5

The compound FsR_2 made by attaching one "atom" of Fs to two "atoms" of R. Note the excess of R.

10. Based on what you have learned in this "experiment," does the law of constant proportions tell you how many atoms of chlorine combine with one atom of zinc in Experiment 6.4, The Synthesis of Zinc Chloride?

11. Why is "Experiment" in quotes in the title of Section 8.4?

12. Is the mass of a ring that is attached to a fastener the same as the mass of a ring that is not attached?

13. Which of the following aspects of the atomic model are addressed in "Experiment" 8.4?

    A. Atoms are very small.

    B. All atoms of a given element are alike.

    C. Atoms attach themselves to each other in a fixed mass ratio.

14. Does the "experiment" with rubber rings and paper fasteners give you any information about the shape of an atom?

15. Suppose that you had either extra fasteners or extra rings remaining in "Experiment" 8.4.

    a. What do these extra fasteners and rings represent?

    b. Relate your answer to part (a) to the class results for Experiment 6.4, The Synthesis of Zinc Chloride.

16. In the synthesis of water described in Section 6.3, different volumes of hydrogen were mixed with a constant volume of oxygen. Then the mixture was ignited by a spark. In part (a) of Figure 6.2, there was some oxygen left over; in part (b), nearly all the oxygen and hydrogen reacted; and in part (c), some hydrogen was left over. Describe these results in terms of the atomic model of matter.

17. Suppose that element A can form a compound with element B but not with element C. Element B can form a compound with element C. How can you use fasteners, rings, and washers to represent these elements?

18. Describe the synthesis of zinc chloride ("Experiment" 6.4) in terms of fasteners, rings, and washers. (Hint: Hydrochloric acid contains hydrogen and chlorine.)

8.5 Constant Proportions and the Atomic Model

You may wonder why you were not asked in the preceding "experiment" to mass one fastener and one ring and find their mass ratio. If you had done so, you would have found this ratio to be the same as you found for all samples of FsR, independent of the number of atoms in the sample. The reason you were not asked to find the ratio in this manner was to be consistent with history. Near the end of the eighteenth century, when Proust and Berthollet were conducting their experiments in the formation of compounds, masses of atoms were not known. Therefore, massing individual fasteners and rings would not have been an accurate portrayal of what the early chemists could do.

To appreciate the importance of knowing the masses of individual atoms, consider the relationship between the mass of a sample of an element and the mass of one atom. That relationship is expressed by the following equation:

Mass of sample = (number of atoms) · (mass of one atom) .

To see how this equation applies to a real sample of atoms, consider the synthesis of zinc chloride in Experiment 6.4. We can apply the previous equation first to the mass of the zinc reacted and then to the mass of chlorine reacted, as follows. (We have replaced the word "number" with the symbol "#"):

Mass of zinc = (# of zinc atoms) · (mass of one zinc atom)

Mass of chlorine = (# of chlorine atoms) · (mass of one chlorine atom) .

Dividing the upper equation by the lower one, we have

$$\frac{\text{Mass of zinc}}{\text{Mass of chlorine}} = \frac{\text{\# of zinc atoms}}{\text{\# of chlorine atoms}} \cdot \frac{\text{mass of one zinc atom}}{\text{mass of one chlorine atom}}$$

The ratio on the left side of the equation is the mass ratio that you found in Experiment 6.4. This ratio is independent of the total mass of the sample (Figure 8.6). The first ratio on the right side of the equation is also independent of the mass of the sample. But this ratio cannot be found unless we know the ratio of the masses of the atoms. We do not know the ratio of how many zinc atoms reacted with how many chlorine atoms. This ratio might have been 1:1 as in FsR or 1:2 as in FsR$_2$. Or it might have been still some other ratio. The first and simplest ratio is illustrated in Figure 8.6 with circles and triangles standing for the atoms of two elements, A and B.

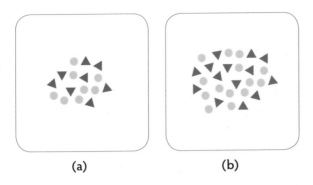

(a)   (b)

Figure 8.6

Two different masses of the same compound. Both samples have the same ratio of numbers of atoms. The ratio of atoms in this example is 1:1. If the ratio were different, such as 1:2, it would still be the same in both samples.

The second ratio on the right side of the equation does not depend on the units used to express the mass of individual atoms of zinc and chlorine. The ratio is the same whether the masses are expressed in grams or in any other unit.

Note that the ratio of the number of A atoms to B atoms does not tell us anything about the way the atoms are arranged in space. All three diagrams shown in Figure 8.7 are possible arrangements of the same compound AB. In Figure 8.7(a), pairs of atoms are far apart from one another. It is clear which atom of A is attached to which atom of B. This arrangement corresponds to a gas. Groups or clusters of atoms attached in a fixed ratio, such as the pairs of atoms shown in Figure 8.7(a), are called *molecules*.

In Figure 8.7(b) the atoms are much closer to one another, and it is hard to tell which atom of A is attached to which atom of B. The density of the compound is much greater than that in Figure 8.7(a). This arrangement of atoms may correspond to a liquid. In some liquids one can recognize molecules; in others, one cannot.

In the third arrangement, Figure 8.7(c), it is impossible to determine which atoms of A are paired with which atoms of B. It is therefore meaningless to talk about molecules. The most we can say is that there are equal numbers of atoms of elements A and B. This kind of arrangement is characteristic of crystals, such as solid sodium chloride.

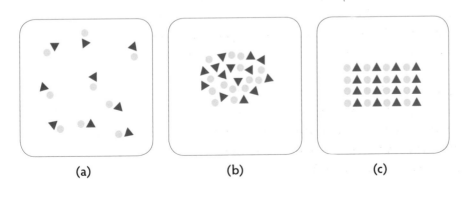

(a)   (b)   (c)

Figure 8.7

Three possible arrangements of atoms A and B forming the compound AB.

19. Write an equation relating the following three quantities: the mass of a handful of identical nails, the number of nails in that handful, and the mass of one nail.

20. From your work on Experiment 6.2, The Decomposition of Water, you can conclude that the mass ratio of oxygen to hydrogen in water is about 8. Suppose you knew that the ratio of oxygen atoms to hydrogen atoms is 1/2. What is the ratio of the mass of one oxygen atom to one hydrogen atom?

21. Suppose you know that the ratio of the mass of a zinc atom to that of a chlorine atom is 1.84.

    a. Use the class results of Experiment 6.4, The Synthesis of Zinc Chloride, to calculate the ratio of the number of zinc atoms to the number of chlorine atoms in zinc chloride.

    b. What is the formula for zinc chloride? Use the symbols Zn for zinc and Cl for chlorine.

EXPERIMENT E

8.6 Flame Tests of Some Elements

As you saw in Chapter 6, it is hard to decompose some compounds into their elements. However, if you hold small samples in a flame, many compounds will reveal the elements they contain.

Place small quantities of different compounds, each of which contains sodium, on tiny loops of nichrome wire and hold them in a flame. Record the color you see for each compound.

Next, try the same experiment using copper and compounds containing copper. Repeat the same procedure with compounds containing strontium, lithium, and calcium.

- How can you recognize sodium in a compound by doing such a flame test?
- How can you recognize copper?
- Can you distinguish among strontium, lithium, and calcium by a flame test?

– – – – – – – – – –

Although the characteristic properties of compounds are different from those of the elements that make them up, it is the individual elements that determine the color of the flame. We can understand the appearance of the colors in terms of the atomic model in the following way: The flame is not hot enough to break up the entire sample. But it can shake off some atoms from their compounds. Once these atoms are separated, they emit light of a color specific to them. It no longer matters which compound they were released from.

A flame test reveals the presence of sodium. Does it also tell you what compound the sodium atoms came from?

22. When you hold a small amount of sodium chloride in a flame, you observe that the flame is bright yellow. What can you do to be sure that the color is due to sodium and not to chlorine?

23. When you spill a few drops of soup or milk on a pale-blue gas flame when cooking, the color of the flame changes to a mixture of colors. Yellow is the most intense color. What do you conclude from this observation?

24. A product containing the compound copper sulfate can be sprinkled on a wood fire to add color to the flame. What color do you expect this compound to add?

EXPERIMENT

E

8.7 Spectra of Some Elements

As you probably just found out, some elements are easy to identify by a flame test. Many other elements are not so easily identified. For such elements, we need to separate the mixed colors in order to detect slight differences. The first step is to spread out the various colors in the light in much the same order they appear in a rainbow. This spread of colors is called a *spectrum* (plural: *spectra*).

You can produce a spectrum using a simple spectroscope. This device consists of a tube with a slit at one end and a transparent plastic disk at the other. The disk has many parallel lines on it that are very close together.

Hold the end with the plastic disk next to your eye and look at several light sources provided by your teacher. When the light source is a thin tube, you may find it more convenient to look at the light with the slit removed.

- What is the major difference between the spectrum of an ordinary light bulb and the spectrum of any of the gas tubes?
- What are the differences between the spectra of the different gas tubes?

8.8 Spectral Analysis

Why can you not see the spectra of oxygen and chlorine by using your burner?

We mentioned compounds of calcium, lithium, and strontium without specifying which compound we were talking about. This may give you the impression that the spectrum of only one of the elements in a compound can be observed. This is not so. The flame of your burner is hot enough to produce the spectra of sodium, lithium, calcium, copper, and a few other elements. It is not hot enough to produce the spectra of elements such as oxygen and chlorine. However, the very high temperatures generated by an electric arc will produce the spectra of all the elements in a compound.

Under such high-temperature conditions, the resulting spectrum is no longer simple. It will most likely contain complicated patterns of many closely spaced lines. Yet each element gives out its own spectrum, one that is different from the spectrum of any other element. It takes accurate measurements of the positions of spectral lines to identify an element. Once this has been done, the presence of any element has been definitely established.

Observed with a good instrument, the sodium spectrum looks like the one illustrated in Figure 8.8. This spectrum shows that the yellow of the sodium flame is not just any yellow. It is a very specific color indeed, which has its own place in the spectrum. No other element has a line at this specific place in the spectrum. The presence of this particular pair

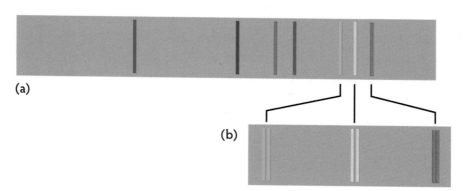

(a)

(b)

Figure 8.8

(a) The spectrum of sodium. The spectrum was in black and white; the color was added later. Therefore, the positions of the lines are accurate, but their colors are not. The yellow line is extremely intense. It has been photographed through an absorbing filter so it can be seen at the same time as the other lines. The almost invisible violet line arises from a potassium impurity. (b) A part of the sodium spectrum has been photographed with a spectroscope that spreads out the light more, enabling us to see more detail. Now we can see that the yellow line is actually made up of two lines that are very close together.

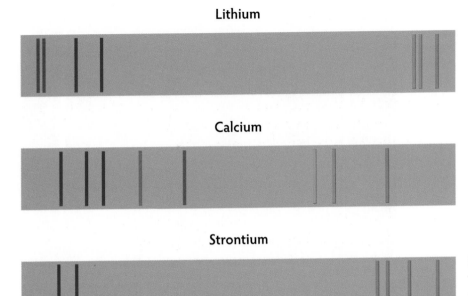

Lithium

Calcium

Strontium

Figure 8.9
The brightest lines in the spectra of lithium, calcium, and strontium.

of yellow lines (Figure 8.8(a)) always means that sodium is present in the light source. Even if the yellow color in the flame is masked by many other colors, the spectroscope will reveal the presence of sodium.

Figure 8.9 illustrates spectra obtained from compounds of calcium, lithium, and strontium. In flame tests, all of these elements display nearly the same color. However, each has its own set of characteristic spectral lines when viewed through a spectroscope.

Unlike the measurement of melting point or density, spectral analysis, or spectroscopy, can be done on very distant objects like our sun and other stars. Analysis of sunlight was one of the very early uses of spectroscopy. Most of the spectral lines observed in sunlight could also be produced with known materials in the laboratory. However, during a solar eclipse in 1868, a new set of spectral lines was found in the spectrum of the light coming from the edge of the sun. This set of lines had never been seen before and could not be produced in the laboratory with any element known at the time. The lines were therefore thought to be from a new element, which was named helium after the Greek word for sun. Eventually, helium was also detected on earth through spectral analysis.

In Section 7.2, we mentioned that the elements produced in the radioactive decomposition of polonium were identified by spectral analysis. The formation of helium in this process was demonstrated for use in this course by the following procedure:

Figure 8.10

A comparison between the spectrum of pure helium (upper half) and the spectrum produced in an evacuated tube containing polonium (lower half). The two faint lines close together in the lower half are polonium lines.

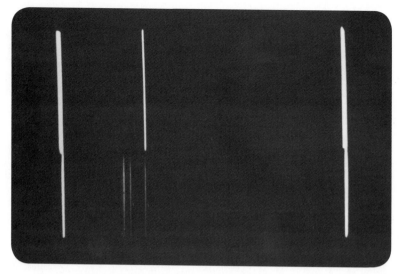

The upper half of Figure 8.10 shows the spectrum of helium contained in a tube like one you may have seen in the classroom. The lower half shows the spectrum obtained from a tube that was prepared this way: 4.5×10^{-3} g of polonium was deposited inside, the air was pumped out, and the tube was sealed. Thirteen days later the spectrum was photographed.

Note that the three lines in the upper half of Figure 8.10 appear at the same positions in the lower half. The exposure was weaker in the lower half (the lines are thinner); this is why the line near the middle is barely visible in the lower half. The mass of the helium in this experiment is calculated in Section 11.4 and found to be 6.8×10^{-6} g—less than seven millionths of a gram!

The usefulness of spectroscopy in recognizing minute quantities of an element is not new. During the first few years of spectroscopy, five elements were discovered that are present on earth only in tiny concentrations. For example, the spectrum of minerals found in the water of a certain spring in Germany was analyzed. Two lines of unknown origin were found in the blue region of the spectrum. This bit of evidence was enough to challenge Robert Bunsen, a German chemist, to search for a new element in the water. He evaporated 40,000 kg of spring water to isolate a sample of the new element, which he named cesium.

In Chapters 5 and 6 you used the characteristic properties of a quantity of matter large enough to be seen and handled in the laboratory to determine the composition of substances. In spectroscopy, the properties of the atoms are used for the same purpose. The results of the two methods always agree completely.

25. Figure A shows some spectra observed with the same spectroscope that was used for Figure 8.9. Which elements can you identify in part (a)? In part (b)?

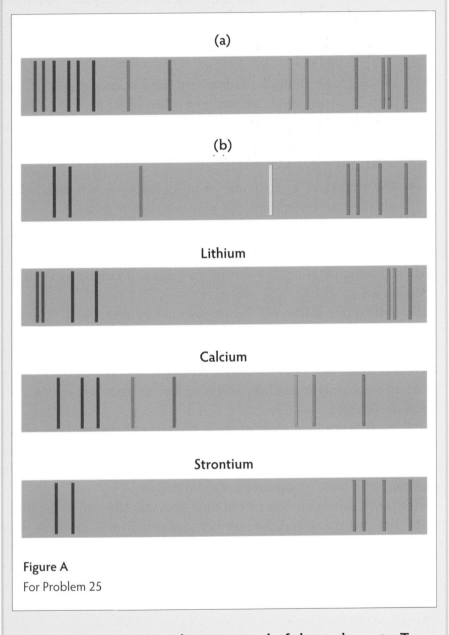

(a)

(b)

Lithium

Calcium

Strontium

Figure A

For Problem 25

26. Suppose a compound is composed of three elements. Two of the elements are sodium and oxygen. Describe how to use spectral analysis to identify the third element.

8.9 An Analog for Radioactive Decay

"EXPERIMENT"
(E)

Having been motivated by observations of radioactivity to develop an atomic model of matter, we are now ready to expand the model to account for what we know about radioactive elements themselves. To do so we will make additional assumptions, which will lead to a testable prediction,

We will make these assumptions:

(1) Whenever an atom of a radioactive element decays, it emits one particle, which affects a counter or other detector.

(2) This process takes place by chance: All atoms have the same chance to decay in any time interval. There is no way of telling which atom will decay next.

(3) The chance of a particular atom decaying is not affected by whether other atoms have or have not already decayed.

Using the power of mathematics, some startling conclusions can be drawn from these assumptions. Instead, you will simulate the mathematical process by using dice instead of rings and fasteners as you did in Section 8.4.

The radioactive atoms will be represented by dice. Each team will begin with 12 dice. The dice will be shaken and thrown onto the table. Dice that land with a six on top will be considered to have decayed and will be removed. They no longer represent an atom of the original radioactive element. By carefully watching for the sixes, you will play the role of the counter.

Shaking the dice gives each of them the same chance to land with a six on top. Also, how any particular die lands is not affected by the other dice. Thus, the dice analog satisfies the assumptions of the model and is consistent with the characteristics of radioactivity.

Each throw stands for some fixed time interval. A record of the number of dice that decay and the number that remain will illustrate what the model says about the decay of a radioactive element over time.

Shake and throw the dice ten times. Make a table showing the number of dice you started with, the number that decayed, and the number that remained after each throw. A sample of such a table is shown in Table 8.1.

A radioactive source producing a small number of counts per minute is considered a weak source. A set of 12 dice is a model for a very weak radioactive source. To see how a strong radioactive source with many more decaying atoms would act, make two more runs. Record the total number of remaining dice and the number of dice decaying from the three runs in two separate columns similar to Table 8.1.

> Why should you remove the dice with a six on top before you throw the dice again?

> Why should you thoroughly shake the remaining dice before the next throw?

Table 8.1		
Number of throw	Number of dice remaining	Number of dice decaying in each throw
0	12	
1	10	2
2	7	3
3	4	3
4	4	0
5	4	0
6	4	0
7	3	1
8	3	0
9	2	1
10	2	0

You can add your decay data to those from the entire class. Now you can graph the class data by drawing a smooth curve that passes quite close to the class data for the number of dice remaining and the number that decayed.

- How many throws did it take for the number of remaining dice to reach half the original value?
- How many throws did it take for the number of dice decaying in each throw to reach half the original value?
- In how many throws did the number of remaining dice drop from half the original value to one quarter of the original value?
- In how many throws did the number of dice decaying in each throw drop from half the original value to one quarter of the original value?

Our dice model of radioactive decay suggests that the number of atoms remaining follows the same kind of curve as the number of atoms decaying per unit time, the *decay rate*.

When you used your record of throws, you counted both the decaying and the remaining dice. However, with a real radioactive element, you can measure only the number of atoms decaying per unit time, that is, the *decay rate*. To see this connection, refer back to Figure 7.7. Compare the shape of the curve in that figure to the shape of the class data graph for the number of dice decaying in this experiment.

Recall that we assumed that the chance of an individual atom decaying is independent of how many atoms are in the sample. Therefore, we expect that the greater the number of atoms in a sample, the greater the decay rate. Or, in other words, the decay rate is proportional to the number of radioactive atoms. We will use this proportionality to find the mass of an atom in Section 11.5.

27. Of the following choices, which describes how the probability that a specific atom of a radioactive element will decay during a 10-minute interval a year from now compares with the probability that it will decay in the next 10 minutes?

   A. Greater

   B. The same

   C. Smaller

28. Suppose your class used a large number of pennies instead of dice and removed those pennies displaying "heads" after each toss.

   a. How many tosses would it take for the number of pennies remaining to reach one-half the original number of pennies?

   b. How many tosses would be required to reduce the number of pennies decaying in each throw to one half of the original number?

29. Recall the assumptions of the model for radioactive decay. Explain in your own words how rolling the dice satisfies these assumptions.

30. a. Is it possible to roll 6 dice and have more display a six than if 12 dice were rolled?

   b. When is it more likely that you will roll a six—when you roll 12 dice or when you roll 6 dice?

8.10 Half-Life

The throwing of dice cannot tell us how much time it will take the decay rate of a radioactive element to drop to half its initial value. But the model makes the following prediction for any radioactive element: Whatever time it takes to reduce the decay rate to one half its initial value, it will take the *same* amount of time to reduce it from one half to one quarter of the initial value. It will take the *same* amount of time to reduce the decay rate from one quarter to one eighth, and so on.

Thus, the model predicts that every radioactive element has a *half-life*, that is, a time during which its decay rate reduces to half its initial value. This half-life is a characteristic property of the element; it is independent of the number of atoms in the sample.

The counting rate measured with a Geiger counter does not equal the decay rate because not all particles enter the counter; some are emitted in other directions. But if we keep the counter always at the same distance from the sample, then the counting rate will be proportional to the decay rate.

The prediction that every radioactive element has a half-life has been tested and verified. The values of the half-lives for a few elements are given in Table 8.2.

Two samples of the same radioactive element have masses of 15 g and 30 g. How do their half-lives compare?

Why is the counting rate measured with a Geiger counter different from the decay rate of the radioactive element?

Table 8.2			
Element	Half-life	Element	Half-life
Uranium	4.5×10^9 years	Polonium	138 days
Radium	1.6×10^3 years	Radon	3.83 days

31. Consider the two quantities *half-life* and *decay rate*.

   a. Which, if either, of these two quantities depends only on the kind of element?

   b. Which, if either, depends also on the number of atoms in the sample?

32. Suppose that at a given moment, you have two samples, one of radon and one of polonium. Each sample contains a billion (1×10^9) atoms.

   a. After 3.83 days, which sample will contain more of the original atoms?

   b. Were there more decays of polonium atoms or of radon atoms during this period?

   c. Which of the two samples has a higher decay rate?

   d. Under the same conditions, which sample will show a greater counting rate?

33. Suppose you repeat "Experiment" 8.9, An Analog for Radioactive Decay, with the following change: On each throw, if one of the dice shows a five or a three, it will be considered to have decayed.

   a. Will the dice still show a half-life? Why?

   b. If your answer to part (a) was yes, how will the new half-life relate to the one you observed in "Experiment" 8.9? Try it.

FOR REVIEW, APPLICATIONS, AND EXTENSIONS

34. Think again of the sealed can referred to in Section 8.1. You are not allowed to pierce the can or break it open. What would you predict about its behavior in each of the following cases?

   a. You lowered the temperature sufficiently.

   b. You raised the temperature sufficiently.

35. Which of the following are *parts* of the atomic model of matter, and which are *illustrations* of the model?

   A. Matter is made up of very tiny particles.

   B. Atoms of the same element are all alike.

   C. A rubber ring combines with a fastener to form FsR.

   D. Atoms of different elements may combine to form compounds.

   E. Marbles can be stacked in a box to represent a solid.

36. In the nineteenth century, Louis Pasteur developed a "germ model" for disease. According to Pasteur, little organisms too small to be seen by the unaided eye were the cause of disease.

   a. How does this model account for the fact that people get sick?

   b. What predictions does the model make about staying healthy?

   c. What are some of the limitations of this model? (Hint: Think of kidney stones or heart attacks.)

37. Suppose that 6 million atoms of hydrogen combine with 2 million atoms of nitrogen to form 2 million molecules of ammonia. How many atoms of hydrogen and how many atoms of nitrogen will there be in each molecule of ammonia?

38. How deep would 40,000 kg of water (the amount evaporated by Robert Bunsen to discover cesium) stand in your classroom?

39. Refer to the graph of the number of remaining dice as a function of the number of throws in Figure B.

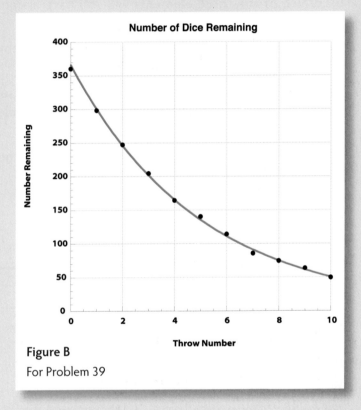

Figure B
For Problem 39

a. How many throws are needed to reduce the number of dice to 80% of the initial number?

b. How many throws are needed to reduce the number of dice to 80% of 80%—that is, to 64% of the initial number?

c. How many throws are needed to reduce the number to 80% of 80% of 80%—that is, to 51% of the initial number?

d. Is "the time needed to reduce the number of atoms of a radioactive element to 80% of the initial number" a characteristic property of the element? If yes, how is this time related to the half-life of the element?

40. Many radioactive elements are waste products in nuclear power plants. Periodically, this waste must be removed and stored safely. Suppose that three radioactive elements are produced. Their half-lives are 30 minutes, 500 years, and 1×10^8 years. Suppose also that when the waste is ready to be shipped, the three elements are present in equal numbers of atoms.

   a. Which of the three elements will have the highest decay rate?

   b. Which of the three elements will still have a significant number of atoms remaining after one year?

   c. If the waste is not stored safely, which of the remaining elements will pose a health hazard after 100 years?

41. a. Since polonium has a half-life of 138 days, it must itself be a product of radioactive decomposition of another element. Why?

   b. Will a freshly prepared sample of polonium have the same half-life as the remainder of an old sample?

THEME FOR A SHORT ESSAY

In or around your house, there are devices that perform particular tasks. You know how to use these devices but you do not know how they work. For you, such devices are black boxes. Choose one of these devices, describe in detail what it does when you operate it, and explain why it is a black box to you.

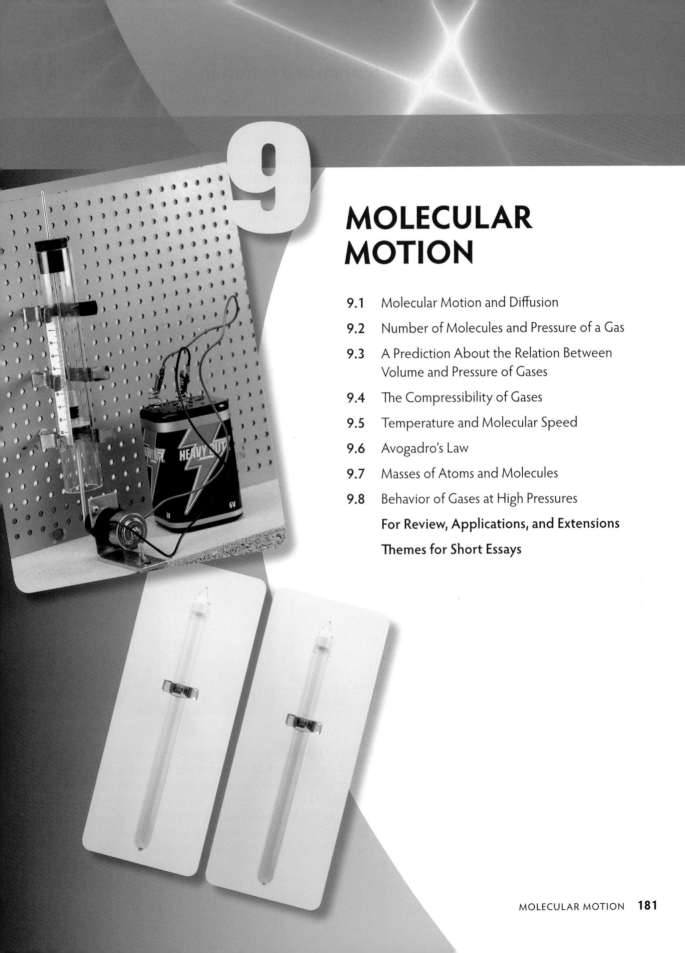

MOLECULAR MOTION

9.1 Molecular Motion and Diffusion

When the cap is removed from a bottle of perfume, you eventually smell it even if you are on the other side of the room. What can you conclude from this observation?

When you put a book on a table, it stays there. But as soon as you take the cap off a bottle of ammonia solution, ammonia comes out of solution, escapes into the air, and spreads in all directions. You can smell it. Hot water evaporates from a bathtub, spreads throughout the room, and often condenses. You can see it on cool mirrors and windowpanes. Water vapor, a gas, moved from the tub to the mirrors and windows. From these observations, we can conclude that molecules of ammonia and water vapor are in motion.

To demonstrate that molecules of a gas move around freely, it is convenient to use a gas that can be liquefied and frozen easily. This gas should also have color so that it can easily be observed. Bromine is an element that has both these properties. It has a deep red-brown color and freezes when cooled by a mixture of dry ice and alcohol.

The photograph on the far left in Figure 9.1 shows a sealed glass tube containing a small quantity of bromine and air. The tube was cooled by

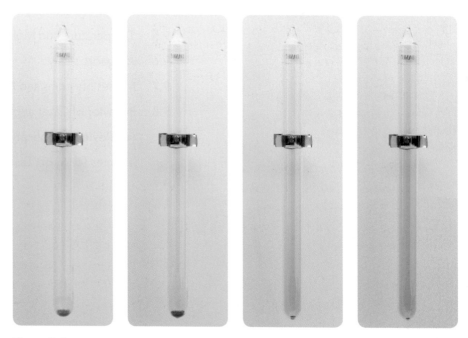

Figure 9.1

A series of photographs of a sealed glass tube containing only bromine and air. It is standing at room temperature. The photograph at the far left was taken 15 seconds after the tube was removed from a mixture of dry ice and alcohol. All the bromine is at the bottom of the tube as a solid. As the tube warms up, the bromine turns to liquid and evaporates. Brown bromine gas slowly spreads upward, gradually darkening the tube until the gas is evenly distributed. The second, third, and fourth pictures were taken 2 minutes, 6 minutes, and 10 minutes after the tube was removed from the dry ice.

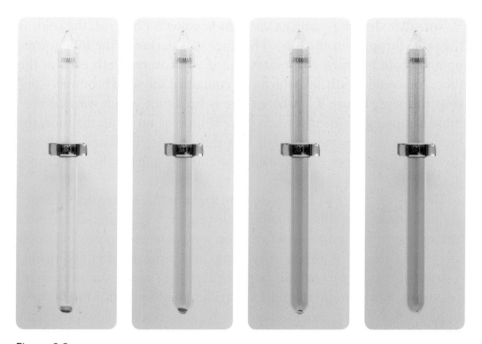

Figure 9.2

The tube shown in this series of photographs is similar to the one in Figure 9.1 except that there is practically no air in it. It was photographed at the same time intervals as the tube in Figure 9.1. Note that as bromine evaporates, it fills the tube evenly, coloring the whole tube a darker and darker shade. Bromine molecules move up the tube more quickly than when air is present in the tube.

a mixture of dry ice and alcohol. All the bromine is seen as a solid at the bottom of the tube, but the air in the tube remained a gas. We know the air remains a gas because nitrogen and oxygen have boiling points much lower than the temperature of dry ice and alcohol.

The other photographs, moving from left to right, show the tube at different times while it was warming. You can see that, as the bromine evaporates, it moves slowly upward until it is evenly distributed throughout the tube. We might think from observing these photographs that bromine molecules move slowly. But is there any other way to interpret these observations?

To find out if the photos shown in Figure 9.1 really tell us something about the speeds of the bromine molecules, we will repeat the experiment with a tube that contains bromine and very little air.

Figure 9.2 shows a set of pictures of a tube that contains bromine and very little air. Most of the air was pumped out, and the tube was sealed while the bromine was frozen. After that, the tube was allowed to warm up and was photographed at the same intervals of time as the tube in Figure 9.1.

What is the evidence that bromine molecules spread faster when air is not present in the tube?

Note that almost as soon as the faintest color is observed, the color is the same throughout the tube. The color gets darker as the tube warms up and more bromine evaporates. But if you covered both ends of the tube, you could hardly tell which end contained the solid bromine. Contrast this with Figure 9.1, where there is no doubt which way the bromine is moving. Evidently, when there is little or no air in the tube, the bromine molecules move so fast that they bounce back and forth and distribute themselves evenly inside the tube so quickly that we cannot perceive it.

There is a way for us to explain why the bromine molecules take longer to move up the tube containing air (Figure 9.1). Think of sprinters attempting to run a 100-meter dash on a track where dozens of people are milling around. A runner may bump into someone after taking only a stride or two. He or she will be pushed aside or may even be bounced backward. After another couple of strides, another collision will have similar results. What would otherwise be a quick dash down the track ends up becoming a zigzag path. It is no wonder that under this condition, it will take longer for the runners to finish than if the track were clear. In this picture, the runners play the role of the evaporating bromine and the milling crowd represents the air in the tube.

What causes the molecules in a gas to move in zigzag paths?

To sum up, molecules of a gas apparently move at high speeds. Because of the many collisions, one gas spreads through another rather slowly. This process of one gas spreading through another is called *diffusion*.

1. What would be different about the photographs in Figure 9.1 if the bromine evaporated more rapidly? If there were more air in the tube?

2. What evidence leads you to believe that atoms are in motion and not at rest?

9.2 Number of Molecules and Pressure of a Gas

The fasteners and rings we used to illustrate the atomic model in Chapter 8 helped us visualize how elements combine to form compounds. But the fasteners and rings were not constantly moving as are the molecules of a gas. If we wish to predict the properties of gases, we must extend the atomic model to include the motion of molecules.

To illustrate the motion of gas molecules and to help us predict some effects of this motion, we will use small steel spheres to represent the gas

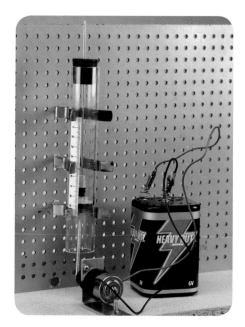

Figure 9.3

A plastic cylinder, with a movable platform near the bottom, contains some small steel spheres. A movable disk lies on top of the spheres. The movable platform is vibrated up and down by a shaft connected to a small electric motor.

Figure 9.4

A close-up view of the movable platform, spheres, and upper disk shown in Figure 9.3.

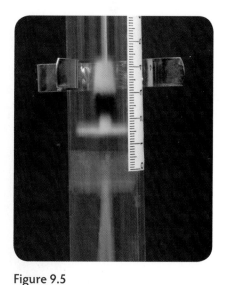

Figure 9.5

The cylinder shown in Figure 9.4, with the bottom platform being vibrated rapidly up and down over a short distance by an electric motor. The cylinder contains 10 steel spheres. The photograph is a time exposure of 4 seconds.

molecules. Of course, steel spheres do not stay in motion on their own. So if we want to study steel spheres moving in a zigzag motion over a period of time, we have to keep them in motion. We can do this with the apparatus shown in Figures 9.3 and 9.4.

The spheres inside the vertical transparent cylinder (Figure 9.3) are resting on a lower platform that is connected to an electric motor. An upper disk is resting on top of the spheres (Figure 9.4). When the motor is turned on, the lower platform vibrates rapidly up and down over a short distance, keeping the spheres in motion. This causes the moving spheres to push the upper disk higher in the cylinder.

Figure 9.5 shows what happens to the platform and the upper disk when the motor is turned on. The shutter of the camera was open for 4 seconds. During this time interval, the "molecules" zigzag about so quickly that they have been smeared out and are practically invisible in the photograph. During any small interval of time, only a few spheres collide with the upper disk. The other "molecules" bounce around in the volume between the disks. Note that the upper disk has been pushed higher in the cylinder by the spheres bouncing off its bottom surface.

In Figure 9.5, there are 10 spheres in the space between the two disks. How does the volume of the "sphere gas" change if we double the number of "molecules" in the tube? Figure 9.6 shows us the answer. After 10 additional spheres have been added, the volume has increased; in fact, it has about doubled.

To force the moving spheres back to the volume they occupied when only 10 spheres were present, we have to add mass to the upper disk. With twice the mass pushing down on the spheres (Figure 9.7), we find that a sample of sphere gas containing 20 spheres occupies about the same volume as a sample with 10 spheres held down by the original mass (Figure 9.5). In other words, twice as many spheres bouncing around in the same volume push on the disk twice as hard. They exert twice the pressure on the disk. From this observation, we learn that the contribution of any sphere to holding up the disk is independent of all the other spheres.

The mass of the individual spheres is not important in this model. Whether we use heavy spheres or light spheres, doubling the number of spheres doubles the pressure.

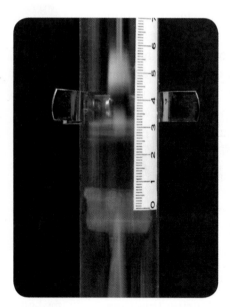

Figure 9.6

With twice as many steel spheres (20) in the cylinder as in Figure 9.5, the volume of the "sphere gas" is close to twice the volume shown in Figure 9.5.

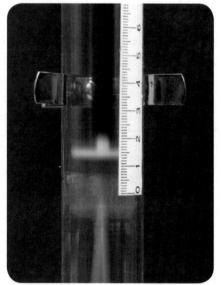

Figure 9.7

Mass was added to the upper disk to double its mass, which reduces the volume occupied by 20 spheres to that occupied by the 10 spheres in Figure 9.5.

3. If a gas sample is compressed until its pressure is doubled, what will happen to the volume of the gas? To the density of the gas?

4. In the sphere-gas machine, what would you expect to happen if the top disk had less mass?

5. Two bricks are placed on each of the pistons shown below in Figure A. In which cylinder does the gas exert the greatest pressure on the piston?

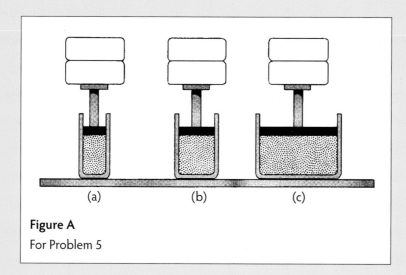

(a)   (b)   (c)

Figure A
For Problem 5

6. Two bricks are placed on each of three wooden dowels resting on clay as shown in Figure B. Which dowel will sink fastest into the clay? Which dowel exerts the greatest pressure on the clay beneath it?

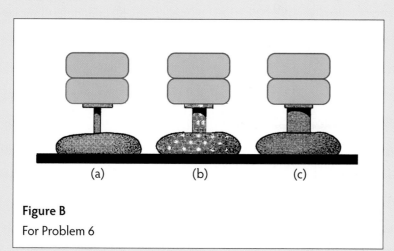

(a)   (b)   (c)

Figure B
For Problem 6

9.3 A Prediction About the Relation Between Volume and Pressure of Gases

We can now generalize the results that we obtained from the sphere-gas machine. Imagine a quantity of gas contained in a cylinder equipped with a piston like that shown in Figure 9.8. If we double the number of gas molecules in the cylinder while keeping the volume and temperature constant, the pressure exerted by the gas on the bottom of the piston will also double. This is just what we would expect based on our sphere-gas model.

Forcing more gas molecules into a given volume is not the only way to increase the pressure. We can also increase the pressure of a gas by decreasing the volume as we keep the number of molecules and the temperature constant. Figure 9.9 shows a cylinder containing a gas. In Figure 9.9(a), the number of molecules in the upper half is almost the

> How can you increase the pressure that a gas exerts on its container without adding more gas to the container?

Figure 9.8

(a) Molecules are spread evenly throughout the cylinder. As they bounce against the piston that seals the top of the cylinder, they create pressure on the piston.
(b) If we double the number of molecules in the cylinder and the piston is kept in the same position as in (a), the pressure exerted by the gas will double.

Figure 9.9

Halving the volume of a gas by moving the piston down to point X will double its density and, we predict, double the pressure.

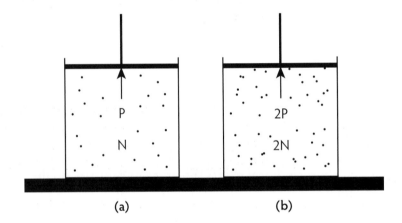

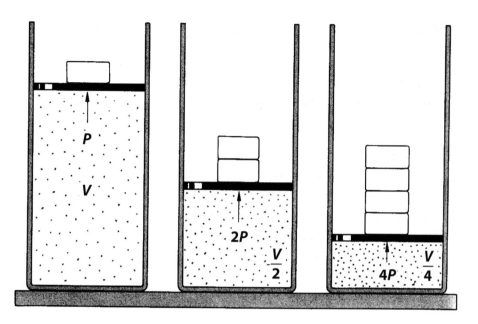

Figure 9.10

The atomic model of a gas predicts that as the volume of a gas is decreased, its pressure rises in the manner shown by the three diagrams.

same as the number of molecules in the lower half. If we push the piston down to position X, we will double the number of molecules in the lower half of the cylinder (Figure 9.9(b)). Based on what we saw with the sphere-gas machine, we can expect that the gas will now exert twice as much pressure as when the piston was at the top of the cylinder.

Suppose we push the piston down still farther so that it is halfway between X and the bottom of the cylinder. If our model still holds, the pressure that the molecules will exert on the piston will double again (Figure 9.10). In other words, we can predict that when the volume of gas is decreased to one-fourth its original volume, the pressure will increase to four times the original pressure.

We can generalize our predictions by saying that if we decrease the volume of a gas by a certain factor, the pressure of the gas will increase by that same factor. This relationship is illustrated by the graph in Figure 9.11.

We have made two basic assumptions in developing this argument:

(1) Molecules of a gas are constantly in motion.

(2) The bouncing of one molecule off the wall of a container is not affected by the presence of other molecules.

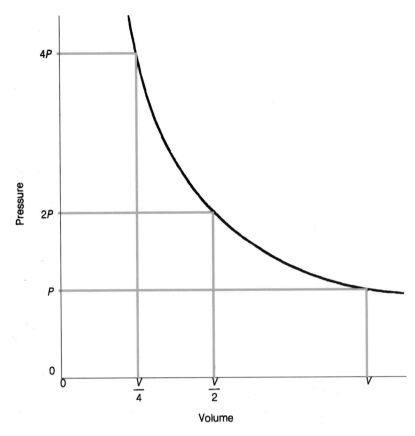

Figure 9.11

A graph of the pressure of a gas as a function of its volume, as predicted from the atomic model.

We made no assumptions about the number of atoms or the types of atoms that are in a molecule of the gas. Thus, if the predicted relation between the pressure and volume of a gas is correct, it should hold true for all gases as long as the two basic assumptions are correct.

7. If no more molecules were added, what would you have to do to the volume of a gas in order to triple its pressure?

8. Suppose that the volume of a sample of gas is allowed to increase until it is five times its original volume. The number of molecules in the sample and the temperature of the sample do not change. What will happen to the pressure of the gas?

9. Look at the graph in Figure 9.11. What is the pressure when the volume is reduced from V to 1/3 V? From V to 3/4 V?

9.4 The Compressibility of Gases

The apparatus shown in Figure 9.12 was used to check the prediction we have just made about the relation between the pressure and the volume of air. By adding bricks to the platform on the top of the syringe's piston, the air in the syringe was compressed.

Before we added bricks to the platform, we adjusted the initial volume of gas in the syringe to about 30 cm³. We did this by pushing the piston down while a length of thin string was held between the inside of the syringe and the piston's seal (Figure 9.13). The string allows air to escape as the piston is pushed down. When the volume reached 30 cm³, we pulled out the string.

Then, by adding bricks to the platform on the top of the syringe's piston, the air in the syringe was compressed. This syringe was stable enough to hold up to four bricks.

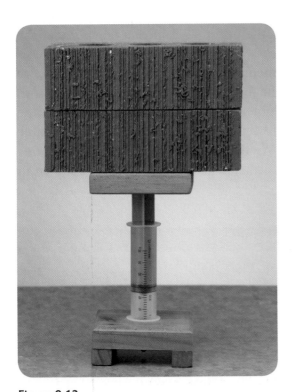

Figure 9.12

A syringe containing air can be used to find the relation between the pressure and the volume of a gas. Air is compressed to smaller and smaller volumes by adding bricks of equal mass to the platform on the top of the syringe.

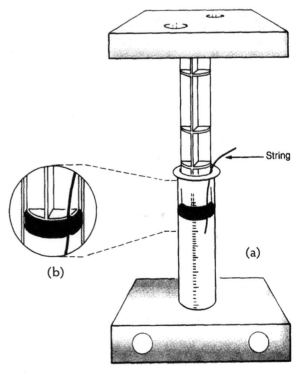

Figure 9.13

The inset in (b) shows how a piece of string is used to hold open the seal of the syringe in (a) when adjusting the initial volume of air in the syringe.

Our procedure is complicated by the effect of friction. When the piston is pushed down, friction prevents it from moving down as far as it would if there were no friction. This results in a larger volume measurement than we would expect from our predicted relation between volume and pressure.

The reverse happens when we remove bricks. If we remove them one by one, friction prevents the piston from rising up as far as we would expect. However, we can overcome this friction problem by taking two readings of each volume—one as we put bricks on the platform and one as we take them off. Averaging each pair of measurements tends to cancel the error introduced by friction.

What procedure can be used to compensate for the effect of friction in this experiment?

To determine the initial volume before adding the first brick, we pulled the platform up a little and let it fall until it settled. We then recorded our first volume for "zero bricks" as 30.0 cm³.

Next, we added the first brick without giving it any downward push, let it come to rest, and recorded the volume. Following this same procedure, we continued to add bricks of equal mass and recorded the volume until we reached a total of four bricks. At this point we had half our volume measurements—those for the piston as it moved down under the pressure of more and more bricks.

To obtain volume measurements for the piston on the way up, we first pushed down slightly on the four bricks and then let go. The piston rose, but it came to rest at a volume slightly below that recorded after the fourth brick was added. This resting point gave us our second volume measurement for four bricks. We then removed the bricks one by one and recorded each volume in turn. The data we obtained are shown in Table 9.1.

Table 9.1				
Down		Up		
Number of bricks	Volume (cm³)	Number of bricks	Volume (cm³)	Average volume (cm³)
0	30.0	0	28.4	29.2
1	22.6	1	20.0	21.3
2	17.8	2	15.7	16.8
3	14.1	3	12.8	13.5
4	11.7	4	10.9	11.3

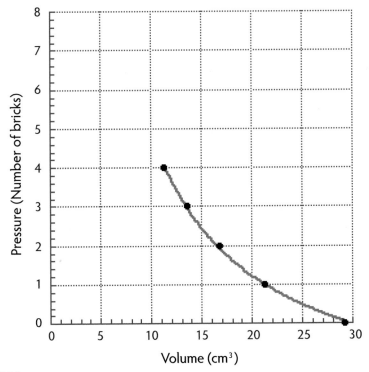

Figure 9.14

The pressure of a gas (air) as a function of volume. The data are plotted from Table 9.1. Note that when the volume is halved, the pressure does not double.

Figure 9.14 shows the graph of these data. The graph looks much like Figure 9.11. But careful examination reveals that there is a significant difference between these two graphs. When the volume is halved from 24 cm³ to 12 cm³, the pressure goes from about 0.6 bricks to 3.6 bricks—a factor of 6, not 2. Is our prediction wrong?

Let's consider again the details of this experiment. We started with no bricks on the wooden platform and then added them one at a time. Is the pressure on the gas in the syringe zero with no brick on the platform? This is not the case. The syringe's piston, the wooden platform, and earth's atmosphere were all pressing on the gas. To find the total pressure on the gas in the syringe, we have to add this pressure to the pressure exerted by bricks. Suppose we plot the total pressure as a function of the number of bricks. The curve will look like the curve in Figure 9.14, except that each point will be raised by the same amount corresponding to the pressure exerted by the atmosphere, platform, and syringe.

How can we find the pressure exerted by the wooden platform, the piston, and earth's atmosphere? Look at Figure 9.14. At 30 cm³, the pressure exerted by the bricks was zero. At half that volume (15 cm³), the pressure on the graph reads 2.4 bricks. According to the atomic model

> What else, other than the bricks, is pressing on the gas in the syringe?

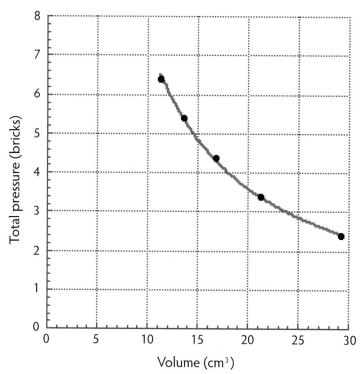

Figure 9.15

The same graph as shown in Figure 9.14, but all points on the curve have been moved vertically upward 2.4 bricks on the pressure scale. This was done to account for the pressure exerted on the gas by the piston, the wooden platform, and the earth's atmosphere.

of a gas, the pressure at 15 cm³ should be double the pressure at 30 cm³. For this to be true, we need to add a pressure equal to 2.4 bricks to every reading (Figure 9.15). Now the total pressure at 15 cm³ reads 4.8 bricks, and at 30 cm³ it reads 2.4 bricks, just as the gas model predicts. Evidently, the piston, the wooden platform, and the earth's atmosphere are pressing on the gas with a pressure equivalent to 2.4 bricks.

To be sure of this conclusion, we need to check some other points on the curve. For example, in Figure 9.15, when the volume decreases from 24.0 cm³ to 12.0 cm³, the pressure increases from 3 to 6 bricks, as expected. Halving the volume does double the pressure. Our prediction, made by use of the gas model, agrees with measurements of the pressure and volume of an air sample as it is compressed in a syringe.

This experiment has been repeated with other gases. If the initial volume is the same as in Figure 9.15, and if the same syringe and bricks are used, the graphs are the same for air, carbon dioxide, propane, and other gases. In other words, under the conditions of our experiment, different gases have the same compressibility, as was predicted by our model.

The relationship we have found between the pressure and the volume of a gas was discovered by Robert Boyle in 1662. Today, it is called *Boyle's law*. We predicted Boyle's law from the atomic model. Boyle, on the other hand, discovered the law by doing experiments similar to the one we have described in this section. He did this before there was an atomic model for gases.

10. In Figure 9.15, when the total pressure is doubled by increasing from 3 bricks to 6 bricks:

    a. What is the ratio of the initial volume to the final volume?

    b. Does your answer agree with the atomic model?

11. Suppose someone claimed that the pressure of the atmosphere, platform, and piston should be equal to the pressure of 3 bricks. How would you refute this claim?

12. A cylinder contains 100 cm^3 of air at a total pressure P (pressure due to piston plus atmospheric pressure). What will the total pressure become if the volume is reduced to 50 cm^3? To 10 cm^3?

13. Figure 9.15 is a graph of pressure as a function of the volume of air over a range of volumes from about 30 cm^3 to about 10 cm^3. What would you predict the total pressure to be (in units of bricks) if the volume of gas were 10 cm^3? 70 cm^3?

9.5 Temperature and Molecular Speed

Let us return to the sphere-gas apparatus used in Section 9.2. What can be done to increase the volume of the "gas" without changing the mass of the upper disk or the number of spheres? You might think that if the spheres are made to move faster, they will strike the upper disk harder and more often. This will increase the pressure on the disk, and make it rise higher in the cylinder—causing the volume to increase. But an opposite effect also occurs. As the disk rises, the spheres must travel farther between collisions with the disk. They will not strike the disk as frequently, and so they exert less pressure on the disk. When these two effects become balanced, the pressure exerted by the spheres on the upper disk is just what it was before the speeds of the spheres were increased. The upper disk stops rising and remains at a higher position,

From the results of the sphere-gas machine, what can you infer happens to the speeds of the molecules in a gas when the temperature of the gas increases?

showing that the volume of the gas has increased as a result of increasing the speed of the spheres.

In the sphere-gas machine, the speeds of the spheres depend on how fast the motor vibrates the lower platform. Speeding up or slowing down the motor will change the speeds of the spheres. Figure 9.16 shows what happens when we have the motor running at different speeds. It is clear that as the speeds of the spheres increase, the volume increases. The fact that the volume of a real gas also increases with temperature suggests that the temperature of a real gas is related to the speeds of its molecules. At higher temperatures, the molecules move faster. At lower temperatures, they move more slowly.

To check this connection between temperature and molecular speed in a real gas, we have to find a way to speed up or slow down the gas molecules and see how the temperature of the gas changes. How can this be done?

When you throw a good tennis ball at a hard wall, it bounces back at almost the same speed it had when it struck the wall. On the other hand, if you strike an oncoming tennis ball with a racket, the ball leaves the racket at a higher speed than it had before the collision. If many tennis balls moving at different speeds each collide with a racket moving toward them, they will all bounce back at higher speeds. As a result, their average speed will have been increased by collisions with the moving racket.

Let's think of something similar using molecules of a gas and a piston moving toward them. Consider air in a tube that is closed at one end and fitted with a piston at the other end. While the piston is being pushed in, the molecules striking it will bounce back at higher speeds. The piston is acting like a tennis racket striking a ball. Hence, when a gas

Figure 9.16

In each of the three photographs, the sphere-gas machine contains the same number of steel spheres, but the speed of the driving motor increases from (a) to (c).

is compressed, we expect its temperature to rise. This effect can be demonstrated very convincingly by placing a few cotton fibers at the bottom of a sealed tube and quickly pushing a piston into the tube. The speeds of the molecules are increased—that is, the temperature of the gas is increased—so that the cotton fibers ignite, as shown in Figure 9.17.

How is the temperature of a sample of gas related to the average speed of its molecules?

> ⓘ **CAUTION: Do not try this with a normal test tube. The tube will burst due to the high pressure.**

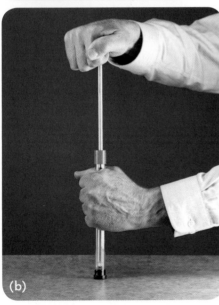

Figure 9.17

A fire syringe. (a) Its parts are a protective outer tube having a cushion at the bottom, a thick-walled glass inner tube, and a metal piston having 3 O-rings. (b) When the piston is rapidly pushed down into the glass tube, the rising temperature of the gas will ignite the cotton fibers. (c) A flash of light from the burning fibers is seen through the protective outer tube.

To sum up, we have seen that the temperature of a gas is related to the average speed of its molecules. When the average speed of the molecules increases, the temperature rises.

We have used the atomic model to discuss the expansion of a gas when its temperature is increased. In doing so, we made use of the same

Figure 9.18

Graphs of the thermal expansion of three different gases that had the same initial volume. The expansion of all three gases is the same, independent of the kind of molecule.

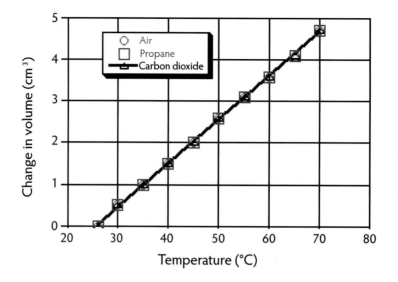

two basic assumptions that we used in the discussion of the compressibility of gases in Sections 9.3 and 9.4:

(1) the molecules of a gas are constantly in motion and

(2) the bouncing of one molecule off the wall of a container is not affected by the presence of other molecules.

The assumptions do not depend on the kinds of molecules that make up the gas. Therefore, the atomic model predicts that, at least at low pressures, equal volumes of all gases expand by the same amount for the same increase in temperature. Figure 9.18 confirms this prediction for three gases.

14. A fast-moving tennis ball strikes a racket that is moving back, away from the ball.

   a. How does the speed of the ball before it hits the racket compare with the speed after it rebounds?

   b. If the piston in Figure 9.18 is pulled up, what happens to the gas molecules when they rebound?

   c. What will happen to the temperature of the gas as the piston rises?

15. Why does a bicycle pump heat up when you pump up a tire?

9.6 Avogadro's Law

In the preceding two sections, we saw something remarkable about all gases. Unlike with density, compressibility and thermal expansion do not depend on what the gas is. The gas may be carbon dioxide, oxygen, nitrogen, or a mixture of all three. What apparently counts is the number of molecules of gas in a given volume.

Consider the following two situations: Suppose we add a volume V of nitrogen to an identical volume V of nitrogen, both at the same pressure and temperature. The pressure will double and so will the number of molecules (Figure 9.19a). Now suppose that we add a volume V of nitrogen to the same volume V of carbon dioxide, again at the same pressure and temperature. The pressure will double as before. Will the number of molecules also double (Figure 9.19b)? In other words, do the same volumes of different gases at the same pressure and temperature contain the same number of molecules?

In 1811, Amedeo Avogadro hypothesized that equal volumes of gas at the same pressure and temperature contain an equal number of molecules.

The chemists of that time objected to Avogadro's hypothesis. Their objections were based on the reasonable assumption that when an element in liquid form evaporates, its atoms leave the liquid's surface one by one. Therefore, they thought, gases of elements such as hydrogen, oxygen, or chlorine would be made up of single atoms; they would be *monatomic*. Only gases of compounds such as carbon dioxide or ammo-

> Did Avogadro's hypothesis involve atoms or molecules?

> What was the main objection that many of the chemists of Avogadro's time had to his hypothesis?

> What does it mean to say that a gas is *monatomic*?

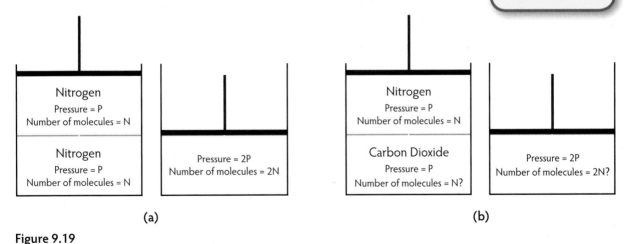

(a)   **(b)**

Figure 9.19

(a) When two equal volumes of nitrogen at the same pressure and temperature are compressed into a single volume, both the pressure and the number of molecules double. (b) When a similar procedure is performed with nitrogen and carbon dioxide, the pressure also doubles.

Figure 9.20

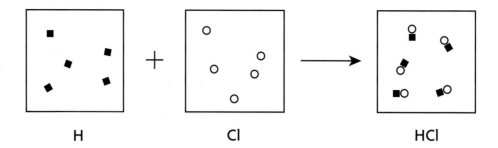

H   Cl   HCl

nia were thought to be made up of molecules containing more than one atom.

Based on this assumption, the chemists correctly argued that Avogadro's hypothesis would predict that the reaction of one volume of hydrogen and one volume of chlorine should form one volume of hydrogen chloride (Figure 9.20). In reality, though, a reaction between equal volumes of hydrogen and chlorine produced *two* volumes of hydrogen chloride at the same temperature and pressure. Therefore— even though they had no evidence for their assumption that the gases of elements are all monatomic—they said that Avogadro's hypothesis must be wrong. This belief was so strong that Avogadro's hypothesis was ignored and almost forgotten.

Close to fifty years later, Stanislao Cannizzaro showed that if the molecules of hydrogen, oxygen, nitrogen, chlorine and some other gaseous elements are assumed to be made up of two atoms, all the objections disappeared. Molecules made up of two atoms are called diatomic molecules. Indeed, applying Cannizzaro's idea about diatomic molecules to the production of hydrogen chloride yields two volumes of hydrogen chloride (Figure 9.21). Avogadro's hypothesis became *Avogadro's law.*

There is a lesson to be learned from the history of Avogadro's law: we must never take things for granted. Even a very attractive assumption must be tested.

> What does it mean to say that a gas is *diatomic*?

Figure 9.21

With diatomic molecules of hydrogen and chlorine, Avogadro's hypothesis correctly accounts for the production of two volumes of hydrogen chloride.

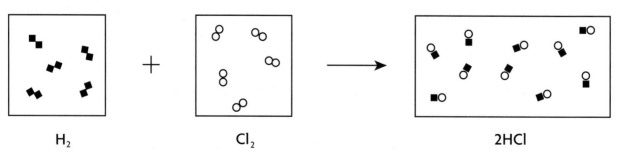

H_2 Cl_2 2HCl

16. Consider a container holding 5.0 liters of chlorine and another container holding 1.0 liter of nitrogen at the same temperature and pressure. What is the ratio of the number of molecules of chlorine to the number of molecules of nitrogen?

17. Consider two containers of equal volumes. One contains a mixture of nitrogen and oxygen; the other contains pure nitrogen. Both gases are at the same temperature and pressure. According to Avogadro's law, is the total number of molecules in each container the same, or is just the total number of nitrogen molecules the same? Explain.

9.7 Masses of Atoms and Molecules

Avogadro's law has very useful consequences; it lets us express the mass of atoms and molecules in terms of the mass of a hydrogen atom.

Consider two samples of propane and hydrogen of equal volume. For each gas, the mass of the sample is given by the product of its density and its volume:

Mass of propane sample = volume · (density of propane)

and

Mass of hydrogen sample = volume · (density of hydrogen).

We now form the ratio of the masses of the two samples:

$$\frac{\text{Mass of propane}}{\text{Mass of hydrogen}} = \frac{\text{volume} \cdot (\text{density of propane})}{\text{volume} \cdot (\text{density of hydrogen})}$$

Because the two samples have the same volume, the volumes will cancel when we calculate the ratio of the masses of the two samples:

$$\frac{\text{Mass of propane}}{\text{Mass of hydrogen}} = \frac{\text{density of propane}}{\text{density of hydrogen}}$$

Why can you ignore the volumes of the propane and hydrogen samples when the ratio of the masses of the samples is calculated?

We can also express the mass of each sample as the product of the number of molecules and the mass of one molecule (See Section 8.5 where we applied the same relation to atoms.):

Mass of propane = (# of propane molecules) · (mass of a propane molecule)

and

Mass of hydrogen = (# of hydrogen molecules) · (mass of a hydrogen molecule).

Again calculating the ratio of the masses of the two samples:

$$\frac{\text{Mass of propane}}{\text{Mass of hydrogen}} = \frac{(\text{\# of molecules}) \cdot (\text{mass of a propane molecule})}{(\text{\# of molecules}) \cdot (\text{mass of a hydrogen molecule})}$$

Why do the numbers of molecules of propane and hydrogen cancel when the ratio of the masses is formed?

We can select the two samples of propane and hydrogen to have equal volumes and be at the same temperature and pressure. According to Avogadro's law, the two samples contain the same number of molecules. Therefore, the number of molecules cancels, and we have:

$$\frac{\text{Mass of propane}}{\text{Mass of hydrogen}} = \frac{\text{mass of a propane molecule}}{\text{mass of a hydrogen molecule}}$$

What are the two equations for the ratio of the masses of the two samples?

We now have two equations for the ratio of the masses of two samples of different gases having the same volume at the same temperature and pressure. Equating the right-hand sides of these two equations, we have:

$$\frac{\text{Mass of a propane molecule}}{\text{Mass of a hydrogen molecule}} = \frac{\text{density of propane}}{\text{density of hydrogen}}$$

This equation holds for any two gases—not just propane and hydrogen. But it is convenient to compare the molecular mass of any gas to that of hydrogen because hydrogen has the lowest density of all gases at the same temperature and pressure (see Table 3.1 on page 55). During the nineteenth century, no one knew what the mass of a hydrogen atom was in grams. So the chemists of that time decided to choose the mass of one hydrogen atom as one mass unit. Later a slightly different unit of mass was chosen. It was given the name *unified atomic mass unit* and the symbol u. The mass of one hydrogen atom, given to two significant digits, is 1.0 u. Therefore, the mass of a hydrogen molecule is very close to 2.0 u. Using 2.0 u for the molecular mass of hydrogen and multiplying both sides of the last equation by 2.0 u, we find

$$\text{Mass of propane molecule (u)} = 2.0\,\text{u} \times \frac{\text{density of propane}}{\text{density of hydrogen}}$$

This equation relates the mass of a gas molecule to measureable quantities—densities. Recall that you measured the density of carbon dioxide in Chapter 3. Indeed, this equation, which is based on Avogadro's law, inspired chemists to measure the densities of many gaseous elements

Table 9.2 The Atomic Masses of Some Elements

Atom	Mass (u)	Atom	Mass (u)
Aluminum	27.0	Mercury	201
Bromine	79.9	Nickel	58.7
Calcium	40.1	Nitrogen	14.0
Carbon	12.0	Oxygen	16.0
Chlorine	35.5	Phosphorus	31.0
Copper	63.5	Polonium	209
Gold	197	Potassium	39.1
Helium	4.00	Sodium	23.0
Hydrogen	1.01	Strontium	87.6
Iodine	127	Sulfur	32.1
Iron	55.8	Thorium	232
Lead	207	Tin	119
Lithium	6.94	Uranium	238
Magnesium	24.3	Zinc	65.4

and compounds. From the ratios of the densities, they were able to calculate many atomic and molecular masses.

Several atomic masses are presented in Table 9.2. The importance of knowing atomic masses will become evident in the next chapter.

18. At room temperature and atmospheric pressure, the density of propane is 1.9×10^{-3} g/cm^3. Under the same conditions, the density of hydrogen is 8.4×10^{-5} g/cm^3. If the mass of a hydrogen molecule is 2.0 atomic mass units (u), what is the mass of one propane molecule in atomic mass units?

19. Iodine is a solid at room temperature. How can the mass of one molecule of iodine be found using Avogadro's law?

20. The density of methane at atmospheric pressure and room temperature is 6.7×10^{-4} g/cm^3.

   a. What is the mass of one methane molecule?

   b. If a molecule of methane is made up of one carbon atom and four hydrogen atoms (CH_4), what is the mass of one carbon atom?

21. In Table 3.1 (page 55), look up the densities of oxygen and carbon dioxide.

   a. What is the mass of a molecule of oxygen?

   b. What is the mass of a molecule of carbon dioxide?

   c. Assume that a molecule of carbon dioxide contains only one atom of carbon. Using your answer for the mass of a carbon atom from Question 20, what is the mass of the oxygen part of a molecule of carbon dioxide?

   d. How many atoms of oxygen have this mass?

   e. What is the formula for carbon dioxide?

9.8 Behavior of Gases at High Pressures

We have seen that gases have the same compressibility at pressures near atmospheric pressure. What happens if we compress gases to very high pressures?

Figure 9.22 is a graph of volume as a function of pressure at 0°C for nitrogen and hydrogen at high pressures. The lowest curve is what would be predicted for both gases using Boyle's law. You can see that both gases follow Boyle's law at pressures less than approximately 150 atmospheres. At relatively low pressures, it is impossible to distinguish between the two gases using their compressibility.

At very high pressures, however, the story is quite different. Neither gas is as compressible as one would expect from Boyle's law, and their compressibilities are different. At greater and greater pressures, the compressibilities of the two gases differ more and more. Therefore, at high pressures, the compressibilities of gases do depend on the kind of molecule that makes up the gas.

In Section 9.3, we assumed that the bouncing of one gas molecule off the wall of a container is not affected by the presence of other gas molecules. This assumption is valid only at low pressures. Gas molecules at high pressures are close together and apparently affect each other's motion. Different kinds of molecules affect each other differently.

The compressibility that we observe for gases at such high pressures is very similar to the compressibility of liquids. For example, the density of nitrogen gas at this high pressure is nearly as great as that of water. From these observations, we would predict that the compressibility of liquids and solids should also depend on the kinds of molecules they are made

At high pressures, are gases more or less compressible than Boyle's law predicts? How do the compressibilities of nitrogen and hydrogen compare at high pressures?

What leads us to predict that the compressibility of liquids and solids depends on the kinds of molecules present in the liquid or solid?

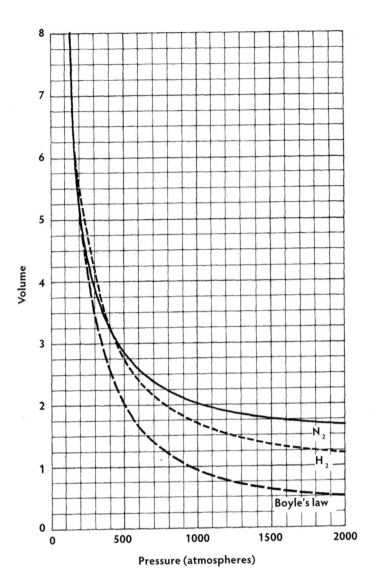

Figure 9.22

The compressibilities of nitrogen and hydrogen at 0°C are shown on this graph of volume as a function of pressure. The lowest line is the curve a gas would have if it satisfied Boyle's law over this wide range of pressures.

of. This, in fact, is the case. Although very high pressures are needed to compress liquids by a measurable amount, the compressibility of a liquid does indeed depend on the kind of molecules making up the liquid.

For Review, Applications, and Extensions

22. Figure 9.2 shows that when bromine vaporizes in a vacuum, the color seems to spread immediately throughout the tube. What can you infer about the speed of the bromine molecules?

23. Would you expect an increase in pressure on the inside walls of the air-filled bromine tube in Figure 9.1 as the bromine evaporates? Why?

24. Do the moving steel balls exert any pressure on the sidewalls of the vertical tube of the sphere-gas machine? What changes would you make in the machine to check your answer?

25. If you run the sphere-gas machine with a long tube and without a top disk, the density of the gas is greatest near the bottom and decreases as you go up the tube. Is there a similar effect in the atmosphere of the earth?

26. What are the different ways that the pressure of a gas can be increased?

27. How is the volume of the steel-sphere gas affected by motor speed? Number of spheres? The mass of the top disk?

28. Diesel engines do not ignite the fuel-air mixture with a spark from a spark plug as gasoline engines do. Instead, air in the cylinder is compressed by a piston. At maximum compression, fuel sprayed into the compressed air ignites and drives the piston back. How can you explain the ignition of the gas when there is no spark to ignite it?

29. The molecules of a gas get closer together when the gas is compressed to very high pressures. How might you get the molecules of a gas close together without applying very high pressure to it?

THEMES FOR SHORT ESSAYS

1. Tell the story in first person about a molecule of nitrogen in the air in the glass cylinder in Figure 9.17 when the plunger is quickly pushed down.

2. Can you think of a situation in which you, or someone you know, took something for granted that turned out not to be true? If so, describe what was taken for granted and what the consequences were of finding out it was not true.

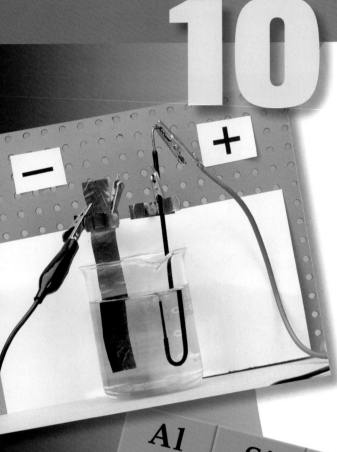

10

THE CLASSIFICATION OF ELEMENTS: THE PERIODIC TABLE

10.1 A Historical Sketch

How did Lavoisier distinguish between compounds and elements?

In 1789, Antoine Lavoisier distinguished between compounds and elements by stating that elements could not be broken down into simpler substances (Section 6.10). A decade later, around 1800, 29 elements were known. They are listed in Table 10.1.

Table 10.1					
Element	Symbol	Year of Discovery*	Element	Symbol	Year of Discovery
Antimony	Sb		Zinc	Zn	1746
Carbon	C		Nickel	Ni	1751
Copper	Cu		Hydrogen	H	1766
Gold	Au		Nitrogen	N	1772
Iron	Fe		Manganese	Mn	1774
Lead	Pb		Oxygen	O	1774
Mercury	Hg		Molybdenum	Mo	1778
Platinum	Pt		Chromium	Cr	1780
Silver	Ag		Tellurium	Te	1782
Sulfur	S		Tungsten	W	1783
Tin	Sn		Yttrium	Y	1789
Arsenic	As	1250	Strontium	Sr	1790
Bismuth	Bi	circa 1400	Titanium	Ti	1791
Phosphorus	P	1669	Beryllium	Be	1798
Cobalt	Co	1735			

* The first 11 of the 29 elements listed have been known since antiquity, long before the distinction between elements and compounds was made.

Which elements were known in ancient times?

Between 1800 and 1850, an additional 26 elements were discovered (Table 10.2), almost doubling the number of known elements.

Fifty-five elements were known by 1850. Evidently, chemists were looking for new elements very intensively in those years. How were these elements discovered?

Some elements—such as gold, silver, copper, and carbon—exist in nature in pure (or almost pure) form. They occur in sufficient concen-

Table 10.2

Element	Symbol	Year of Discovery	Element	Symbol	Year of Discovery
Niobium	Nb	1801	Chlorine	Cl	1810
Tantalum	Ta	1802	Iodine	I	1811
Cerium	Ce	1803	Cadmium	Cd	1817
Iridium	Ir	1803	Lithium	Li	1817
Osmium	Os	1803	Selenium	Se	1817
Palladium	Pd	1803	Silicon	Si	1824
Rhodium	Rh	1803	Zirconium	Zr	1824
Potassium	K	1807	Aluminum	Al	1825
Sodium	Na	1807	Bromine	Br	1826
Barium	Ba	1808	Thorium	Th	1828
Boron	B	1808	Vanadium	V	1830
Calcium	Ca	1808	Uranium	U	1841
Magnesium	Mg	1808	Ruthenium	Ru	1844

trations and large enough pieces that they can be collected by sifting. These elements were known in antiquity and were found free in nature. They may also be found in compounds.

The chemists who discovered most of the elements during the first half of the nineteenth century basically used the same methods that you used and read about in Chapters 5 and 6. To arrive at pure substances, they dissolved and filtered as well as using fractional crystallization and fractional distillation. Then they heated alone, heated with carbon, reacted with acids, or electrolyzed, as the case may be. As the technologies for these processes improved, chemists were able to decompose compounds that could not be broken down earlier (Section 6.10).

A particularly interesting example of the contribution of improved technology involved the discovery and separation of neon, argon, krypton, and xenon during the last decade of the nineteenth century. These elements were discovered only after new technologies made it possible to fractionally distill air at very low temperatures.

Another gas, helium, had been identified on the sun in 1868 when a spectral analysis (Section 8.8) of sunlight was performed during a solar eclipse. It was discovered on earth about 30 years later.

> What does it mean to say that an element is found "free" in nature?

Why was the name given to the "inert gases" changed in the 1960s?

For years after the discovery of these gases, no compounds could be made from them. They were known as the "inert gases" for six decades. As has happened before, a new discovery was made that caused an old name to be altered. Compounds of xenon were synthesized in 1962. These five gases are now called the *noble gases* rather than inert gases.

1. Which of the elements listed in Table 10.1 are known to you, at least by name?

2. How was it possible for people in antiquity to discover silver and gold when their abundance near the surface of the earth is less than 0.001 percent by mass? (See Section 6.11.)

10.2 Some Families of Elements

For the most part, the noble gases do not form compounds, and they are all monatomic gases at room temperature. No other elements share these two properties with the noble gases. This is why the noble gases form a natural group or *family* of elements. Table 10.3 lists their atomic masses and notes the fact that they do not form compounds like other elements.

Why was the grouping of elements into families important to chemists?

At the middle of the nineteenth century, chemists had a difficult task in deciding how to put elements into families. With new elements being discovered at a rapid pace, chemists were trying to discover some pattern or order to the growing collection of elements by studying their characteristic properties. Such a pattern might be useful in answering the question of how many more elements there may be, and where and how one should look for them. Which properties of the elements and their atoms should be used to place elements into families? Two proper-

What two properties can be used to begin organizing the elements?

Table 10.3			
Element	Atomic mass (u)	Sodium compound	Chlorine compound
Helium	4.0	None	None
Neon	20.2	None	None
Argon	39.9	None	None
Krypton	83.8	None	None
Xenon	131	None	None

ties played a key role in this process. One was the combining ratio of the atoms of an element with atoms of other elements. This ratio is usually expressed by the simplest formulas of their compounds. The other property was the electrode to which the element moved during electrolysis. You will use both properties in the activity in the next section.

A group of elements that have very similar properties are lithium, sodium, and potassium. These elements are not found free in nature because they react violently with water. All three of these elements form oxides having the same ratio of atoms (2:1). Also, all three chlorides have the same ratio of atoms (1:1). These metallic elements are placed in a family called *alkali metals.*

Another family consists of beryllium, magnesium, calcium, and strontium. These metallic elements are called *alkaline earth metals.* Alkaline earth metals, especially beryllium and magnesium, are not nearly as reactive as alkali metals. These four metallic elements combine with the same ratios of atoms in both their oxides (1:1) and their chlorides (1:2).

Both alkali metals and alkaline earth metals move to the negative electrode during the electrolysis of their water solutions. But they cannot be collected on the negative electrode. Because of their immediate reaction with water, they stay in solution. (See Sections 6.2 and 6.10.)

Other elements, such as silver and zinc, combine with oxygen and chlorine in the same ratios as the alkali metals and the alkaline earth metals. However, they hardly react with water, and they can be collected at the negative electrode from their water-soluble compounds. Should such elements be included in either of these families? As you will see shortly, a key consideration in answering this question is the atomic mass of the element.

Table 10.4 displays data for both alkali metals and alkaline earth metals.

Table 10.4 Compounds of Alkali Metals and Alkaline Earth Metals			
Element	Atomic mass (u)	Compound	
		Oxide	Chloride
Lithium	6.9	Li_2O	LiCl
Sodium	23	Na_2O	NaCl
Potassium	39	K_2O	KCl
Beryllium	9.0	BeO	$BeCl_2$
Magnesium	24.3	MgO	$MgCl_2$
Calcium	40.1	CaO	$CaCl_2$
Strontium	87.6	SrO	$SrCl_2$

How many atoms of sodium will combine with one atom of chlorine?

How many atoms of lithium will combine with three atoms of oxygen?

What is the combining ratio of each of the alkaline earth metals with oxygen? With chlorine?

What is the combining ratio of each of the alkali metals with oxygen? With chlorine?

Another family of elements—fluorine, chlorine, bromine and iodine—also have similar properties. All four are reactive elements that never appear in nature as free elements. During electrolysis of their sodium compounds, these elements move to the positive electrode as did the oxygen in Experiment 6.2, The Decomposition of Water. This family of elements is called the *halogens*. Halogens form compounds with sodium only in a combining ratio of 1:1, with calcium only in a ratio of 2:1, and with hydrogen only in a ratio of 1:1 (Table 10.5).

Table 10.5 Compounds of Halogens				
Halogen	Atomic mass (u)	Sodium compound	Calcium compound	Hydrogen compound
Fluorine	19.0	NaF	CaF_2	HF
Chlorine	35.5	NaCl	$CaCl_2$	HCl
Bromine	79.9	NaBr	$CaBr_2$	HBr
Iodine	127	NaI	CaI_2	HI

3. How can you use combining ratios to distinguish the alkali metals from the alkaline earth metals?

4. Alkali metals and alkaline earth metals were discovered within a short time span (Table 10.2). Which new technique was used to separate these elements from their compounds? (See also Section 6.10.)

5. Silver combines with the halogens in an atomic ratio of 1:1 and with oxygen in a ratio of 2:1. In electrolysis, silver moves to the negative electrode. Why is silver not considered to be an alkali metal?

6. Table 10.4 lists three alkali metals.

   a. In the table, find three alkaline earth metals that have atomic masses slightly greater than each of the three alkali metals.

   b. There is an element with an atomic mass of 85.5 u. On the basis of the information provided in Table 10.4, what do you expect some of the properties of this element to be?

7. Examine Tables 10.3 and 10.4. Are there any pairs of noble gases and alkali metals that are close in atomic mass?

8. Why are deposits of pure sodium metal or pure potassium metal not seen in nature?

9. Examine Tables 10.4 and 10.5.

   a. What is the combining ratio of potassium with bromine? With iodine?

   b. Write the simplest formulas for the potassium compounds referred to in part (a).

ACTIVITY A 10.3 Atomic Mass and Other Properties of Atoms

In the discussion so far, we have intentionally selected elements that are easily classified according to their properties: noble gases, alkali metals, alkaline earth metals, and halogens. You also noticed some relationships between the atomic masses of members of different families (Questions 6 and 7). Do these observations hint at the existence of a greater pattern—one that may provide guidance for the discovery of new elements?

To answer this question, we have summarized some important properties of 24 elements and recorded them on individual cards for ease of comparison (see Figure 10.1 for an example). Each element is identified by its name, its symbol, its atomic mass (u) and its common combining ratio with chlorine as expressed by the simplest formula of its compound. For elements produced by electrolysis, we list the electrode to which they move during electrolysis.

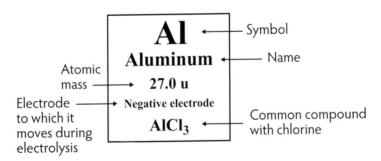

Figure 10.1

A sample element card.

To begin, arrange the 24 element cards in a single horizontal row in order of increasing atomic mass from left to right. When you have done this correctly, hydrogen (H) will appear at the far left and rubidium (Rb) will be at the far right. Identify each of the noble gases. To highlight their locations, move each noble gas card slightly toward you.

Let us now check the location of elements belonging to the alkali metals. Identify these elements and move their cards slightly toward you, as you did with the noble gases.

Notice that the alkali metals are near the noble gases. With the exception of potassium, all occur immediately to the right of a noble gas. Rather than being to the right of argon, potassium is to the left.

- Calculate the difference in mass between adjacent pairs of the alkali metals and noble gases. Which pair has the smallest difference?

To keep the order of all four pairs the same and because the difference in mass between argon and potassium is very small, switch the order of argon and potassium. To see the usefulness of this interchange, arrange the elements from hydrogen to argon in the following way:

1. Arrange the noble gases to form a column, so that each noble gas occupies the rightmost position in its horizontal row (Figure 10.2).

2. Place the other elements in the rows to the left of the noble gases. Be sure to keep the elements in order of increasing atomic mass from left to right within each row, as indicated in Figure 10.2.

3. Put the remaining cards (potassium through rubidium) aside for future use.

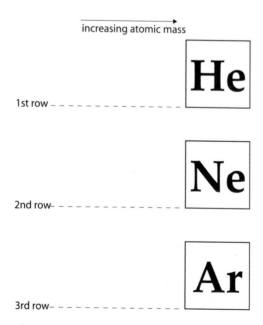

Figure 10.2

The proposed arrangement of the elements from hydrogen to argon in three rows. The noble gases appear in the rightmost column.

- Does each of the noble gases have the highest atomic mass in its row? If not, recheck the ordering of your elements.
- Ignoring hydrogen for the moment, what is the name of the family of elements in the first column at the left? The second column? The seventh column?

10. Interchanging the positions of potassium and argon created an exception to the pattern of increasing atomic mass when all the elements were in a single row. Are there similar exceptions in the columns that you have formed? If so, what are they?

11. Summarize the arguments for placing hydrogen:
    a. in the seventh column.
    b. in the first column.
    c. by itself.

10.4 The Elements in the Third Through Sixth Columns

Before you started ordering elements by their atomic masses, you already knew some of the named families of elements. These included the noble gases, the halogens, the alkali metals, and the alkaline earth metals. The elements in each of these families displayed similar properties. So, when you started rearranging elements to construct a table in Activity 10.3, it was reassuring to see that the first, second, seventh, and eighth columns each contained elements of only one family.

What about the elements in the third through the sixth columns? Do the elements in each of these columns have similar properties? Do the properties of elements in any column differ from the properties of the elements in the adjacent columns?

Comparing the properties of boron and aluminum (in the third column) shows that they have much less in common than, say, lithium and sodium (in the first column). Boron is a black powder and a nonmetal. Like other nonmetals, it is a poor conductor of heat and cannot be produced by electrolysis. Aluminum, on the other hand, is a shiny metal that can be produced by electrolysis; it is collected at the negative electrode. Yet boron and aluminum generally combine in the same atomic ratios with other elements. For example, in addition to the chlorides BCl_3 and $AlCl_3$ listed on the cards, they form similar oxides, B_2O_3 and

Al_2O_3. For these reasons, boron and aluminum are placed in the same family. But as we can see, placing elements in families is a matter of judgment. Whether the judgment is good or bad is determined by the usefulness of the grouping.

The situation is somewhat simpler when we compare the properties of carbon and silicon in the fourth column. Neither of these elements is a metal, and neither can be produced by electrolysis. Both form many compounds with other elements in the same atomic ratios. For example, in addition to CCl_4 and $SiCl_4$ listed on the cards, they form CH_4 and SiH_4, and CO_2 and SiO_2.

The sixth column has some problems. Although both oxygen and sulfur combine in the same ratio with hydrogen (H_2O and H_2S), many other compounds are dissimilar. However, keeping sulfur in the sixth column leaves other elements of known families in their respective columns. Later in the chapter we shall develop better arguments in favor of the placement of sulfur.

12. **Boron and aluminum are both in the third column of your table. Which of the following properties do they share?**

    A. Color

    B. Classification as a metal

    C. Produced by electrolysis

    D. Combining ratio with chlorine

    E. Combining ratio with oxygen

ACTIVITY

A

10.5 The Elements in the Fourth Row

Reconstruct the table of elements the way you left it at the end of Section 10.3. Then place the remaining cards so that krypton is in the column with the noble gases. (We intentionally did not provide enough elements to complete a row.)

- Which of the elements can you confidently place in their proper columns?
- What are the difficulties in placing the remaining elements?

10.6 The Fourth and Fifth Rows: A Historical Perspective

The preceding activity ended with a difficulty: How can we fit copper, zinc, and other elements into a table so that elements with similar properties will appear in vertical columns? In addition, the atomic mass should increase in each row, at least in most cases.

Dmitri Mendeleev (pronounced MEN-duh-LAY-uff), a Russian chemist, first proposed such a table in 1871. The first five rows of a modern version of his table are shown in Figure 10.3. Because the elements are arranged in a pattern that repeats, the table is called *the periodic table of the elements*. The rows in the table are often referred to as *periods*. A complete periodic table of the elements may be on display in your science classroom.

We can look at the periodic table as a model. To be useful, a model must accomplish two goals: (1) It must account for and organize known facts, and (2) it must enable us to make testable predictions (Section 8.1). Was this table useful when Mendeleev proposed it?

Let us examine Figure 10.3 more closely. Except for hydrogen, all elements in the first column are alkali metals. All elements in the second column are alkaline earth metals. Beginning with the fourth row, Mendeleev added new columns where he placed other known elements according to their increasing atomic masses. Where necessary, he left blank spaces in order to keep the remaining families in vertical columns. For example, the elements in the column headed by carbon all form similar compounds with other elements. Therefore, they form a family. Similarly, all of the halogens are in one column.

Although it is still difficult to see why oxygen and sulfur are in the same family, the elements below sulfur have much in common with sulfur. For example, their oxides—SO_2, SeO_2, and TeO_2—all dissolve

H 1.0																	He 4.0
Li 6.9	Be 9.0											B 10.8	C 12.0	N 14.0	O 16.0	F 19.0	Ne 20.2
Na 23.0	Mg 24.3											Al 27.0	Si 28.1	P 31.0	S 32.1	Cl 35.5	Ar 39.9
K 39.1	Ca 40.1	Sc 45.0	Ti 47.9	V 50.9	Cr 52.0	Mn 54.9	Fe 55.8	Co 58.9	Ni 58.7	Cu 63.5	Zn 65.4	Ga 69.7	Ge 72.6	As 74.9	Se 79.0	Br 79.9	Kr 83.8
Rb 85.5	Sr 87.6	Y 88.9	Zr 91.2	Nb 92.9	Mo 95.9	Tc 98.9	Ru 101.1	Rh 102.9	Pd 106.4	Ag 107.9	Cd 112.4	In 114.8	Sn 118.7	Sb 121.8	Te 127.6	I 126.9	Xe 131.3

Figure 10.3

The first five rows of the periodic table. The shaded elements had not yet been discovered when Mendeleev proposed his table.

in water and form similar acids. All (including oxygen) combine with hydrogen in the same ratio: H_2O, H_2S, H_2Se, and H_2Te. The periodic table clearly accounts for and organizes these and other known facts.

The truly amazing part of Mendeleev's achievement is that the periodic table allowed him to make predictions. The elements shaded in yellow and blue in Figure 10.3 had not been discovered when he proposed the table. For the ones shaded yellow, he left empty spaces and gave them temporary names. Moreover, on the basis of the properties of adjacent elements, he predicted what their properties would be. Within fifteen years, all three elements were discovered. Their properties were indeed close to what Mendeleev had predicted.

Particularly impressive was his prediction about the properties of the element that he called "eka-silicon" ("following silicon"). It is called germanium (Ge) today. A comparison between the predicted properties and the observed properties is shown in Table 10.6.

Table 10.6 Comparison of Eka-silicon to Germanium		
Property	Eka-silicon	Germanium
Atomic Mass (u)	72	72.6
Density (g/cm³)	5.5	5.47
Color	Dirty gray	Grayish white
Density of oxide (g/cm³)	4.7	4.70
Density of chloride (g/cm³)	1.9	1.89
Boiling point of chloride (°C)	<100	86

Today, with much more experimental and theoretical knowledge, we understand the periodic table in a deeper way. But—as is usually the case in science—such an understanding brings with it new questions and new challenges.

13. **Cesium (Cs) appears in the first column on the complete periodic table. What do you expect its properties to be?**

14. The element barium appears in the second column on the complete periodic table. What do you expect the molecular formula to be for the compound formed from barium and oxygen? From barium and chlorine?

FOR REVIEW, APPLICATIONS, AND EXTENSIONS

15. Radon (see Section 7.7) is a noble gas.
    a. How does this fact explain why radon comes to the surface from within the earth?
    b. Why does radon accumulate in basements rather than in higher floors?

16. Why do you think the Declaration of Independence of the United States is stored in a sealed case containing helium rather than air?

17. Silver, gold, and platinum are used in jewelry. What properties do they have in common that make them ideal for this use?

18. Mercury is a liquid at room temperature and is considered to be a metal. Why is this so?

19. A student claims that oxygen and sulfur should not be in the same family because one is a gas and the other is a solid at room temperature. How might you counter this claim?

20. a. Examine Figure 10.3. Aside from potassium and argon, are there other exceptions to the ascending order of atomic masses? If so, what are they?

    b. How do the mass differences between the pairs of elements you identified in part (a) compare with the difference in atomic mass between potassium and argon?

    c. For one of the pairs that you identified in part (a), give a reason why the elements were placed in the order that they appear in the periodic table.

Before he published his periodic table, Dmitri Mendeleev presented his ideas in a lecture to the Russian Chemical Society. Suppose you had attended that lecture as a science reporter for a newspaper. Write a brief report of the lecture.

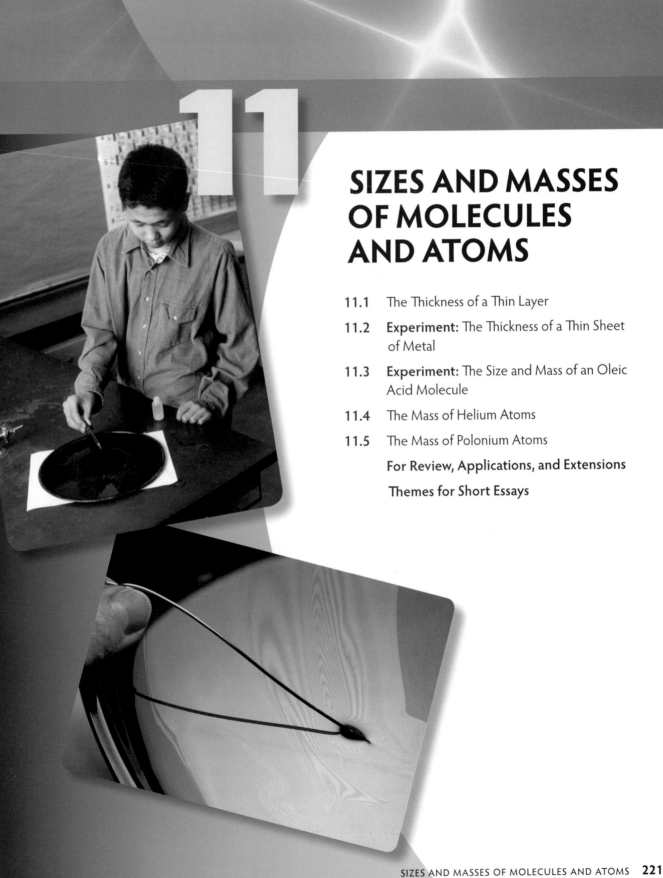

11

SIZES AND MASSES OF MOLECULES AND ATOMS

At the end of Chapter 9, we followed the work of nineteenth century-chemists on the masses of atoms and molecules. Their unit of mass was the mass of a hydrogen atom. For comparison with the mass of other atoms or molecules, this is as good a unit as any. Nevertheless, you have the right to ask, "What is the mass of one atom in grams?" After all, you have been using grams throughout the school year. You deserve an answer.

Now, if you ask someone "What is the time?" or "How do I get to the football stadium?" you would be satisfied with a simple, straightforward answer. You would not follow up with the question "How do you know?" because you have a good idea what the answer is based on.

It is quite different when it comes to the question "What is the mass of an atom?" The answer (in grams) is such a small number that you have every right, even an obligation, to follow with the question "How do you know?" In this chapter you will see how we know. The method we will use is not the most accurate, but it is based entirely on what you have learned in this course.

Molecules and atoms are not visible even under powerful optical microscopes. How, then, can you answer any of the following questions: How big is an atom? What is the mass of one atom? How many atoms are in a sample of matter that you can work with in the laboratory? These three questions are related. If you can measure any one of these quantities, you can calculate the others. You will do just that in this chapter. However, you will use indirect methods. The first method is introduced in Section 11.1.

11.1 The Thickness of a Thin Layer

Consider a rectangular solid. Its volume V is equal to its length times its width times its height, or $V = lwh$ [Figure 11.1(a)]. Since lw is the area of the base, we can say that the volume equals the area of the base times the height.

Figure 11.1(b) shows another rectangular solid with the same volume as that in Figure 11.1(a). The material has been formed into a different rectangular shape that has a larger base and a much smaller height. Its volume is still the area of its base times its height. If the material were spread out into an even thinner layer, its volume would be unchanged and would still be equal to the area of its base times its height.

Now suppose you have a thin rectangular sheet of some material—a metal foil, for example—whose volume you know. From measurements of its length and width, you can calculate the area of its base. To find the thickness, you divide the known volume by the area of the base.

Two rectangular solids have the same volume. The base of Solid A has a larger area than the base of Solid B. How do the heights of these solids compare?

Suppose you know the volume and the area of the base of a rectangular sheet. How would you find the thickness of the sheet?

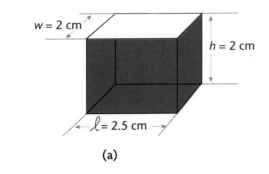

(a)

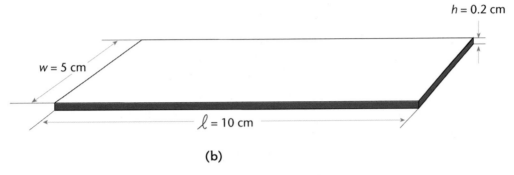

(b)

Figure 11.1

The piece of matter in (a) has a volume of lwh = 2.5 cm × 2.0 cm × 2.0 cm = 10 cm³. In (b) the same piece of matter has been flattened. It has the same volume as in (a). The volume of the thin slab in (b) is lwh = 10 cm × 5 cm × 0.2 cm = 10 cm³.

The same method works for finding the thickness of a circular sheet. The volume of a circular sheet is also equal to the area of the base times the height. In the case of a circular sheet, or cylinder, the base area is equal to πr^2, where r is the radius of the base. You will apply this method to both rectangular and circular objects later in this chapter.

1. A rectangular solid has a length of 10.0 cm, a width of 5.0 cm, and a volume of 10.0 cm³. Which of the following is the thickness of the solid in centimeters?

   A. 0.20

   B. 2.0

   C. 500

2. A circular solid (cylinder) has a diameter of 20 cm and a volume of 30 cm³. What is the height of the cylinder?

11.2 The Thickness of a Thin Sheet of Metal

EXPERIMENT

E

You can find the thickness of a rectangular sheet of aluminum foil from its length, width, and volume. To find the volume, you need to know the mass of the sheet and the density of the material (2.7 g/cm³).

- From your calculation of the foil's thickness, what is the maximum thickness of an aluminum atom?
- Can you say anything about how thin the atom can be?

- - - - - - - - - -

Goldsmiths do not make gold foil with a thickness less than about 10^{-5} cm. Why?

Metals do not flatten out into thin layers by themselves; they have to be rolled or hammered. Hammering, however, is a crude process. Even the most skilled goldsmith, making thin gold leaf for lettering on store windows, must stop when the gold leaf is about 10^{-5} cm thick. In such cases, the minimum thickness is determined not by the size of the atoms of gold but by the difficulty of handling such a thin sheet.

Liquids, on the other hand, tend to spread out into thin layers by themselves. If you pour water on the floor, it spreads out quickly to form a thin layer. You can calculate the thickness of this layer if you know the volume of the water you pour out and the area it covers.

In the next experiment, you will use a liquid that spreads out even more thinly than water. To calculate such a small thickness, it will be convenient to express the numbers in *scientific notation*. If you are unfamiliar with scientific notation, you may find it helpful to study Appendix 1 on page 347.

3. In a small-boat harbor, a careless sailor dumps overboard a quart (about 1,000 cm³) of diesel oil. Assume that this oil will spread evenly over the surface of the water to form a layer whose thickness is 1.0×10^{-4} cm. What area will be covered with oil?

4. A tiny drop of mercury has a volume of 1.0×10^{-3} cm³. The density of mercury is about 14 g/cm³. What is the mass of the drop?

5. A goldsmith hammers 19.3 g of gold into a thin sheet of foil 100 cm in length and 100 cm in width. The density of gold is 19.3 g/cm^3.

    a. What is the volume of the gold?

    b. What is the area of the gold sheet?

    c. What is the thickness of the gold sheet?

6. The following measurements were recorded for a rectangular slab of aluminum. (The density of aluminum is 2.7 g/cm^3.)

Length	7.60 cm
Width	2.50 cm
Mass	30.78 g

What is the height of the aluminum slab?

11.3 The Size and Mass of an Oleic Acid Molecule

You are now ready to calculate the size and the mass of a single molecule. The starting point will be finding the thickness of a very thin layer of a substance. To do that, you will follow the same approach that you used in Experiment 11.2, The Thickness of a Thin Sheet of Metal.

Under proper conditions, oil and certain other substances can spread out even more thinly than water. Oil does not dissolve in water, it floats on top of it. You often see oil spread out on a water surface in a thin, rainbow-colored film. Oleic acid, a compound made of hydrogen, carbon, and oxygen, does not dissolve in water either but spreads out into an even thinner layer than oil does. In fact, a single drop of this liquid from a medicine dropper will spread in a layer one molecule thick—so thin that it will cover the entire surface of a small wading pool.

To make it possible to do the experiment in a small tray, we must dilute the solution of oleic acid in alcohol. In this experiment you will be using a solution that is 1 part oleic acid in 500 parts of solution, or 2×10^{-3} parts of oleic acid.

Pour tap water into a tray to a depth of about half a centimeter. Allow the water to stand for a few minutes until all movement has stopped. Then sprinkle just enough fine powder on the water to make a barely visible layer. When a drop of dilute solution of oleic acid is dropped

Is oleic acid soluble or insoluble in water? How do you know?

Figure 11.2

A close-up of the tray with motionless water (a) after a thin layer of powder has been sprinkled on the water; (b) after a drop of dilute solution of oleic acid has been dropped from a medicine dropper.

onto the water surface, the powder will be pushed aside. This will allow you to see the oleic acid film when it spreads out across the water (Figure 11.2).

To prove that it is the oleic acid and not the alcohol that pushes the powder aside, first put one drop of pure alcohol from a medicine dropper in the center of the tray.

- What do you observe?

Now put one drop of the dilute solution in the center of the tray.

- If the area covered by the film is very nearly circular, what is the diameter of the circle?
- If the area is only roughly circular, how will you find its average diameter?
- What is the area of the thin film?

To find the volume of the thin layer of acid, you must first find the volume of one drop of the dilute solution. You can do that by counting the number of drops that will add up to 1.0 cm³ in a graduated cylinder.

- What is the volume of one drop of solution?
- What is the volume of oleic acid in one drop of the solution? (Remember that only 1/500 of the solution is oleic acid.)
- From your volume and area measurements, what is the thickness of the layer?

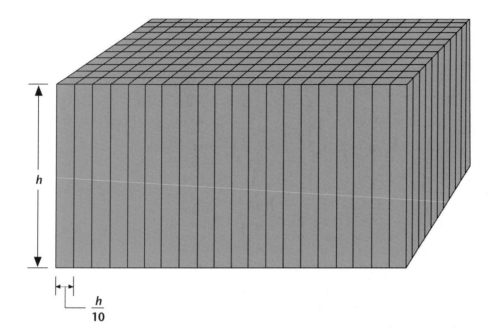

Figure 11.3

A simplified picture of a submicroscopic piece of a film of oleic acid one molecule thick.

So far, you have found only the height of a molecule of oleic acid. Other experiments show that oleic acid molecules are long and thin, with a height about 10 times the width of their base. They stand nearly upright on a water surface when they form a thin layer. Thus a tiny piece of a layer of oleic acid one molecule thick might look roughly like the collection of tiny rods in Figure 11.3. The area of the base of each rod is then equal to the width of the base squared, as shown in Figure 11.4.

Suppose that all the molecules of oleic acid touch one another, as in Figure 11.3. Then,

Area of layer = (number of molecules) · (base area of one molecule)

or

$$\text{Number of molecules} \ = \ \frac{\text{area of layer}}{\text{base area of one molecule}} .$$

- From your data for the height of one molecule and the fact that the width is about 1/10 of the height, what is the area of the base of one molecule?
- What is the number of molecules in the layer?
- What does this tell you about the number of molecules in the droplet you started with?

From the volume of the oleic acid in one drop of dilute solution and the density of oleic acid, you can calculate the mass of oleic acid in one

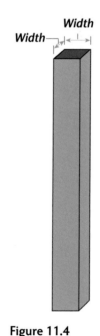

Figure 11.4

An enlarged view of a simplified picture of a single oleic acid molecule. The area of the base (the darker region) is equal to (width) ^{2}.

drop of dilute solution. The density of oleic acid is 0.87 g/cm³. Since this is a very rough calculation, you may substitute 1 g/cm³ for the density of oleic acid.

- What is the mass of the droplet of oleic acid?

Knowing the number of molecules in the droplet, you can now use the relation

$$\text{Mass of one molecule} = \frac{\text{mass of sample}}{\text{number of molecules in sample}}$$

to find the mass of a single molecule of oleic acid.

- What is the mass of one molecule of oleic acid?

7. Can the height of a single molecule of oleic acid be greater than the thickness of the layer of oleic acid?

8. Can the size of an atom of hydrogen, carbon, or oxygen be greater than the width of an oleic acid molecule?

9. Suppose the mass of 1.3×10^{18} molecules of oleic acid is 3.8×10^{-5} g. Which of the following choices shows the calculation you can use to find the mass of one molecule of oleic acid?

A. $\dfrac{1.3 \times 10^{18}}{3.8 \times 10^{-5}}$

B. $\dfrac{3.8 \times 10^{-5}}{1.3 \times 10^{18}}$

C. $(1.3 \times 10^{18}) \times (3.8 \times 10^{-5})$

10. a. What is the volume of oleic acid in 1.0 cm³ of solution prepared by dissolving 2.0 cm³ of oleic acid in 98 cm³ of alcohol and mixing thoroughly?

   b. If 50 drops of the solution in part (a) occupy 1.0 cm³, what is the volume of one drop of this solution?

   c. What is the volume of oleic acid in one drop of this solution?

11. If 3×10^{-5} cm³ of pure oleic acid forms a film with an area of 150 cm², how thick is the film?

11.4 The Mass of Helium Atoms

By indirect but simple means, you were able to determine the mass of a single molecule of oleic acid. Now we will describe an experiment in which the mass of a single helium atom is found. The experiment was done for *IPS* students at the Mound Laboratory of the Monsanto Research Corporation. This experiment is shown in the film *The Mass of Atoms*. Figures 11.5 through 11.7 and Figure 11.10 are from the film.

As in your experiment with oleic acid, an indirect method was used. The main idea of the experiment was to prepare a sample of helium of known mass and known number of atoms. The mass of a single atom was then calculated by division:

$$\text{Mass of one atom} = \frac{\text{mass of sample}}{\text{number of atoms in sample}}.$$

The helium was produced by the radioactive decay of polonium. A small amount of polonium was placed inside a quartz tube of known diameter. The air was pumped out and the tube was sealed (Figure 11.5).

After 21 days, the seal was broken underwater. The water rose into the tube and compressed the helium to atmospheric pressure (Figure 11.6). From the volume of the helium and its known density at atmospheric pressure, the mass of the helium sample was calculated. The number of helium atoms can be measured by recording the counting rate and the length of time during which the polonium decayed.

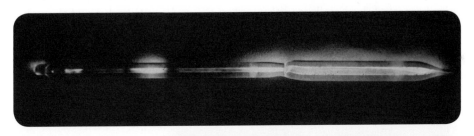

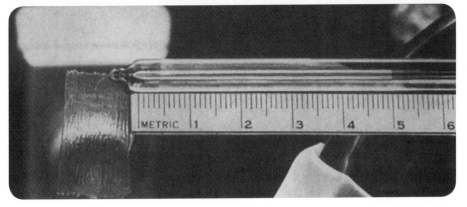

Figure 11.5

The sealed quartz tube containing polonium. A blue glow is produced by the emitted helium particles when they strike the quartz. This photograph was taken in the light from the blue glow.

Figure 11.6

The quartz tube containing helium after being opened underwater. The length of the gas column is 5.0 cm.

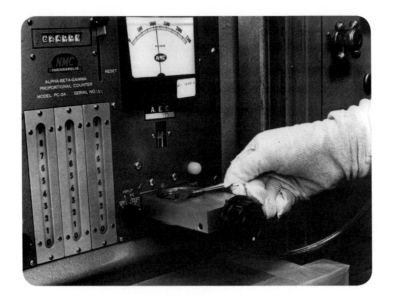

Figure 11.7

A metal plate containing polonium being removed from a radiation counter after a count.

In principle, the polonium could now be removed from the tube and placed in a counter in order to find the number of decays or *disintegrations* per minute. However, in practice this is not possible. A sample large enough to produce a measurable amount of helium in three weeks would give off too many helium particles per minute for the counter to count. Therefore, the polonium was first dissolved completely in a large quantity of nitric acid. The solution was further diluted with water. In both steps, the solution was thoroughly mixed to make sure the polonium was evenly distributed throughout. Finally, a tiny drop of the solution was put on a small plate, the acid was evaporated, and the plate was placed in a counter (Figure 11.7).

Here is the record of the data of the experiment:

Production of Helium

On March 3 the polonium was sealed in the evacuated quartz tube. The seal was broken on March 24. The water rose in the tube and the helium was compressed to a length of 5.0 cm in the tube (Figure 11.6).

The area of the circular cross section of the inside of the quartz tube, checked beforehand, was 8.1×10^{-3} cm^2. Thus the volume of helium in the tube was

$$\begin{aligned} \text{Volume} &= \text{length} \times \text{area of cross section} \\ &= (5.0 \text{ cm}) \times (8.1 \times 10^{-3} \text{ cm}^2) \\ &= 4.1 \times 10^{-2} \text{ cm}^3 . \end{aligned}$$

> Why was it necessary to dissolve the polonium sample in nitric acid and dilute it with water before measuring the radioactivity of a single drop?

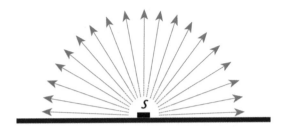

Figure 11.8

Helium particles flying off from a thin polonium source *S* on a metal plate. Those emitted in the directions shown by the arrows can be counted. Half of the helium particles are emitted downward into the plate and are not counted.

The density of helium at atmospheric pressure and room temperature is 1.7×10^{-4} g/cm^3. The mass of the sample of helium is

$$\begin{aligned} \text{Mass} &= \text{volume} \times \text{density} \\ &= (4.1 \times 10^{-2}\ \text{cm}^3) \times (1.7 \times 10^{-4}\ \text{g/cm}^3) \\ &= 7.0 \times 10^{-6}\ \text{g}. \end{aligned}$$

Dilution

To start with, the small sample of polonium was dissolved in 1.0×10^3 cm^3 of nitric acid. Therefore, one cubic centimeter of this solution contains 1/1,000 of the original amount of polonium.

A volume of 1.0 cm^3 of this solution was then thoroughly mixed with 99 cm^3 of water. So 1.0 cm^3 of this dilute solution contained only 1 part in 10^5 (or 1.0×10^{-5}) of the original sample of polonium. Even this was too much to be counted!

Therefore, only 1.0×10^{-3} cm^3 (one one-thousandth of a cubic centimeter) of the very dilute polonium solution was placed on the plate to be counted. This meant that only

$$(1.0 \times 10^{-5}) \times (1.0 \times 10^{-3}) = 1.0 \times 10^{-8},$$

or 1 part in 100 million, of the original polonium was counted. Two trials were run with samples of this size.

Counting

> Trial 1: 2.4×10^5 counts/minute
> Trial 2: 2.0×10^5 counts/minute.

This step introduces the largest experimental error in the experiment so far. Using the average of the two readings, we have 2.2×10^5 counts/minute.

The counter used in this experiment does not count those helium particles that fly off into the plate; it counts only those that fly off upward (Figure 11.8). Thus the true disintegration rate was twice the recorded number, or 4.4×10^5 counts/minute.

> Why is the experimentally measured radioactivity of the sample only one-half of the total radioactivity?

Why is the disinte-
gration rate of
4.4×10^5 counts/
min multiplied by
1×10^8?

This large number of counts is produced by only 1.0×10^{-8} of the original sample. The number of disintegrations per minute of the whole sample is

$$(1.0 \times 10^8) \times (4.4 \times 10^5 \text{ counts/min}) = 4.4 \times 10^{13} \text{ counts/min.}$$

Now recall that the quartz tube containing the polonium was sealed on March 3 and opened on March 24. This is a period of 21 days or

$$(21 \text{ days}) \times (24 \text{ hours/day}) \times (60 \text{ min/hour}) = 3.0 \times 10^4 \text{ min.}$$

If the sample of polonium had decayed at the same rate over the entire duration of the experiment, then the total number of counts would have been

$$(4.4 \times 10^{13} \text{ counts/min}) \times (3.0 \times 10^4 \text{ min}) = 1.3 \times 10^{18} \text{ counts.}$$

Of course, the counting rate is not constant; it decreases with time. Like all radioactive elements, polonium has a half-life. (Section 8.10.) The half-life of polonium is 138 days (Figure 11.9). After 21 days the rate

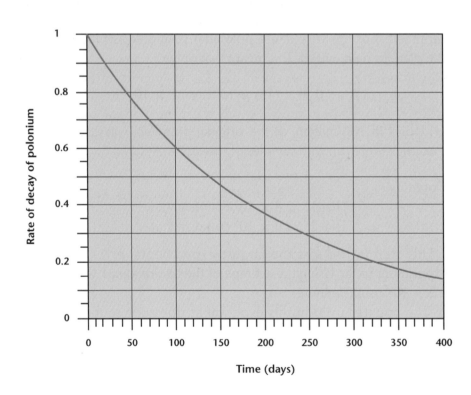

Figure 11.9

The rate of decay of a sample containing polonium as a function of time. The rate (number of polonium atoms that disintegrate per unit time) is expressed as a fraction of the rate measured at zero days. The rate reaches 0.5 of the original value at 138 days, the half-life of polonium.

of decay is 0.90 of the original rate. So the average rate of decay over the first 21 days is about 0.95 of the original rate. Thus the counting rate measured after 21 days must be divided by 0.95 to give the average counting rate over the 21 days. This correction will increase the total number of counts during the experiment to about 1.4×10^{18}.

Therefore, we will use the value 1.4×10^{18} for the total number of counts during the experiment.

We said earlier that we shall assume that each decay signals the formation of one helium atom. Thus the number of helium atoms produced by the polonium sample during the three weeks is:

$$\text{Number of helium atoms} = 1.4 \times 10^{18}$$

and the mass of one helium atom is

$$\text{Mass of one atom} = \frac{\text{mass of sample}}{\text{number of atoms in sample}}$$

$$= \frac{7.0 \times 10^{-6}\,\text{g}}{1.4 \times 10^{18}} = 5.0 \times 10^{-24}\,\text{g}$$

As we said at the beginning of this chapter, the experiment described here is by no means the first or the most accurate one to find the mass of a helium atom. But it is perhaps the most direct. A repetition of this experiment, which you may see in the film *The Mass of Atoms*, gave a similar result: 7.5×10^{-24} g. For higher precision, different methods are used and give a mass of 6.64×10^{-24} g for a helium atom.

Before studying this experiment, you had no way of guessing what the mass of a single atom might be. The mass might have been a billion times larger than 10^{-24} g—that is, about 10^{-15} g—or perhaps 10^{-33} g, a billion times smaller. Thus, being able to conclude that the mass of a helium atom is close to 6×10^{-24} g is an impressive achievement.

The mass of a helium atom is 4.0 u; that of a hydrogen atom is 1.0 u (see Table 9.2 on page 203). Therefore, using the more accurate value for the mass of a helium atom, the mass of a hydrogen atom is

$$\frac{6.64 \times 10^{-24}\,\text{g}}{4.0} = 1.66 \times 10^{-24}\,\text{g}.$$

12. If the mass of a hydrogen atom is 1.66×10^{-24} g, how many hydrogen atoms are there in 1 g of hydrogen?

13. A cylindrical tube with a cross-sectional area of 2 cm^2 and a height of 50 cm is filled with hydrogen. What is the volume of the hydrogen in the tube?

14. Write a brief summary of the steps followed in finding the mass of helium atoms by radioactive decay.

15. In the experiment on the mass of helium, how many lead atoms were formed? What assumptions are made to get this number?

11.5 The Mass of Polonium Atoms

We can apply the relation

$$\text{Mass of one atom} = \frac{\text{mass of sample}}{\text{number of atoms in sample}}$$

to polonium as well as to helium. We assumed that one atom of polonium disintegrates into one atom of lead and one atom of helium. Therefore, the number of atoms of polonium that disintegrated during the three weeks of the experiment equals the number of helium atoms formed. This number we calculated in the preceding section. To calculate the mass of one polonium atom, we must know the mass of the polonium that disintegrated.

As we saw in the preceding section, the rate of decay of polonium after 21 days is 0.90, or 90 percent, of the original rate. Since the rate of decay is proportional to the number of polonium atoms present, 0.90 of the original mass of polonium remained in the quartz tube. In other words, 0.10 of the initial sample had decayed.

All this can be seen from Figure 11.9. However, to find out how much polonium decayed, you have to know the mass of the original sample of polonium. Although we did not mention it before, the polonium was massed before it was placed in the quartz tube (Figure 11.10).

Massing polonium is difficult. Because of the intense and dangerous radiation, the polonium must be massed inside a small closed container. The procedure resembles the massing of a liquid. Here we state only the final result, found by massing the container plus polonium and then subtracting the mass of the container.

$$\text{Mass of polonium sample} = 4.5 \times 10^{-3} \text{ g}$$

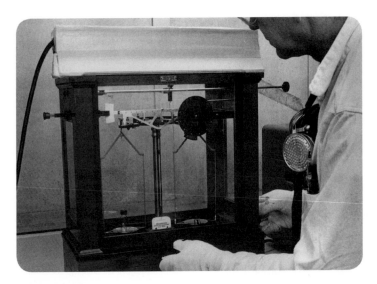

Figure 11.10
A few milligrams of polonium being weighed on a sensitive balance. The polonium is in a small glass tube in the sealed bottle on the left pan. The bottle is sealed to prevent contamination of the balance and the laboratory by the polonium.

Since only 0.10 of the sample decayed, we can find the mass of the polonium that decayed.

$$\text{Mass of polonium that decayed} = 0.10 \times 4.5 \times 10^{-3} \text{ g}$$
$$= 4.5 \times 10^{-4} \text{ g}$$

Since the number of polonium atoms is the same as the number of helium atoms produced, we can calculate the mass of one polonium atom.

$$\text{Number of atoms of polonium that decayed} = 1.4 \times 10^{18}$$

$$\text{Mass of one polonium atom} = \frac{4.5 \times 10^{-4}}{1.4 \times 10^{18}} = 3.2 \times 10^{-22} \text{ g}$$

To more easily compare the mass of one polonium atom to the mass of a helium atom (5.0×10^{-24} g), we express both of the masses to the same power of ten. The mass of a polonium atom will now be expressed as 320×10^{-24} g. We see that polonium atoms are about $320/5.0 = 64$ times as heavy as helium atoms.

As in the case of helium, more accurate experiments yield a mass of 349×10^{-24} g for the mass of a polonium atom, a difference of only 9%.

> Why was the total mass of the polonium multiplied by 0.10 to determine the mass of polonium that decayed?

> Why was 320 divided by 5.0 to find the ratio of the mass a polonium atom to the mass of a helium atom?

16. A rectangular object 3.0 cm × 4.0 cm × 5.0 cm is made of many tiny cubes, each 1.0×10^{-2} cm on an edge. How many cubes does the object contain?

17. The diameter of a tennis ball is about 0.07 m, and the dimensions of a tennis court are about 10 m × 24 m. How many tennis balls will be required to cover the court?

18. Spherical lead shot are poured into a square tray, 10 cm on a side, until they completely cover the bottom. The shot are poured from the tray into a graduated cylinder, which they fill to the 20-cm^3 mark.

    a. What is the diameter of a single shot?

    b. How many shot were in the tray?

    c. If the 20 cm^3 of shot had a mass of 130 g, what would be the mass of a single shot?

19. If the molecules of the oleic acid layer you made could be placed end to end in a line, about how long would it be?

20. If a 0.001-g sample of radium produces 4×10^7 counts/min, how much radium would give 100 counts/min?

21. The rate of decay of the sample of polonium described in this chapter had a counting rate of 4.4×10^{13} counts/min. How does this number compare with the number of seconds in a million years?

22. Suppose you buy a 2-kg bag of dried beans that has been contaminated with small stones. How would you go about finding the approximate number of stones in the bag without separating all the stones in the bag from the beans? What assumptions have you made?

23. A cubic millimeter (10^{-3} cm^3) of blood contains about 5×10^6 red blood cells. The volume of blood in an adult human body is about 5×10^3 cm^3. About how many red blood cells are there in an adult human body?

24. Some polonium is dissolved in 1,000 cm³ of nitric acid, and a 0.01-cm³ sample of the solution is counted. The number of disintegrations per minute is found to be 3×10^3. How many disintegrations per minute occurred in the original solution?

25. If 10^{18} atoms of polonium disintegrate to produce lead and 10^{-5} g of helium, what is the mass of a helium atom?

26. a. What fraction of a sample of pure polonium will decay in 100 days? (See Figure 11.9.)

    b. If a counter initially records 5×10^4 counts/min for the sample, what should you expect it to record after 100 days?

27. Compared to gases, solids are practically incompressible. The atomic model can account for this by considering atoms to be hard spheres that touch one another. Applying this idea provides a way to calculate the diameter of one atom of polonium.

    a. Using the mass of polonium that decayed (Section 11.5) and the density of polonium (9.4 g/cm³), find the volume of polonium that decayed.

    b. Using your answer to part (a) and the number of atoms of polonium that decayed, find the volume of one atom of polonium.

    c. Assume that the atoms of polonium are arranged as shown in Figure A. What is the diameter of one atom of polonium?

    d. Why is it important that we assume that in a solid, atoms touch one another?

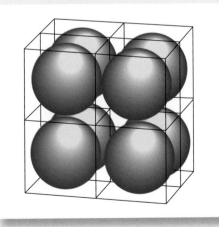

Figure A
For Problem 27

Spheres touching all faces of the cubes containing them. The diameter of a sphere equals the length of the edge of a cube.

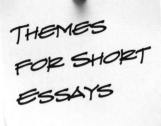

1. A few grains of sand can be placed on an overhead projector and projected onto a wall. The images are large enough to be measured with a ruler. To be able to calculate the size of the grains of sand, you also need to project an object of known size. Do this investigation and find the size of one sand grain. Then, using the results of your own experimentation on the volume of sand (Experiment 1.4, Measuring Volume by Displacement of Water), write a research report, "The Number of Sand Grains in a Cup of Sand."

2. Write an experimental section for an *IBS (Introductory Biological Science)* textbook to count the hairs on a person's head.

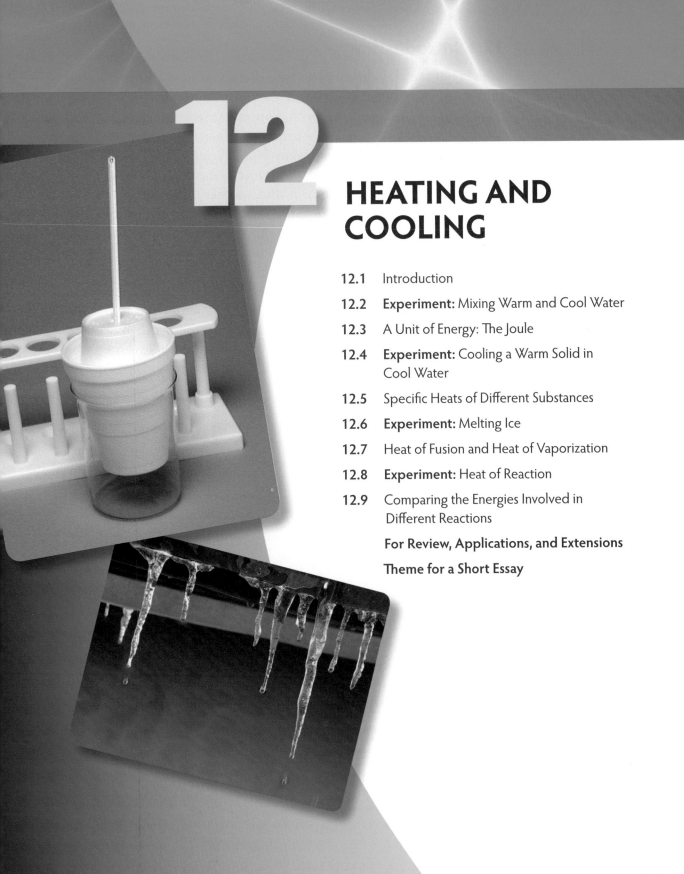

12

HEATING AND COOLING

12.1 Introduction

In many of the experiments you have done, you used a burner to heat substances or a water bath to cool them. In Experiment 3.11, Boiling Point, for example, you did both. You measured the temperature of water as you heated it with a burner, and then you cooled and condensed the resulting steam in a water bath (Figure 12.1). You may have noticed that the water bath became warmer as the steam cooled.

Bringing any object into contact with another that is hotter or colder will cause the temperatures of both objects to change. Like the steam and the water bath, the warmer object cools down while the cooler object heats up. An increase in the temperature of one object is accompanied by a decrease in the temperature of the other.

Direct contact with a hotter or colder object is not the only way to create a temperature change. For example, in Experiment 6.4, The Synthesis of Zinc Chloride, the pieces of zinc and the hydrochloric acid were both at room temperature. Yet as zinc chloride and hydrogen were formed, the temperature of the test tube and its contents increased.

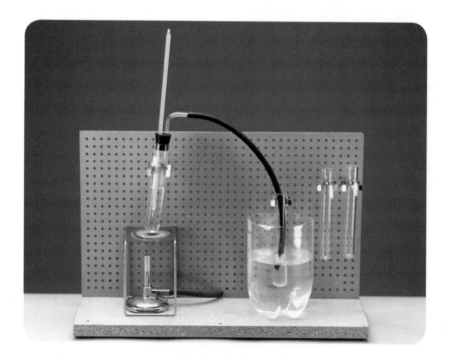

Figure 12.1

The water in the test tube is heated by a burner. Steam is cooled in the water bath. As the steam cools, the water bath warms up.

Aside from the experiments you have done, you may have observed another example of an increase in temperature. You may have smelled burned rubber when the driver of a car slammed on the brakes and came to a screeching stop. Apparently, the tires warmed up a great deal without coming into contact with a warmer object. However, this warming was accompanied by another change—the car stopped.

Perhaps you have slid down a rope and burned your hands. The rope was not any warmer than your skin, but here again there was another change taking place. Your position changed. You ended up at a lower point on the rope than your starting point.

In each of these examples, a change in temperature was accompanied by another change. Table 12.1 lists some common processes where changes in temperature are accompanied by a variety of other changes.

Table 12.1 A Temperature Change Accompanied by Other Changes		
Process	Temperature Change	Other Changes
A hot piece of metal is placed in cold water.	The metal cools down.	The water warms up.
A hot piece of metal is placed in a slush of ice and water.	The metal cools down.	The temperature of the slush remains at 0°C, but some ice melts.
A car travels down a long, steep road at constant speed.	The brakes heat up.	The car loses elevation.
The brakes are applied to a fast-moving car on a level road.	The brakes heat up.	The car slows down.
Zinc is placed in hydrochloric acid.	The solution heats up.	A new substance is produced.

Items in the second column in Table 12.1 describe either an increase or decrease in temperature. The changes listed in the third column are quite different from each other, but each is accompanied by the change in temperature noted in the second column. We shall call any of the changes listed in either column a *change in energy*. A change in temperature indicates a change in *thermal energy*. In this chapter and the next one, you will investigate some energy changes like those mentioned in the third column of Table 12.1. You will begin with the simplest case: mixing warm and cool water.

How will you know if a change in thermal energy occurs?

1. What other changes take place as each of the following occurs?

    a. A hot frying pan cools down when water is added to it.

    b. A nail gets warm when a hammer hits it repeatedly.

    c. The cold water in a mountain stream warms up when it flows into a warmer river.

    d. Molten rock cools as it flows out of a volcano.

EXPERIMENT E — 12.2 Mixing Warm and Cool Water

Suppose that you mix two samples of water having equal masses but different temperatures. How will their temperatures change? Does the result depend on how large the equal masses are? Will the results be different if unequal masses are used?

To answer these questions, you must try to insulate the mixed samples of water from the surroundings. You will do this to prevent any other substances, such as the air in the room, from changing temperature. Mixing the liquids in a well-insulated container called a *calorimeter* will eliminate most of the effects of the surroundings. A simple calorimeter is shown in Figure 12.2.

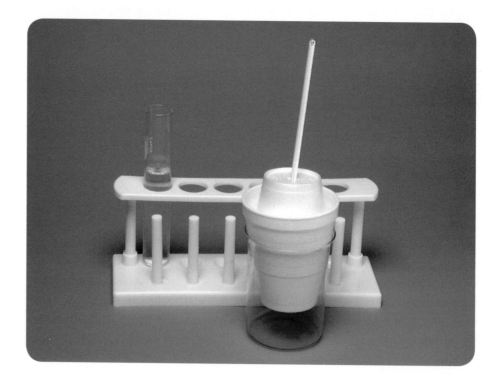

Figure 12.2

A calorimeter constructed from four Styrofoam cups and a beaker. The beaker provides additional insulation and prevents the calorimeter from tipping over. The test tube contains the room-temperature water.

The thermometers you will use in this experiment have been designed for high resolution between 10°C and 40°C. Examine the scale on the thermometer to convince yourself that the markings are 0.2°C apart.

As you saw in Section 1.3, there are three possibilities when the reading on a scale falls between two marks. The reading could be halfway between two marks, it could be closer to the lower mark, or it could be closer to the higher mark. To read the temperature when the liquid is halfway between two marks, you should add 0.10°C to the temperature that corresponds to the lower mark. This result will be more precise than if you simply rounded to the nearest 0.2°C. When the top of the liquid is closer to the lower mark, add only 0.05°C to value of the lower mark to increase the precision of the measurement. When the top of the column is closer to the higher mark, add 0.15°C to the value of the lower mark (see Figure 12.3). A magnifying glass can help you with this task.

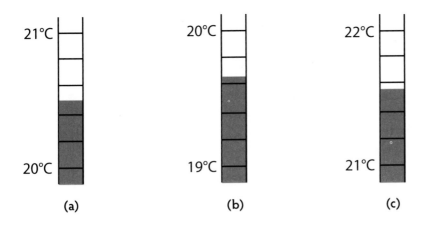

Figure 12.3

Each division on the thermometer represents 0.2°C. If the liquid is halfway between two marks (a), you should add 0.10°C to the value of the lower mark. Here the temperature reading would be reported as 20.50°C. When the top of the liquid is closer to the lower mark (b), add only 0.05°C. The reading here is 19.65°C. When the top of the column is closer to the higher mark (c), add 0.15°C to the value of the lower mark. The temperature is 21.55°C.

Part A

Begin with two samples of water of equal mass. Your teacher will assign a mass of water between 30 g and 50 g for you to use in this part of the experiment. It is best to have the cool water at room temperature and the other sample between 30°C and 35°C. To save time in measuring the assigned mass of water, you can use the fact that the density of water is 1.00 g/cm³. This allows you to measure the water in a graduated cylinder rather than massing it on a balance. (See Section 1.2.)

It is best to pour the cool water into a large test tube that is also initially at room temperature, as was shown in Figure 12.2. Place an equal mass of warm water (at a temperature between 30°C and 35°C) in the calorimeter.

- Why is this procedure better than putting the cool water in the calorimeter and the warm water in the test tube?
- Which water sample's temperature should you measure first, the one at room temperature or the warm one? Why?

Measure the temperatures of both samples just before you mix them. As soon as you record their initial temperatures, pour the cooler sample into the calorimeter and quickly replace the lid. Swirl the calorimeter in a circular motion to mix the samples. When the temperature of the mixture remains constant for several seconds, record it as the final temperature of the mixture.

- What is the decrease in temperature for the warm-water sample?
- What is the increase in temperature for the cool-water sample?
- What is the ratio of the warm-water temperature decrease to the cool-water temperature increase?
- How does your ratio compare with those of your classmates?
- Does this result depend on the size of the equal masses you use?
- What can you conclude about the temperature changes that occur when two equal-mass samples of the same substance with different initial temperatures are mixed?

> Does a change in thermal energy depend on mass for a given change in temperature?

Consider now the results of two teams that did this experiment. Suppose that each team mixed 30 g of warm and cool water. Both teams observed the same gain and loss in temperature. So, since you learned in Section 12.1 that a change in temperature indicates a change in thermal energy, it makes sense to assume that both teams had the same gain and loss in thermal energy. If this is true, then a third team using 60 g of warm and cool water would have twice the gain and loss in thermal energy with the same changes in temperature as the earlier two teams.

How do the temperatures and thermal energies change when the masses of the water samples are different? Part B will answer this question.

Part B

In Part A, the ratio of the masses of the two samples was 1:1. Will the ratio of the decrease in warm-water temperature to the increase in cool-water temperature be different if the ratio of the masses is different? To find out, repeat the experiment with a 60.0-g (60.0-cm³) sample of warm water and a 30.0-g (30.0-cm³) sample of cool water. As before, it is best to place the warm water in the calorimeter.

- What is the temperature decrease for the 60.0-g warm-water sample?
- What is the temperature increase for the 30.0-g cool-water sample?
- What is the ratio of the warm-water temperature decrease to the cool-water temperature increase?
- What is the ratio of the mass of the warm water to the mass of the cool water?
- What is the relationship between these two ratios?

2. Figure A shows the tops of the liquid columns in three thermometers. How would you record the temperature indicated by each thermometer?

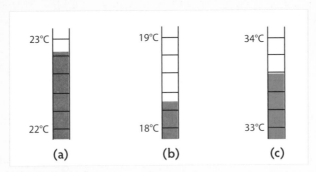

(a)   (b)   (c)

Figure A
For Problem 2

3. Why is it important to put the top back on the calorimeter immediately after adding the cool water to the warm water?

4. Was it important to note the temperature readings on the thermometer before you measured the temperatures of the warm and cool water?

5. Why is it that a Styrofoam™ cup filled with 250 cm³ of water is better able to maintain a constant temperature than one containing only 50 cm³ of water?

6. Suppose that instead of mixing 30 g of cool water and 30 g of warm water in the first part of this experiment, you used 90 g of each.

   a. Assuming that you started with the same initial temperatures that you recorded in your experiment, how would this change affect the final temperature of the mixture?

   b. How would it affect the change in temperature for each of the samples?

12.3 A Unit of Energy: The Joule

In the preceding experiment, you compared the ratio of masses with the ratio of temperature changes. You may have found the relationship between these two ratios on your own. If not, here are additional data taken with the same equipment that you used (Table 12.2).

Table 12.2 Temperature Changes for Unequal Masses of Water				
Trial number	Mass of warm sample (g)	Warm-water temperature decrease (°C)	Mass of cool sample (g)	Cool-water temperature increase (°C)
1	90.0	3.25	30.0	9.70
2	80.0	2.05	20.0	8.05
3	100.0	1.75	20.0	8.75

We observe in every trial that the larger mass had a smaller temperature change. For example, in Trial 1, the temperature of the 90.0-g sample of warm water decreased 3.25°C, while the temperature of the smaller, 30.0-g sample of cool water increased 9.70°C. Furthermore, the ratios of the masses are very close to the reciprocals of the ratios of the temperature changes (Table 12.3). Note that in Trial 1 the ratio of masses of warm to cool water was 3.00 and the reciprocal of the temperature change ratio was 2.99.

Table 12.3 Ratios of Masses and Ratios of Temperature Changes for Data in Table 12.2			
Trial number	Ratio of masses (warm/cool)	Ratio of the temperature change (warm decrease/cool increase)	Reciprocal of the temperature change ratio (cool increase/warm decrease)
1	3.00	0.335	2.99
2	4.00	0.255	3.92
3	5.00	0.200	5.00

We can sum up these results in an equation:

$$\frac{\text{Mass of warm water}}{\text{Mass of cool water}} = \frac{\text{Increase in cool-water temperature}}{\text{Decrease in warm-water temperature}}$$

We can multiply both sides of this equation by the product of the two denominators and get:

(Mass of warm water) · (temperature decrease) = (mass of cool water) · (temperature increase)

Indeed, as Table 12.4 shows, the products of mass and temperature decrease (or increase) in each of the three trials are equal within the uncertainty of the measurements. (The products are shown in boldface type in the table.)

Table 12.4 Mass Times Temperature Change for Unequal Masses of Water						
Trial number	Mass of warm water (g)	Decrease in warm-water temperature (°C)	Mass · (decrease in warm-water temperature) (g·°C)	Mass of cool water (g)	Increase in cool-water temperature (°C)	Mass · (increase in cool-water temperature) (g·°C)
1	90.0	3.25	**293**	30.0	9.70	**291**
2	80.0	2.05	**164**	20.0	8.05	**161**
3	100.0	1.75	**175**	20.0	8.75	**175**

We can now define the change in thermal energy (ThE) of a sample to be proportional to the product of its mass and its change in temperature:

(Change in ThE) is proportional to (mass · change in temperature)

Then, inserting a proportionality constant (see Appendix 2), we have

Change in ThE = (constant) · mass · (change in temperature).

> Examine Table 12.4. How is it possible for the change in thermal energy of a water sample to be large if its temperature change is small?

With this definition, the increase in thermal energy of the cool water equals the decrease in thermal energy of the warm water. We can make this statement even though we have not chosen a unit for energy. However, to say how much the thermal energy of the cool water has increased, we must choose a unit for energy. The unit of energy we choose determines the value of the proportionality constant. (See Appendix 2 on page 352 for help with proportionality.)

Quite a few different units of energy have been used over the years. The standard unit of energy in science today is the *joule* (J). (The reason for choosing the joule as a unit of energy will be seen later in the course.) To express a change in thermal energy in joules, the proportionality constant must be expressed in J/(g·°C). This constant is the amount of thermal energy, in joules, required to raise the temperature of one gram of a substance by one degree Celsius. It is called the *specific heat* of the substance.

$$\text{Change in ThE} = (\text{specific heat}) \cdot \text{mass} \cdot (\text{change in temperature})$$

The specific heat of water is 4.18 J/(g·°C).

As an example, we calculate the decrease in thermal energy of the warm water in Trial 1. From Table 12.4, we know that the temperature of 90.0 g of water decreased by 3.25°C. The decrease in thermal energy in joules is:

$$\text{Decrease in ThE} = 4.18 \ \frac{J}{g \cdot °C} \ \times \ 90g \ \times \ 3.25°C \ = \ 1{,}223J$$

> How much energy is released when 1.0 g of water cools 1°C?

7. The temperature of a 40-g sample of water increases by 8.5°C. How much thermal energy did the water gain?

8. Use the data in Table 12.2 to verify the data in Table 12.3.

9. Suppose a freshly poured mug of tea contains 200 g of water at 75°C. If the tea cools down to room temperature (22°C), what is the decrease in thermal energy of the water?

10. The temperature inside a refrigerator often reads 7°C. Suppose a 1.0-L bottle of water that has been in a refrigerator for some time is allowed to warm up to room temperature. What is the increase in the thermal energy of the water?

EXPERIMENT E — 12.4 Cooling a Warm Solid in Cool Water

Suppose a warm piece of metal is put into room-temperature water. We would expect the final temperature of the water and metal to be somewhere between the initial temperature of the water and the initial temperature of the metal. Assume the masses of the metal sample and the water sample are the same. Will the final temperature of the two be midway between the initial temperatures, as it was when you mixed equal masses of water?

To find out, mass a large metal washer and tie a string to it. Submerge the washer in warm water between 30°C and 35°C, with the string hang-

ing over the lip of the container so that you will be able to easily pick it up (Figure 12.4).

- How will you know when the washer and the water are at the same temperature?

Measure a volume of room-temperature water that has a mass equal to the mass of the washer, and place it in your calorimeter.

- Which temperature should you measure first, that of the metal washer or that of the water in the calorimeter? Why?

Measure the temperatures of both, then quickly remove the washer from the warm water and submerge it in the water in the calorimeter. Swirl the calorimeter gently.

- What is the increase in the temperature of the water? The decrease in the temperature of the washer?
- What is the increase in the thermal energy of the water?

The water and the washer in the calorimeter are quite insulated from the surroundings. Therefore,

Decrease in ThE of metal = increase in ThE of water.

The decrease in the thermal energy (see Section 12.3) of the washer is given by the following equation:

Decrease in ThE of metal = (specific heat of metal) · mass · (decrease in temperature).

11. What reasons can you give for first placing the sample of cool water, rather than the washer, into the calorimeter in Experiment 12.4?

12. Consider a 150.0-g piece of the same metal used to make the washer you worked with in Experiment 12.4. If the temperature of this piece is raised by 10.0°C, by how much will its thermal energy increase?

12.5 Specific Heats of Different Substances

Your results in the preceding experiment may have surprised you, but they are quite valid. We did the same experiment, using the same equipment, with equal masses of water and aluminum. The data are shown in Table 12.5.

Table 12.5 Data for Experiment 12.4 Using Warm Aluminum and Cool Water				
Sample	Mass (g)	Initial temperature (°C)	Final temperature (°C)	Change in temperature (°C)
Aluminum	46.40	33.60	24.00	-9.60
Water	46.40	21.90	24.00	2.09

The gain of thermal energy by the water is:

$$(4.18 \text{ J/(g} \cdot \text{°C)} \times 46.40 \text{ g} \times 2.09\text{°C} = 405 \text{ J}.$$

This gain equals the loss of thermal energy of the piece of aluminum:

$$(\text{Specific heat of aluminum}) \times 46.40 \text{ g} \times 9.60\text{°C} = 405 \text{ J}$$

or

$$\text{Specific heat of aluminum} = \frac{405 \text{J}}{46.40 \times 9.60 \text{ °C}} = 0.91 \frac{\text{J}}{\text{g} \cdot \text{°C}}$$

The specific heats for several substances are listed in Table 12.6. Notice that the specific heat of water is much higher than most other substances. This is generally true; very few substances have a specific heat as great as that of water.

Table 12.6 Specific Heats of Some Common Substances

Substance	Specific heat (J/g·°C)
Hydrogen	14
Water	4.2
Ice	2.1
Water vapor	1.9
Ethanol	2.4
Ethylene glycol	2.4
Olive oil	2.0
Air	1.0
Aluminum	0.90
Granite rock	0.79
Iron	0.45
Copper	0.39
Lead	0.13
Gold	0.13

13. Samples of copper and lead were each heated 5.0°C. What was the increase in the thermal energy per gram for each sample?

14. To raise the temperature of a sample of a metal from 20.0°C to 25.0°C required 12 J.

    a. How much thermal energy is required to raise the temperature of the sample by 1.0°C?

    b. What additional information must you have to determine the specific heat of the substance that makes up the sample?

15. A 50.0-g piece of metal is added to 60.0 g of water. When mixed, the temperature of the water increases 2.0°C while the temperature of the metal decreases 22.8°C. Calculate the specific heat of the metal and use Table 12.6 to identify it.

EXPERIMENT

E

12.6 Melting Ice

For ice to melt, it must be in contact with something at a higher temperature. For example, you can put ice in warm water. When you do, the water cools as the ice melts. If you combine the ice and warm water in a calorimeter, we can argue that the water lost thermal energy as it cooled. Therefore, the ice must have gained thermal energy as it melted. The purpose of this experiment is to determine how much thermal energy is required to melt one gram of ice at 0°C.

You will use a known amount of warm water. When this warm water is added to a mixture of ice and water in a calorimeter, some of the ice will melt. To find out how much melts, you will need to know how much ice is in the calorimeter just before you add the warm water. Plan a strategy to mass the ice rapidly and return it to the calorimeter before much melting can take place. Having a balance nearby will help.

⚠ **CAUTION: Be sure to use standard −10°C to 110°C thermometers to make all measurements in this experiment. The more sensitive thermometers used previously could be damaged by temperatures outside their normal range.**

Pour about 25 g of water into a calorimeter and add two or three ice cubes. The ice cubes need not be completely covered with water. Stir the mixture until the temperature no longer changes.

- What is the temperature of the ice-water mixture?
- What is the mass of the ice?

Now you are ready to add about 35 g of warm water (at about 40°C) to the mixture of ice and water. The exact amount is not important as long as you measure its mass and temperature accurately.

- What is the mass of the warm water?
- What is the temperature of the warm water?

Gently swirl the calorimeter and mixture until the temperature no longer changes.

- What is the final temperature of the mixture?
- How much ice has melted?
- How much thermal energy was lost by the warm water?

- How much thermal energy was lost by the warm water to melt one gram of ice?

16. Why was it necessary to mass only the ice, but not the water, at 0°C before adding the warm water in the experiment?

12.7 Heat of Fusion and Heat of Vaporization

The results of the preceding experiment can be summarized as follows: in a calorimeter, some warm water cooled down and some ice melted to become water without a change in temperature. The melting of the ice is a change and, as explained in Section 12.1, we associate that change with a change in energy. This change is measured by the loss of thermal energy by the warm water. The gain in energy when one gram of ice at 0°C becomes one gram of water at 0°C is called the *heat of fusion* of water. When one gram of water at 0°C freezes, it loses this amount of energy. The surroundings gain an equal amount of thermal energy.

What would you expect a temperature vs. time graph for ice to look like during the interval when the ice is absorbing its heat of fusion?

Table 12.7 lists the heats of fusion for a few substances. As you can see, the heat of fusion varies a great deal from substance to substance. The table also includes the *melting point* for each of these substances—that is, the temperature at which the transition from solid to liquid takes place.

Table 12.7 Heats of Fusion and Melting Points for Some Common Substances		
Substance	Heat of fusion (J/g)	Melting point (°C)
Nitrogen	25.7	–210
Sulfur dioxide	115	–72.7
Ethanol	109	–117
Isopropanol	16.2	–89.5
Tin	60.9	231.7
Lead	24.7	327.3

Does a higher melting point mean that a substance will have a larger heat of fusion?

How much does the temperature of a sample of water increase as it boils?

Just as there is a change in energy (the heat of fusion) associated with the melting of ice, there is also a change in energy associated with the boiling of water. To see this, think of an experiment similar to Experiment 12.4, Cooling a Warm Solid in Cool Water. Instead of cool water, we have water close to boiling. Instead of a washer, we have a stone at a temperature of several hundred degrees Celsius. When the stone is dropped into the water, the water will boil and the stone will cool down. However, a thermometer will show that the temperature of the boiling water remains constant (100°C at sea level). Thus, water evaporates while the temperature of the stone decreases. The change in energy associated with the evaporation of one gram of water is called the *heat of vaporization*. To measure this energy, you would need to find the decrease in thermal energy of the stone.

Table 12.8 lists the heats of vaporization for several common substances along with the *boiling point* of each.

Table 12.8 Heats of Vaporization and Boiling Points for Some Common Substances		
Substance	Heat of vaporization (J/g)	Boiling point (°C)
Nitrogen	200	−196
Sulfur dioxide	383	−10.0
Ethanol	855	78.5
Water	2,260	100
Isopropanol	669	82.4
Tin	2,490	2,260
Lead	859	1,740
Helium	20.9	−269

> Does a higher boiling point mean that a substance will have a larger heat of vaporization?

17. How do the values for the heats of fusion in Table 12.7 compare with the value you found for ice in Experiment 12.6, Melting Ice?

18. Suppose that it rains when the temperature of the ground, and the air just above the ground, is below the freezing point of water (0°C). The rain freezes. Will the freezing lower or raise the temperature near the ground? Explain.

19. How does the heat of vaporization of water compare with those of the other substances listed in Table 12.8?

20. How do the heats of fusion and vaporization of the same substance compare?

12.8 Heat of Reaction

EXPERIMENT

E

When you reacted zinc with hydrochloric acid in Experiment 6.4, you placed the test tube in a beaker to keep the acid solution cool. To find out how much thermal energy was released in the reaction, you might consider repeating the experiment in a calorimeter and measure the increase in temperature of the solution. However, even with a calorimeter, considerable thermal energy would leak to the room because the reaction took a long time. To find out how much thermal energy is released when a metal reacts with hydrochloric acid, you will use magnesium, which reacts very fast.

⚠ CAUTION: Safety glasses are required throughout this experiment. Be careful not to spill any of the solution on your clothes. If some acid spills on your hands, wash them thoroughly with water.

Measure and place 40 cm³ of room-temperature hydrochloric acid in a calorimeter.

- The density of the hydrochloric acid solution is 1.02 g/cm³. What is the mass of the hydrochloric acid solution you are using?

About 0.05 g of magnesium is all you need to get a significant rise in temperature when the magnesium reacts with the acid. This is too small a mass to measure with sufficient accuracy on your balance. The magnesium that you will use comes in thin strips. Your teacher will tell you the mass per centimeter of the magnesium strip, having measured the mass and length of a long strip.

- What is the length of the piece of magnesium that you received?
- What is its mass?
- Do you need to be concerned about recording the temperature of the hydrochloric acid before the magnesium is added? Why or why not?
- When should you measure the final temperature of the acid solution after you put the magnesium in the acid?
- The specific heat of the hydrochloric acid solution is 3.9 J/(g·°C). What was the increase in the thermal energy of the solution?
- In this reaction, how much thermal energy is released per gram of magnesium reacted?

In a reaction, the amount of thermal energy released (or absorbed) per gram of reactant is known as the *heat of reaction*. It has the units of joules per gram, or J/g.

- What is the heat of reaction for this reaction between magnesium and hydrochloric acid?

21. Equal volumes of liquids A and B are mixed together. If the initial temperature of both was 25°C, could the final temperature be different from 25°C? Explain.

22. In calculating the heat of reaction, why could you ignore the thermal energy absorbed by the magnesium chloride and hydrogen that are formed in the reaction?

12.9 Comparing the Energies Involved in Different Reactions

What does a negative heat of reaction mean?

Table 12.9 shows the heats of reaction for some common reactions. In most of these reactions, energy is released so the heat of reaction is positive. However, when nitrogen combines with oxygen to form nitrogen oxide, energy is absorbed in the reaction. To indicate this, the heat of reaction is stated as a negative number.

Table 12.9 Heats of Reaction for Some Common Reactions		
Substance	Reaction	Heat of reaction (J/g)
Methanol	Methanol + oxygen → carbon dioxide + water	2.3×10^4
Gasoline	Gasoline + oxygen → carbon dioxide + water	4.8×10^4
Heating oil	Heating oil + oxygen → carbon dioxide + water	4.6×10^4
Hydrogen	Hydrogen + oxygen → water	14.3×10^4
Nitrogen	Nitrogen + oxygen → nitrogen oxide	-0.63×10^4
Sodium	Sodium + chlorine → sodium chloride	1.8×10^4
Copper	Copper + sulfur → copper sulfide	0.76×10^4
TNT (trinitrotoluene)	TNT → nitrogen + hydrogen + water + carbon monoxide + carbon dioxide	0.46×10^4

How do heats of reaction compare to heats of fusion and heats of vaporization? Almost all substances have heats of fusion between 15 J/g and 840 J/g. In contrast, heats of vaporization are almost always in the range 200 J/g to 2,500 J/g. As you can see in Table 12.9, heats of reaction are often even larger.

23. When a medical "cold pack" is activated, the reaction that takes place causes the pack to feel quite cold. Is the heat of reaction positive or negative in this case?

24. Does Table 12.9 indicate why liquid hydrogen is one of the best fuels for propelling rockets that carry satellites into orbit?

25. Suppose some astronauts landed on a planet whose atmosphere was composed of hydrogen.

   a. What could they use for fuel in such an atmosphere?

   b. How much thermal energy per gram of fuel would they obtain? (See Table 12.9.)

FOR REVIEW, APPLICATIONS, AND EXTENSIONS

26. Suppose you heat 100 g of room-temperature water in a small beaker and 1,000 g of room-temperature water in a large beaker until the temperature of each sample is 60°C. Do both water samples gain the same amount of thermal energy? Explain your reasoning.

27. Equal masses of olive oil and water are heated in identical containers for the same length of time on the same hot plate. If the temperature of the water increases by 5°C, approximately how much will the temperature of the olive oil change?

28. A few metal washers, whose total mass is 200 g, are heated in boiling water at 100°C and then placed in 100 g of water at 20°C. The final temperature of both is 25°C.

   a. What is the specific heat of the metal?

   b. Based on this specific heat, what metal do you think the washers might be made of?

29. The specific heat of zinc is 1.62 J/(g·°C). How much thermal energy is required to raise the temperature of 4.00 g of zinc by 2.0°C?

30. Figure B shows the cooling curves for four 50-g samples of water. The temperature of each water sample was recorded as a function of time and then graphed on the same set of axes.

a. Which arrangement makes for the best calorimeter? Why?

b. What was the approximate decrease in temperature for each sample during the first 2 min?

c. What was the approximate decrease in temperature for each sample during the last 2 min?

d. Room temperature was about 22°C. As the temperature of the water approached room temperature, was the decrease in temperature in a 2-min interval greater than or less than at the beginning?

e. Why were the experiments in this chapter carried out at close to room temperature?

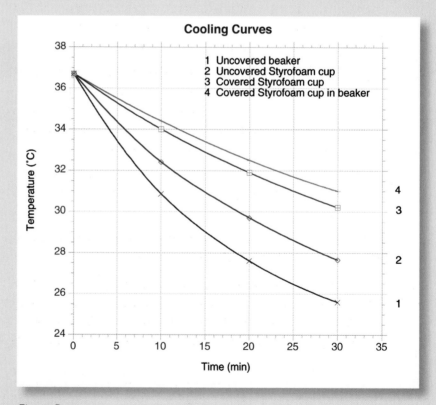

Figure B
For Problem 30

31. Suppose the volume of water in a swimming pool can be approximated by a rectangular box of length 9.6 m, width 4.8 m, and average depth 1.7 m.

   a. What is the volume of the water in cubic meters? In cubic centimeters?

   b. What is the mass of the water in grams?

   c. Suppose the pool's owner wants to raise the temperature of the water by 5°C. By how much will the thermal energy of the water increase, in joules, as this temperature change takes place? (Ignore any loss of thermal energy to the air and the walls of the pool.)

   d. Swimming pools are usually heated electrically. The electric company uses the kilowatt-hour (kWh) as the unit of energy in its billings: 1 kWh = 3.6×10^6 J. What is the needed increase in thermal energy in kWh?

   e. Check your family's electricity bill for the current price of a kilowatt-hour. How much would it cost to increase the temperature of the water in this swimming pool 5°C?

32. One-hundred-gram samples of aluminum, copper, and lead are placed in boiling water. After several minutes, the samples are removed and placed into separate containers, each with 100 g of water at 20°C. Which metal will cause the greatest temperature change in the cool water? (See Table 12.6.)

33. You can put your hand into a hot oven for a moment without harming yourself. Yet holding your hand over steam at 100°C can cause a serious burn. Why?

34. Suppose that 1 g of ice at 0°C is changed into 1 g of steam at 100°C. What is the total increase in energy?

35. A century ago, farmhouses in colder parts of the country often had unheated cellars for storing vegetables. To keep the vegetables from freezing, people placed large buckets of water in the cellar. Explain how the water helped prevent the vegetables from freezing.

36. Eggs will cook just as quickly at a low boil as at a high boil. Why?

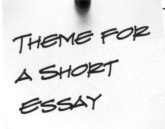

THEME FOR A SHORT ESSAY

Suppose a friend admits to being confused about the difference between temperature and thermal energy. Write a short essay using examples from daily life that will highlight the distinction between these two terms.

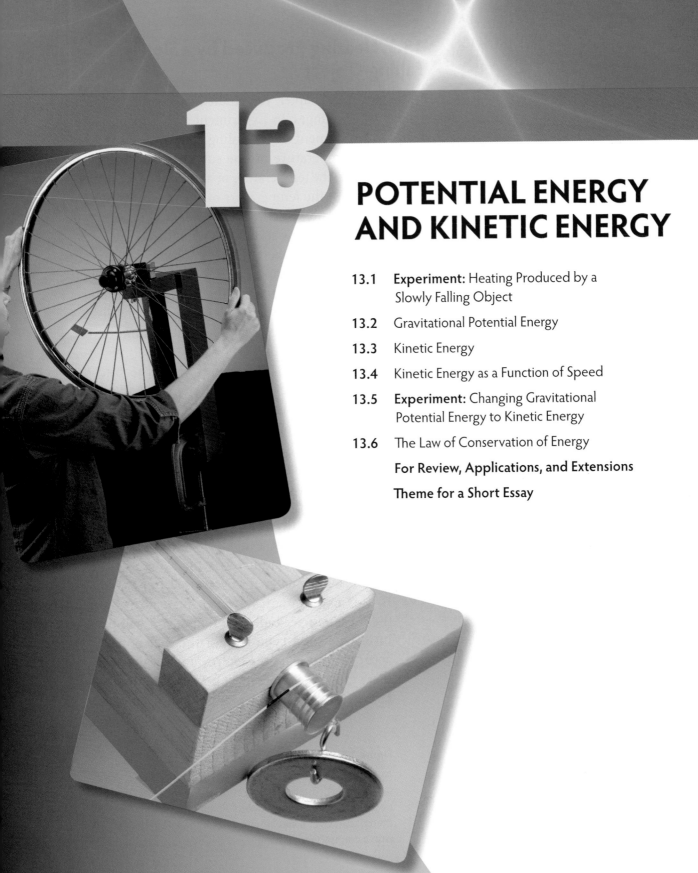

13

POTENTIAL ENERGY AND KINETIC ENERGY

13.1 Heating Produced by a Slowly Falling Object

EXPERIMENT **E**

In the previous chapter, you studied changes in temperature accompanied by other changes. In Experiment 12.2, Mixing Warm and Cool Water, and in Experiment 12.4, Cooling a Warm Solid in Cool Water, an increase in the temperature of one substance or object was accompanied by a decrease in the temperature of another. In Experiment 12.6, Melting Ice, a decrease in the temperature of the water was accompanied by the melting of ice. And in Experiment 12.8, Heat of Reaction, a temperature change occurred as new substances were formed.

In all of those experiments, once the objects or substances were put together in the calorimeter, they remained in the calorimeter. Their positions did not change. In this experiment, the position of an object will change; a plastic bottle containing water will fall very slowly. Fishing line attached to the falling bottle will rub against an aluminum cylinder, raising its temperature (Figure 13.1).

> If this is the purpose, what will you need to measure?

The purpose of this experiment is to find out how the increase in thermal energy of the cylinder is related to the mass of the falling bottle. This knowledge will provide a way to define a new kind of energy.

To obtain reliable results, there are several precautions and preparations you will need to make. Their details are described below.

Notice that the aluminum cylinder has a hole drilled in it so that a thermometer can be inserted into it. The thermometer is the same high-resolution thermometer that you used in Chapter 12. In this experiment, however, instead of placing the thermometer bulb in a liquid, you will place it inside the solid cylinder. For the thermometer to accurately measure the temperature of the cylinder, there must be good contact between the thermometer bulb and the cylinder. This contact is most easily

Figure 13.1

Apparatus for measuring the heating produced by a slowly falling object. The fishing line supporting the water-filled bottle is looped around a fixed aluminum cylinder. The line then passes over a steel guide rod on the left and is anchored with a counterweight hanging from the end.

achieved by putting a small amount of paste into the cylinder hole. The paste will conduct thermal energy from the cylinder to the thermometer.

Before clamping the cylinder in place and inserting the thermometer, be sure you know the mass of the cylinder, including the paste. Then firmly clamp the cylinder so that it cannot rotate.

Place the thermometer in the groove and gently slide it into the cylinder as far as it can go. Carefully turn the thermometer as you insert it. This will provide better contact by allowing air bubbles that may be trapped in the paste to escape. It will also allow you to position the thermometer so that it can be read most conveniently.

Once the thermometer is in place, the fishing line can be wrapped around the cylinder. Hang a large washer on one end of the line and a counterweight on the other end (Figure 13.2). Together, the washer and counterweight will keep the line taut so that it does not unwind and fall off the cylinder. During the actual experiment, the water-filled bottle will replace the washer. The counterweight will be left in place to hold the line taut so that it rubs against the aluminum cylinder as the bottle falls.

You can use a balance to find the mass of the empty bottle. Your teacher will assign each lab group a volume of water to be added to the bottle. The mass of the water is most conveniently found by measuring its volume and then using its density to calculate its mass.

Still another factor to be considered is the amount of friction between the line and the cylinder. This friction depends on the number of times the line is wrapped around the cylinder. With too many turns, the friction will be so great that the bottle will not fall. With too few turns, the friction will be so low that the bottle will fall too rapidly and the cylinder will not warm up. Before performing the experiment, you will

Why is a small amount of paste put into the hole in the aluminum cylinder?

Figure 13.2

The apparatus before the first run. The thermometer projects from the rear of the cylinder, and a washer is in place to keep the line taut until the water-filled bottle is attached.

Figure 13.3

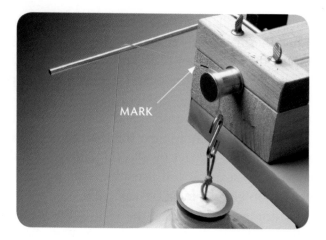

A close-up of the apparatus shown in Figure 13.1 at the start of a run. The loops have been pulled to the front rim of the cylinder and the water-filled bottle has been attached.

MARK

need to determine how many times to wrap the fishing line around the cylinder so that the bottle takes between 5 s and 15 s to fall to the floor. You can begin by wrapping the fishing line around the cylinder four or five times, and then adjust the number of turns until the bottle falls at an appropriate rate.

You may have noticed that as the hanging bottle slowly falls, the loops of fishing line creep along the cylinder. To provide enough distance for this creep and prevent the loops from piling on top of each other, wind the fishing line around the cylinder in a clockwise direction as shown in Figure 13.2. Then slide the loops to the front rim of the cylinder so that they are touching and form a single layer (Figure 13.3).

There is another quantity that must be considered before you can perform the experiment—the amount of thermal energy lost to the surrounding air. In Chapter 12, you used a calorimeter to reduce this loss. But the aluminum cylinder is not in a calorimeter. As the fishing line heats the cylinder, a significant amount of the thermal energy could be lost to the room.

To prevent this, you can pre-cool the aluminum cylinder so that it is slightly below room temperature at the beginning of each run and slightly above room temperature at the end of each run. This will allow the cylinder to gain thermal energy from the room while it is below room temperature and lose thermal energy to the room when it is above room temperature. In this way, the thermal energy gains and losses will roughly balance. Measure the room temperature with the sensitive thermometer before each run. Pre-cooling the cylinder to about 0.3°C to 0.6°C below room temperature will be sufficient for the falling mass you will be using. Practice pre-cooling the cylinder several times using an ice cube in a plastic bag. If necessary, you can warm the cylinder by touching it briefly with your hand to bring it back up to the desired temperature.

> Why is it important that the ice cube be in a plastic bag? Why can't you simply touch the ice cube directly to the cylinder?

Your teacher will tell you the height to use for the fall of the bottle. Attach the bottle to the fishing line at the appropriate height with the line wrapped the proper number of turns. Then mark the line where it begins to wrap around the cylinder. This is shown by the arrow in Figure 13.3. This will allow you to repeat the experiment with the bottle released from the same height each time.

As the bottle falls, the counterweight is lifted. To determine the net mass that is actually falling, you will need to subtract the mass of the counterweight from the mass of the bottle and the water it contains.

Now you are ready to do the experiment. With the fishing line in place and the cylinder cooled correctly, attach the bottle at the assigned height and make a measured run. Repeat the experiment several times. Then, using the temperature changes, the mass of the cylinder, and the specific heat of aluminum, calculate the increase in thermal energy of the cylinder for each run.

- How will you calculate the increase in the thermal energy of the cylinder?

Using data from the entire class, graph the increase in thermal energy as a function of the net falling mass.

- Why should you consider the origin as a data point?
- How is the amount of thermal energy gained by the cylinder related to the net falling mass?

Why is it important that you always release the bottle from the same height?

What is meant by "net mass"? Why do you *not* need to be concerned about the masses of the identical hooks on the ends of the fishing line?

1. Suppose you arrange the apparatus in Experiment 13.1 so that it takes the object 10 min to reach the floor. What rise in temperature would you expect to find?

2. Suppose that the aluminum cylinder had twice the mass of the cylinder that you used. How would this affect the rise in temperature in your experiment?

3. How would your experimental results have been affected by each of the following?

   a. You began with the temperature of the aluminum cylinder a degree or two above room temperature.

   b. You forgot to subtract the mass of the counterweight from the mass of the container.

4. How would your experimental results have been affected if you had used the same volume of candle oil instead water? (The density of candle oil is 0.76 g/cm^3.)

13.2 Gravitational Potential Energy

How is the increase in thermal energy of the cylinder related to the vertical falling distance (Figure 13.4)?

In the preceding experiment, the class results showed that the increase in thermal energy of the cylinder is proportional to the net mass when the falling distance is kept constant. How does the increase in thermal energy depend on the falling distance? To answer this question, we have to vary the falling distance while keeping the mass constant. Figure 13.4 presents data obtained from just such an experiment. The net falling mass was 5.00 kg.

We now have two conclusions. (1) If the falling distance is kept constant, the increase in thermal energy is proportional to the net falling mass. (2) If the mass is kept constant, the increase in thermal energy is proportional to the distance. To satisfy both these conclusions, the increase in the thermal energy (ThE) of the cylinder must be proportional to the product of the net mass and the falling distance. (See Appendix 2, Proportionality.)

Increase in ThE (J) is proportional to mass (kg) · distance fallen (m)

so

Increase in ThE (J) = constant · mass (kg) · distance fallen (m)

How can we find the proportionality constant for this relationship? We take any point on the graph in Figure 13.4 and divide the increase in the thermal energy by the distance fallen. For example, in a 1.00-m fall, the thermal energy of the 5.00-kg object increased by 50.0 J. For a 1.00-kg object, the increase for a fall of the same distance would be just

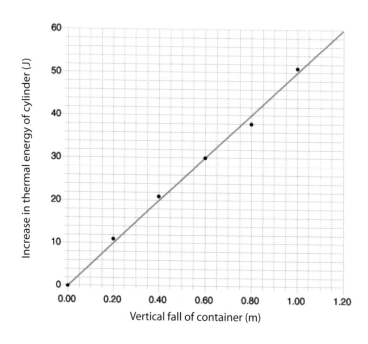

Figure 13.4

A graph of the increase in thermal energy of the cylinder as a function of the distance that a 5.0-kg object has fallen.

10.0 J. This means that the value of the proportionality constant is 10.0 J/(kg·m). More accurate experiments have shown the proportionality constant to be 9.8 J/(kg·m).

To sum up:

Increase in ThE (J) = 9.8 (J/kg·m) · mass (kg) · distance fallen (m)

Note that the left side of this equation depends only on the cylinder: its mass, its substance, and its temperature change. The right side of the equation depends only on the falling object: its mass and the distance it falls. We now use this equation to define a new form of energy. Because it depends on gravity, it is called *gravitational potential energy* (GPE):

Decrease in GPE (J) = increase in ThE (J)

Equating the decrease in gravitational potential energy of a falling object with the increase in thermal energy of the cylinder means that the sum of the two energies stays constant. It also means that when an object rises, its gravitational potential energy increases.

Increase in GPE (J) = 9.8 (J/kg·m) · mass (kg) · distance raised (m)

Similarly, as an object falls, its gravitational potential energy decreases.

Decrease in GPE (J) = 9.8 (J/kg·m) · mass (kg) · distance fallen (m)

In fact, we can use Figure 13.4 to describe the change in gravitational potential energy of the 5.00-kg object by simply changing the labels on both axes (Figure 13.5).

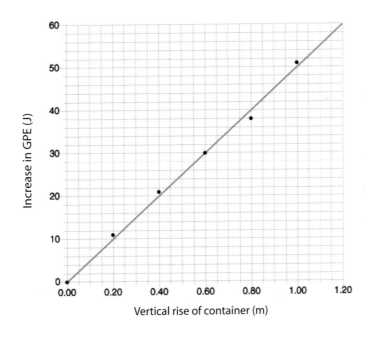

Figure 13.5

The same graph as in Figure 13.4 but with changed labels on the axes. The graph shows the increase in gravitational potential energy of a 5.0-kg object as a function of the distance it is raised.

5. A one-gallon bottle of water has a mass of about 4 kg. How much gravitational potential energy does the bottle gain if it is lifted each of the following distances?

    a. 1 m   b. 2 m   c. 10 m

6. Which gains more gravitational potential energy, a 4.00-kg object lifted 3.00 m or a 5.00-kg object lifted 2.00 m?

(a)

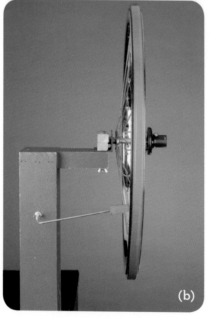

(b)

13.3 Kinetic Energy

Have you ever wondered what would happen if you tried to stop a rapidly spinning bicycle wheel by holding your hand against the tire? You may have even tried it! If so, you know that your hand heats up as the wheel slows down. In fact, your hand might even be burned. An increase in thermal energy occurs even though the wheel has neither fallen nor been lifted. This happens whether the wheel spins in a vertical or a horizontal plane, so there is no change in the gravitational potential energy of the wheel. Therefore, the heating up of your hand must be related only to the slowing down of the wheel and not to a change in the gravitational potential energy of the wheel. Once again, as in Sections 12.1 and 13.2, we define a form of energy. This form of energy, which is associated with motion, is called *kinetic energy* (KE).

Decrease in KE (J) = increase in ThE (J)

What does kinetic energy depend on? Suppose you stopped two identical wheels that were spinning on the same axis. Together, the wheels have twice the mass of one wheel, and so they will double the increase in the thermal energy of your hand. Apparently, kinetic energy is proportional to the mass of a moving object.

Figure 13.6

(a) A wheel ready to be spun. The rim is a steel ring that may be covered with red or black tape. (b) A metal pointer fastened to the stand is lightly tapped by a piece of tape attached to one of the spokes. When the tape hits the pointer, it produces a click that can be used to count and time 10 rotations of the wheel.

Figure 13.7

A close-up of the center of the wheel and the aluminum cylinder just before it is inserted into the plastic extension of the hub.

How does kinetic energy depend on speed? This question can be answered by experiment. Figure 13.6 shows a bicycle wheel that can be spun using both hands. The tire has been replaced by a solid ring of steel about 1.5 cm thick, effectively shifting the entire mass of the wheel, which in this case was 4.60 kg, to the rim. A plastic extension of the hub contains a hole into which an aluminum cylinder can be inserted (Figure 13.7). After the wheel has been spun and its rate of spinning determined, the wheel is brought to rest by friction between the hub and the cylinder. The rise in temperature of the cylinder is read on a thermometer like the one you used in Experiment 13.1 (Figure 13.8).

Figure 13.8

The wheel after being stopped by friction between the extension of the hub and the aluminum cylinder. A thermometer inserted in the cylinder detects any rise in the temperature of the cylinder.

The results for this experiment are displayed in Table 13.1.

Time for 10 rotations (s)	Initial Speed of rim (m/s)	Increase in temperature (°C)	Increase in thermal energy (J)
	Table 13.1 Data from Spinning Wheel Experiment		
15.4	1.23	0.30	4.1
13.0	1.45	0.30	4.1
10.8	1.75	0.45	6.1
10.6	1.78	0.50	6.8
10.0	1.89	0.65	8.8
10.0	1.89	0.50	6.8
9.7	1.95	0.65	8.8
8.6	2.20	1.00	13.5
8.0	2.36	1.00	13.5
7.0	2.70	1.05	14.2
6.6	2.86	1.55	20.9
6.4	2.96	1.30	17.6

Since the mass of the wheel is concentrated in the rim, one complete rotation of the wheel is essentially the same as having the total mass of the wheel move a distance equal to the circumference of the wheel. The speed of the rim was calculated by dividing the circumference of the rim by the time for one rotation:

$$\text{Speed} = \frac{\text{circumference}}{\text{time for one rotation}}.$$

The circumference of the wheel is π times the diameter. Therefore,

$$\text{Speed} = \frac{\pi \cdot \text{diameter}}{\text{time for one rotation}}.$$

The diameter of our wheel, measured from the middle of the steel rim, was 0.603 m.

If the time for one rotation is doubled, the speed is cut in half. This is why the entries in the first column of Table 13.1 are in descending order, while those in the second column are in ascending order.

The increase in thermal energy in the fourth column was calculated by multiplying the increase in temperature by the product of the mass of the cylinder and its specific heat. The mass of the cylinder used in this experiment was 15.0 g and the specific heat was 0.91 J/(g·°C).

Figure 13.9 contains a graph of the data in the second and fourth columns of Table 13.1. The origin was added to the data because we are absolutely certain that a wheel at rest will cause no increase in thermal energy. Two features of the graph are evident: the data points are quite scattered, and the smooth curve is not a straight line.

Figure 13.10 shows the same data, but the labels on both axes have been changed. The horizontal axis now shows the speed of the rim as the wheel spins faster, beginning from rest. The vertical axis now shows the kinetic energy of the rim as its speed increases.

Why the origin included as a data point in the graph is shown in Figure 13.9?

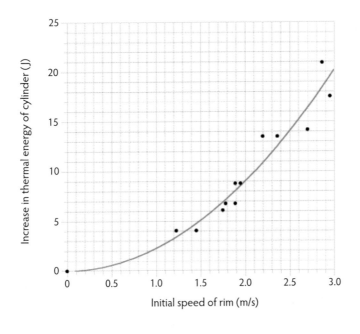

Figure 13.9

A graph of the increase in thermal energy of the cylinder as a function of the initial speed of the rim. The point at the origin was added to the values in Table 13.2.

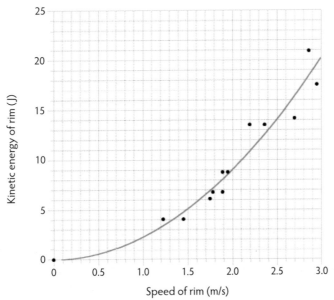

Figure 13.10

The same graph as in Figure 13.9, but with the axes renamed.

7. Confirm the first and last entries in the second and fourth columns in Table 13.1. Use the information given in the text about the diameter of the wheel and the product of the mass and specific heat of the aluminum cylinder.

8. Look at the sixth row of Table 13.1. The temperature increase of 0.50 °C came from an initial temperature of 21.35 °C and a final temperature of 21.85 °C.

    a. Another experimenter might have read the initial temperature as 21.30 °C. Assuming that the final temperature reading was unchanged, what would this experimenter calculate for the increase in the thermal energy of the cylinder?

    b. How would this reading affect the position of this data point in Figure 13.9?

    c. The time of 10 rotations was measured with a stopwatch. The reading of 9.7 s might have been off by 0.1 s either way. How would a reading of 9.6 s or 9.8 s affect the position of the data point in Figure 13.9?

    d. Which data reading—time or temperature—has a greater effect on the position of the data points?

13.4 Kinetic Energy as a Function of Speed

As we have already seen, the graph in Figure 13.10 is not a straight line. Is there a simple way of expressing the relationship between speed and kinetic energy?

Figure 13.10 is a good representation of all the data points, considering their uncertainties, so let's look more carefully at that graph. The kinetic energy of the wheel at 1.00 m/s is 2.2 J. At 2.00 m/s the wheel has a kinetic energy of 8.8 J, or four times the kinetic energy at 1.00 m/s. At 3.00 m/s the kinetic energy is 20 J, or nine times the value at 1.00 m/s. This suggests that we calculate the squares of the speeds and plot the kinetic energy as a function of the square of the speed. The resulting graph is shown in Figure 13.11.

Indeed, the straight line through the origin shows that the kinetic energy of the rim is proportional to the square of the speed. We already know that kinetic energy is proportional to the mass of a moving object. If it is also proportional to the square of the speed, then kinetic energy

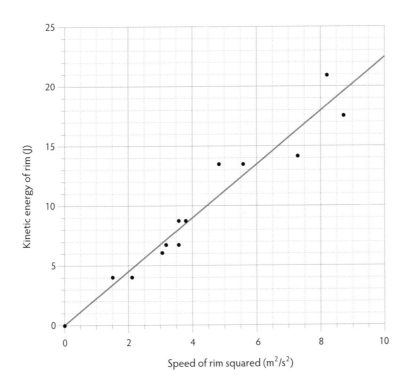

Figure 13.11

A graph that shows the relationship between the square of the speed of a wheel and its kinetic energy.

(KE) must be proportional to the product of the mass and the square of the speed. That is,

$$KE = \text{proportionality constant} \cdot \text{mass} \cdot \text{speed}^2.$$

We can now find the proportionality constant by reading a speed-squared value and the corresponding kinetic energy from the graph. We then divide the kinetic energy by the speed squared and the mass.

In Figure 13.11, a value of 10.0 $(m/s)^2$ for the square of the speed corresponds to a kinetic energy of 22.5 J for the wheel. The mass of the wheel, which is almost all in the rim, is 4.60 kg. Therefore, the proportionality constant will be

$$\frac{22.5 \text{ J}}{4.60 \text{ kg} \times 10.0 \ (m/s)^2} = 0.49 \ \frac{\text{J}}{\text{kg} \cdot (m/s)^2}.$$

More accurate experiments show that the proportionality constant is 0.500 for a wide range of speeds and masses. It is generally written as the fraction ½ rather than as 0.500.

To sum up, the kinetic energy of any object is given by the following formula:

$$KE = \tfrac{1}{2} \cdot \text{mass} \cdot \text{speed}^2.$$

If the mass is given in kilograms and the speed in meters per second, the kinetic energy is in joules.

9. A compact car has a mass of about 1,000 kg.

   a. What is its kinetic energy at each of the following speeds?
      0.5 m/s, 10 m/s, and 30 m/s

   b. When would a car be moving at these speeds?

10. Can two people be moving at different speeds and have the same kinetic energy? Explain.

11. Can two moving cars of different mass have the same kinetic energy? Explain.

12. Consider a cart moving at constant speed. What will increase its kinetic energy more, tripling its mass or doubling its speed?

EXPERIMENT E 13.5 Changing Gravitational Potential Energy to Kinetic Energy

In Section 13.2, we defined the loss of gravitational potential energy by the relation

Decrease in GPE (J) = 9.8 (J/kg·m) · mass (kg) · distance fallen (m).

In Section 13.4, we defined kinetic energy by the relation

$$KE = \tfrac{1}{2} \cdot mass \cdot speed^2.$$

Both of these definitions were based on experiments involving thermal energy. In the first case, fishing line tied to a slowly falling mass rubbed against an aluminum cylinder, raising its temperature. In the second case, a rotating wheel was stopped by having it rub against an aluminum cylinder. What happens if a slowly falling mass causes a wheel to rotate (Figure 13.12(a))? Does the loss of gravitational potential energy equal the gain in kinetic energy as defined by the above relations?

Begin by massing the empty bottle, hooks, and dowel. Your teacher will tell you how much water to add to the bottle.

• What is the total mass that will be falling in this experiment?

You are now ready to connect the looped end of a piece of fishing line to the screw on the hub (Figure 13.12(b)). If necessary, adjust the length of the line so that it will fall off the screw just as the bottle reaches the floor. Lift the bottle by turning the wheel so that the fishing line winds around the hub. When the bottle is at the desired height, make a mark

Figure 13.12

(a) A bottle containing water hangs from fishing line that is wrapped around the hub of a wheel. When the wheel is released, the bottle falls slowly, the fishing line unwinds, and the wheel begins to spin. (b) A close-up shows how a loop at the end of the fishing line is hooked over a pin in the hub. This allows it to release from the hub automatically when it is unwound.

where the fishing line touches the hub. This will help you to easily perform several runs starting at exactly the same height.

- How far will the bottle fall?
- What is the decrease in the gravitational potential energy of the falling mass?

When you are ready, release the wheel and allow the bottle to fall. As soon as the fishing line falls away from the hub, you can use a stopwatch and the piece of tape (Figure 13.6) to time 5 rotations of the wheel. As you count the rotations, be sure to start with 0 and stop timing when you reach 5.

- How much time is needed for the wheel to make 5 rotations?
- What is the average speed of the rim of the wheel?
- What is the kinetic energy of the wheel?

To compare the gain in kinetic energy with the loss in gravitational potential energy, it is best to calculate their ratio.

- What is the ratio of the increase in kinetic energy of the wheel to the decrease in gravitational potential energy of the falling mass?

Make a histogram of the ratios obtained by the entire class.

- Considering the histogram, how would you answer the question "Does the loss of gravitational potential energy equal the gain in kinetic energy?"

---

13. **Suppose that the bottle fell four times as far while attached to the hub of the wheel.**

   a. **How would this affect the decrease in the gravitational potential energy of the bottle?**

   b. **How would this affect the increase in the kinetic energy of the wheel?**

   c. **How would this affect the ratio of the decrease in gravitational potential energy to the increase in kinetic energy?**

   d. **How would this affect the speed of the wheel?**

13.6 The Law of Conservation of Energy

The results of the preceding experiment show that the definitions of gravitational potential energy and kinetic energy are useful. They enable us to predict the kinetic energy and the speed of the wheel if we know the vertical distance a mass has fallen.

Just as gravitational potential energy can change into kinetic energy, so can kinetic energy change into gravitational potential energy. This can be shown using the same wheel that is pictured in Figure 13.12. In Figure 13.13(a), a heavy object hangs from a string wrapped around the hub of the wheel. Unlike in Experiment 13.5, Changing Gravitational Potential Energy to Kinetic Energy, the end of the string is securely fastened to the hub. When the wheel is released, the string unwinds and the falling object causes the wheel to turn. Clearly, the falling object loses gravitational potential energy and gains kinetic energy.

In Figure 13.13(b), the object is momentarily at rest at its lowest point, and the wheel spins the fastest. At this instant, the spinning wheel begins to slow down as it pulls the object back up. During this portion of the motion, the wheel loses kinetic energy as the object gains gravitational potential energy.

In Figure 13.13(c), the object and the wheel are again at rest. Notice that the object almost returns to its original height. Some loss is inevitable due to friction in the bearings and with the air. Had we measured the height and speed of the object and the speed of the rim at various

> How do you know that the kinetic energy of the wheel is at its maximum when the object reaches its lowest point?

Figure 13.13

(a) A string holding a heavy object is tied around the hub of the wheel. When the wheel is released, the object begins to fall and the wheel begins to turn. (b) The string is completely unwound. The object is momentarily at rest at its lowest point. The wheel turns at its highest speed. (c) The wheel and the object are again at rest. The object is almost back to its starting position.

times, we would have found that the loss in gravitational potential energy was nearly equal to the gain in kinetic energy at all times throughout the motion.

A similar experiment is shown in Figure 13.14. The object has been replaced by a stretched spring. In Figure 13.14(a), the spring is stretched all the way to the rim of the wheel, as shown by the small ring at the top end of the spring. In Figure 13.14(b), the spring has contracted to its natural length and the wheel spins the fastest. At this moment, the wheel

Figure 13.14

(a) A stretched spring is attached to the hub of a wheel by a string. (b) The stretched spring contracts and turns the wheel. (c) The spring is stretched by the turning wheel until it returns almost to its original position when the wheel comes to rest.

begins to slow down as the spring stretches. In Figure 13.14(c), the wheel is again at rest and the spring is almost back to its initial length. Apparently the stretched spring has a potential energy that can be transformed into kinetic energy. This form of potential energy is called *elastic potential energy*.

The experiments illustrated in Figures 13.13 and 13.14 are just two examples of gains and losses of different forms of energy that always balance. Many other experiments lead to the same conclusions: when all changes are taken into account, the losses equal the gains. Energy is neither created nor destroyed; it only *transforms* from one form to another. Saying it differently, the sum of all forms of energy involved in any process remains the same. This generalization is called *the law of conservation of energy*.

No process has ever been observed in which the law of conservation of energy has been violated. For example, you would never see that mixing equal masses of water in a calorimeter at 30°C and 50°C would produce a final temperature of 20°C. However, not every process that could satisfy the law will necessarily take place. You have seen that if you place a hot washer in cool water, the washer will cool down and the water will warm up until they reach the same temperature. This process satisfies the law of conservation of energy. The opposite process would also satisfy the law of conservation of energy. But you will never see a washer warming up and the water cooling down if both start at the same temperature.

14. How is the law of conservation of energy similar to the law of conservation of mass?

15. When it falls, the heavy object in Figure 13.13 never reaches the floor. Describe the energy changes of the object and the wheel until all motion stops.

16. Figure A shows an object hanging from a spring. In (a), the object is also supported by a block of wood. When the block is removed, the object falls. In (b), the object has reached its lowest position. Its next highest position is shown in (c).

   a. Describe the energy changes taking place between (a) and (b), and between (b) and (c).

   b. Consider an instant between (a) and (b). Will the decrease in gravitational potential energy of the object equal the increase in elastic potential energy of the spring?

c. Based on the sequence of photographs, do you think the object will continue to bounce up and down forever?

d. Does your answer to part (c) violate the law of conservation of energy?

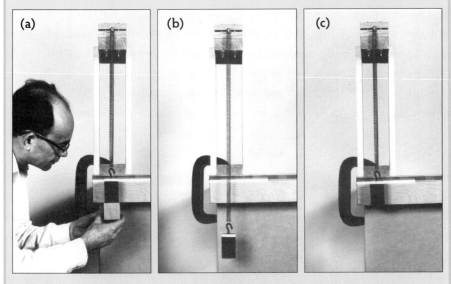

Figure A
For Problem 16

For Review, Applications, and Extensions

17. Ten students whose combined mass is 700 kg ride down 30 m (about 10 floors) in an elevator. How much thermal energy is produced in the elevator system by the loss in gravitational potential energy of the students?

18. An object with mass *m* is moving at speed *v*. How is the kinetic energy of the object affected when each of the following changes takes place?

    a. *m* is doubled while *v* remains constant.

    b. *v* is halved while *m* remains constant.

    c. Both *m* and *v* are doubled.

    d. *m* is doubled and *v* is halved.

    e. *m* is halved and *v* is doubled.

19. In Figure B, a cart loaded with bricks can roll down a slanted board. Like the falling object in Experiment 13.1, Heating Produced by a Slowly Falling Object, the cart is tied to fishing line wrapped around an aluminum cylinder. Also as in that experiment, a thermometer has been inserted into the cylinder.

Figure B
For Problem 19

The experimenter can change how much the board is tilted. When the board is less steep, the cart travels a longer distance for the same decrease in height (Figure C).

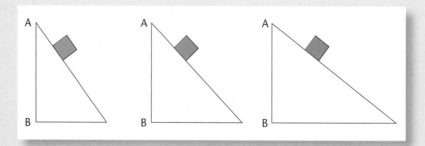

Figure C
For Problem 19

The table below shows the results of several runs.

Run number	Distance cart travels along board (m)	Decrease in height of cart (m)	Increase in temperature of cylinder (°C)
1	0.50	0.50	1.8
2	0.58	0.50	1.8
3	0.72	0.50	1.8
4	0.83	0.50	1.8
5	0.97	0.50	1.8

    a. In which run was the board vertical?

    b. In which run was the board the least steep?

    c. Which determines the loss of gravitational potential energy of the cart—the distance traveled along the board or the decrease in height?

20. Suppose the friction in the wheels of the cart described in Problem 19 was so great that it could not be neglected. How would this affect each of the following?

    a. The total change in gravitational potential energy of the cart

    b. The total increase in thermal energy of the wheels and the aluminum cylinder as the cart travels down the slanted board

    c. The change in temperature of the aluminum cylinder.

21. To quickly stop a car moving on a horizontal road, you must apply the brakes. To keep a car at a constant speed while it is traveling down a hill, you also must apply the brakes.

Consider two identical cars each having a mass of 1,000 kg. One, moving horizontally, is brought to a stop from an initial speed of 25 m/s (about 55 mph). The other travels down a 300-m-high hill (about 1,000 ft) at constant speed and is not stopped. For which car will the increase in thermal energy of the brakes be greater?

22. Suppose that a 110-lb student slowly walks down three floors in a building (a total height of about 10 m).

    a. What is the student's loss of gravitational potential energy?

    b. If this loss could be converted into a gain of thermal energy by the aluminum cylinder used in Experiment 13.1, what would be the rise in temperature of the cylinder?

    c. Why would the student not feel any rise in temperature?

23. Suppose a pendulum is hung from a ceiling. When the pendulum is pulled to one side and released, it swings back and forth.

    a. When is the gravitational potential energy of the pendulum increasing? When is it decreasing?

    b. When is the kinetic energy of the pendulum increasing? When is it decreasing?

24. Suppose that you had a setup of a spring and a wheel similar to that shown in Figure 13.14(a), except that the spring would fall free as soon as it reached its natural, unstretched length. How would you use this set up to study the dependence of elastic potential energy on the amount of stretch?

THEME FOR A SHORT ESSAY

The word "potential" is used both in everyday language and as an adjective describing a form of energy. Discuss the similarities and the differences between the two uses.

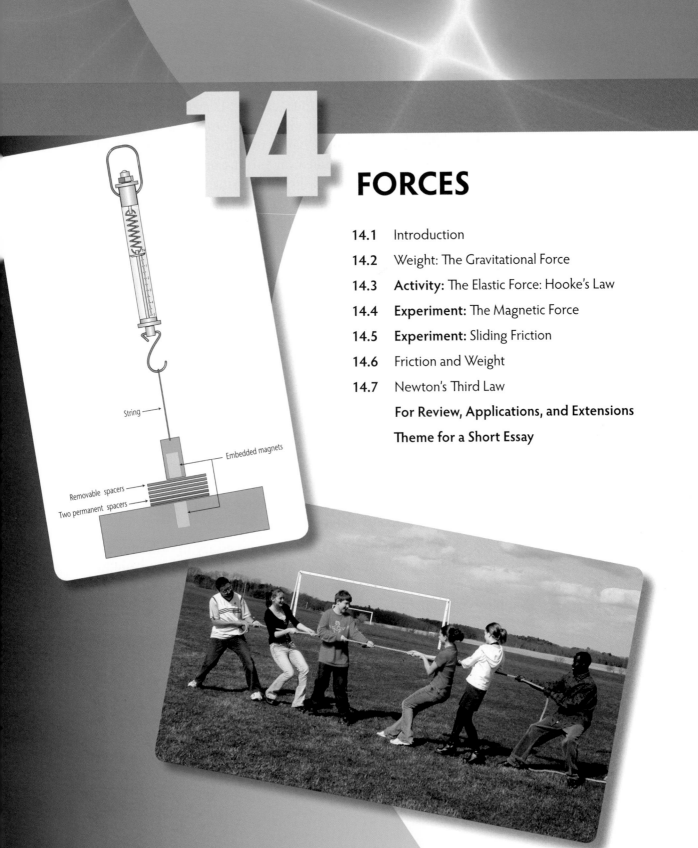

14

FORCES

String

Embedded magnets

Removable spacers

Two permanent spacers

14.1 Introduction

The energy changes that you studied in Chapter 13 were all associated with pulls and pushes. In Section 13.1, you lifted a heavy object and then, as the earth pulled it back down, friction heated an aluminum cylinder. In Section 13.4, you pushed a heavy wheel to make it spin.

Pushes and pulls are not new experiences for you. From early childhood you have pushed and pulled on various objects. As long as they were not too heavy, you could easily observe the effect of your push or pull. For example, pulling on the handle of a wagon makes it move. If a ball is at rest—that is, not moving—it will begin to move when you kick it. A kick is a very brief push.

Since a push and a pull produce quite similar results, they have been given a common name—a force. In this chapter we will study forces in some detail.

What if you push or pull on something and it does not move? Something else must be pushing or pulling just as hard in the opposite direction. This equal force acting in the opposite direction balanced your force.

Based on the above examples, you can tell whether a force is acting on the object by using the following rules:

(1) If the object was at rest and begins to move, a force must have acted on it.

(2) If the object does not begin to move when a force is applied, then there must be at least one other force acting on the object, and the forces balance each other.

Direct contact (touching) is not always necessary in order for a force to be exerted. As an example, you have observed a magnet pulling or pushing an object without touching it. In these cases, the same rules apply as when there is contact.

Tie a string to a pencil and hold it over your desk. When the pencil hangs at rest from the end of the string, the forces on it must be balanced. This means that there must be another force balancing the upward pull exerted by the string. How do we know this? Cut the string. When the force exerted by the string is removed, you can see that there was another force acting on the pencil. That force made the pencil move downward.

In this chapter, you will learn how to measure a number of forces and find out how strong they are under different conditions.

14.2 Weight: The Gravitational Force

Have you ever seen a photograph of someone standing next to a big fish that he or she caught? Chances are the fish was hanging from a device that showed its *weight*. On earth, weight is the pull of the earth on an object. Such a force is called a *gravitational force*, and the device that measures it is called a *spring scale*. In this course, you will use a laboratory version of a spring scale (Figure 14.1).

By hanging something from a spring scale, you can determine its weight just as you can use an equal-arm balance to determine its mass. But are weight and mass related? To find out, let us consider what you have already learned about mass.

When the beam of an equal-arm balance is horizontal, the masses of the objects on the two pans are equal (Figure 14.2). This is true no matter what materials the objects are made of or what their shapes, colors, or volumes might be. Will any two objects that have the same mass also have the same weight?

Suppose that we adjust two identical spring scales so that each reads zero when nothing is hanging from it. If we then hang the equal masses that were used in Figure 14.2, one from each spring

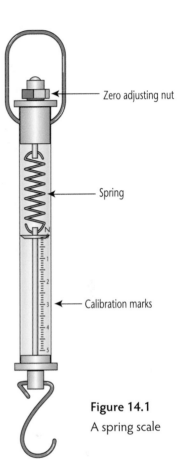

Zero adjusting nut

Spring

Calibration marks

Figure 14.1
A spring scale

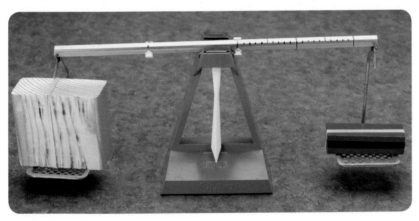

Figure 14.2
The horizontal beam shows that the objects in the two pans have equal masses.

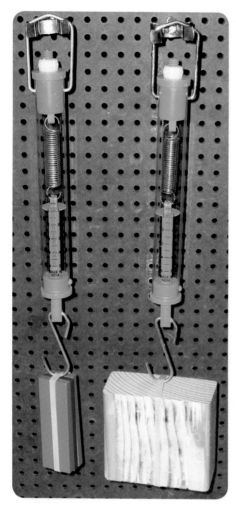

Figure 14.3

When the equal masses are hung from identical spring scales, we can see that they have equal weights.

Which changes with elevation—mass or weight? How is this possible if mass and weight are proportional?

scale, we can compare the weights of the two objects (Figure 14.3). As you can see, if the masses are equal, the weights are also equal even when the volumes are considerably different.

The total mass of two identical objects is twice the mass of one of the objects alone. Similarly, the total weight of two equal masses is twice the weight of either one. Three objects having the same mass would have three times the weight of one, four would have four times the weight, and so on. In other words, weight is proportional to mass:

Weight = (proportionality constant) · mass.

The value of the proportionality constant depends on the units that we use for weight and mass. For everyone to be able to compare the results of different weight measurements, we need a standard unit for weight. The standard for weight, and for all forces in the metric system, is the newton. A newton is about the weight of a small apple or a quarter-pound burger (before cooking!). The abbreviation for newtons is N. Since the unit of weight is the newton and the unit of mass is the kilogram, the proportionality constant in the equation just stated must have units of N/kg.

Suppose you mass a stone on an equal-arm balance in New York, which is at sea level. You then travel with the balance, stone, and standard masses to Denver, Colorado, at an elevation of 1,600 m. The stone will have the same mass it had in New York. This is true even if you would use a more sensitive balance.

The spring scales you will use in this course are not sensitive enough to detect differences in an item's weight in two cities at different elevations, such as New York and Denver. However, using much more sensitive devices, it has been shown that the weight of an object does depend on its elevation.

Since the weight of an object depends on its elevation but its mass does not, the value of the proportionality constant between weight and mass must be different at different elevations. Careful measurements have shown that the value of the proportionality constant does vary slightly at different elevations (Table 14.1).

Table 14.1 Values of the Proportionality Constant Between Weight and Mass at Different Elevations		
Location	Elevation (m)	Proportionality Constant (N/kg)
New York, New York	0	9.803
Denver, Colorado	1,600	9.796
La Paz, Bolivia	3,600	9.780
Top of Mt. Everest	8,848	9.763

The proportionality constant is usually referred to as *g*. Notice that all the values listed in Table 14.1 are very close to 9.8 N/kg. So, for our measurements on earth, we do not need to be concerned with changes in the constant at different elevations. We will simply use a value of 9.8 N/kg in our calculations.

$$\text{Weight (N)} = 9.8 \text{ N/kg} \cdot \text{mass (kg)}$$

The number 9.8 should be familiar to you. It appeared in Section 13.2 in the expression for the increase in the gravitational potential energy (GPE) of an object being lifted a given distance:

$$\text{Increase in GPE (J)} = 9.8 \text{ (J/kg·m)} \cdot \text{mass (kg)} \cdot \text{distance raised (m)}.$$

That the number 9.8 appears in both equations is no coincidence. The joule and the newton were chosen in such a way that

$$1 \text{ J} = 1 \text{ N·m}.$$

Therefore, substituting 1 N·m for 1 J in the equation for the increase in GPE results in

$$\text{Increase in GPE (J)} = 9.8 \text{ (N m/kg·m)} \cdot \text{mass (kg)} \cdot \text{distance raised (m)}.$$

Canceling the meters (m) inside the parentheses results in

$$\text{Increase in GPE (J)} = 9.8 \text{ (N/kg)} \cdot \text{mass (kg)} \cdot \text{distance raised (m)}.$$

The product of the first two factors—9.8 (N/kg) · mass (kg)—on the right side of this equation is the weight of the object being lifted, in newtons. Thus

$$\text{Increase in GPE (J)} = \text{weight (N)} \cdot \text{distance raised (m)}.$$

If an object is falling a given distance rather than being lifted, we have

$$\text{Decrease in GPE (J)} = \text{weight (N)} \cdot \text{distance fallen (m)}.$$

Why do we use a value of 9.8 N/kg for *g*, even though the value of the proportionality constant is different at different elevations?

By using the units for energy (Section 12.3) and force (Section 14.1), we have developed a straightforward relationship between the increase or decrease in gravitational potential energy, the weight of an object, and the distance the object is raised or lowered.

3. In Figure A, what amount of force is indicated by each spring scale?

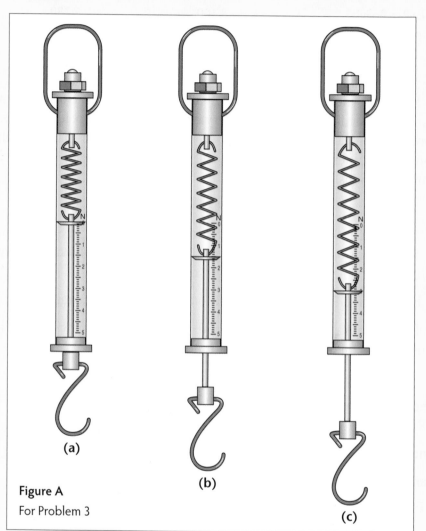

(a)

(b)

Figure A
For Problem 3

(c)

4. Suppose that two objects are individually hung from a spring scale and that each object stretches the spring by the same amount. Which of the following properties of the objects— size, shape, weight, color—must be the same and which could be different?

5. Do equal volumes of water have equal weights? Explain your reasoning.

6. What is the weight of each of the following food items, expressed in newtons?

    a. 5.0 kg of apples

    b. 3.5 kg of grapes

    c. a 1.8-kg cantaloupe

7. In a supermarket, weights are often given in pounds (abbreviated as lb, an old English unit). One pound is equivalent to 4.45 N. What is the mass of each of the following food items? (Hint: First convert from pounds to newtons.)

    a. 1.00 lb of meat

    b. 5.00 lb of sugar

    c. 10.0 lb of flour

8. Suppose you took a spring scale and some standard masses with you to the moon.

    a. How could you use the spring scale to measure weight on the moon?

    b. How could you use the spring scale to measure mass on the moon?

ACTIVITY A · 14.3 The Elastic Force: Hooke's Law

Examine the spring scale provided by your teacher. Note the two scales marked on the outer cylinder, one in newtons and one in grams.

- How can the same device measure both weight and mass?

Hold the spring scale vertically, and adjust the nut at the top so that the top edge of the disc is at the zero mark. (See Figure 14.1.) Hang a light object on the spring scale. The object will stretch the spring some distance and come to rest.

- How are the forces acting on the object related after the object comes to rest?

The force exerted by the spring is called the *elastic force.* How does the force exerted by the spring depend on the stretch? To find out, you will need to measure the distances on the spring scale from the 0-N mark to each of the marks representing whole numbers of newtons. Since it is awkward to measure these distances on the spring scale itself, your teacher will provide you with a photograph of the spring scale. When you have completed your measurements on the photograph, plot a graph of the elastic force as a function of the amount of stretch.

- What do you conclude about the relation between the force exerted by the spring and the stretch of the spring?

If you were given a photograph of a second, different spring scale, make the necessary measurements and plot the elastic force as a function of stretch for this spring scale.

- What is similar and what is different about the two graphs?

The relation between the elastic force and stretch of a spring is called *Hooke's Law*. Hooke's law holds only over a limited range. If you stretch a spring too much, it will not return to its original length when you release it. This is why your spring scales are constructed in such a way that you can only stretch them a safe amount.

The force of gravity always points downward. The elastic force, however, can point in any direction depending on the direction that the spring scale is held. You will use a spring scale in both vertical and horizontal positions in the next two experiments.

9. If a new spring scale reads 1.5 N when it is stretched 3 cm, how much will it be stretched when it reads 3.0 N?

10. If two variables, such as stretch and weight, are proportional, what do you know about the value of one of the variables if the value of the other is zero?

11. The 5-N and 20-N spring scales contain different springs.

a. Pull gently on the two springs. Describe the difference between them.

b. Suppose you hang identical objects on each spring scale. When the objects are at rest, which spring will stretch more? Explain.

c. Does one spring exert a greater force on the object than the other spring? Explain.

14.4 The Magnetic Force

EXPERIMENT E

What happens when two magnets are brought closer to each other? Does the force between them increase or decrease? You have probably played with magnets in the past. You know that whether the magnets are pulling together (*attracting*) or pushing apart (*repelling*), the force between them will be greater when the magnets are closer to each other. What is the quantitative relationship between the magnetic force and the separation distance? For example, if the separation between the magnets is doubled, what happens to the force? In this experiment you will investigate how force and separation are related.

(!) **CAUTION: The magnets used in this experiment can damage sensitive electronic devices such as computers and ID cards with magnetically encoded information. Keep the magnets at least 40 cm from such devices.**

The apparatus that you will use is shown in Figure 14.4. There are two cylindrical magnets. One is embedded in the base, the other in a dowel glued to a string. The string can be attached to a spring scale. Spacers are used to separate the magnets a specific amount so that the force can be measured. All spacers, except the bottom two, are removable, so you can change the separation between the magnets. The lowest two spacers are glued in place to prevent the magnets from striking each other and breaking.

To find the separation between the magnets, you must know the thickness of one spacer.

- How will you use the fact that all the spacers are of the same thickness to find the most accurate value for the thickness of one spacer?

- What is the thickness of one spacer in millimeters?

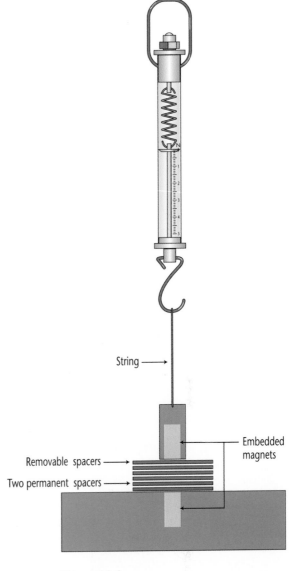

String

Embedded magnets

Removable spacers

Two permanent spacers

Figure 14.4

The magnetic force apparatus.

Why are the two bottom spacers glued to the block containing the lower magnet?

Why must the spring scale be adjusted to zero after the magnet is suspended on it?

Why should you keep the *lower* magnet away from the spring scale as you zero it?

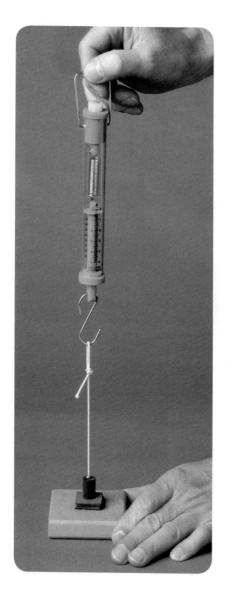

Create a table and record your measurements of the magnetic force at several separation distances.

⚠ **CAUTION: Safety glasses must be worn throughout this experiment.**

A spring scale can be used to measure the magnetic force. But first you must make sure that the spring scale reads only the magnetic force. The weight of the top magnet must be excluded. To do this, use the string to hang the top magnet from the hook on the spring scale. Then adjust the spring scale to read zero by turning the nut at the top of the scale. (Refer to Figure 14.1 on page 285.) You have now "zeroed" the spring scale for this experiment with the top magnet in place.

Begin with a total of eight spacers (six removable spacers plus the two permanent ones) on top of the lower magnet. Carefully lower the top magnet onto the spacers as you hold the string. The hanging magnet will position itself directly above the base magnet. When you begin pulling up on the spring scale, the upper magnet will not move until the pull of the spring becomes greater than the pull of the lower magnet (Figure 14.5).

To observe the force reading on the spring scale at the exact moment the magnets separate, call out the readings as you slowly increase the upward pull. To improve your results, have your lab partner listen carefully and repeat each measurement. Be sure to record both the separation and the force in your data table.

Now remove spacers from the stack one at a time, and measure the force required to separate the magnets at each new separation. Make a graph of the magnetic force, in newtons, as a function of the separation of the magnets, in millimeters.

Figure 14.5

Hold the base and pull straight up on the spring scale to determine the amount of force needed to pull the magnets apart.

Draw a smooth curve that fits the data points you have plotted. Remember that your curve does not need to touch all the data points. Do not connect the dots!

- How would you describe your graph to someone who cannot see it?
- According to your graph, what happens to the magnetic force as the separation between the magnets gets larger?

---

12. Use the graph you constructed for this experiment to answer the following questions.

   a. What do you expect the magnetic force to be at a separation of 4.0 mm? 9.0 mm?

   b. What do you expect the magnetic force to be at a separation of 50 mm?

   c. What separation is needed between the magnets to provide a magnetic force of 0.40 N? 1.80 N?

EXPERIMENT

E

14.5 Sliding Friction

When you pull a sled through snow or push a cardboard box across a level floor, you encounter another force. You can feel a resistance to your push or pull. This additional force is called the *force of friction* or the *frictional force*. However, when you hold a book above a table, there is no friction between the book and the table. For there to be any friction at all, there must be contact.

Does a horizontal tabletop exert a frictional force on a book resting on it? To find out, push very gently in a horizontal direction on a book resting on a table. If you push gently enough, the book will not move. Yet you can feel that you are pushing on the book. A frictional force is balancing your push.

Now push the book with the same force in another direction. The book remains at rest. Apparently, the frictional force also changed direction. It opposes your force just as it did before.

Push the book a little harder. The book still may not move. The frictional force has increased and is once again exactly balancing your push. Of course, once you push hard enough, the book will move. The frictional force is an odd force! It does not appear until some other force is present and, up to the point at which movement begins, its strength depends on the strength of that other force.

Figure 14.6

Equipment used to study sliding friction. Nonskid material covers two sides of the friction block.

What factors affect the frictional force between two objects? To help answer this question, you will use a spring scale and a wooden block (Figure 14.6). The block has wide surfaces and narrow surfaces. One wide and one narrow surface are covered with a nonskid material.

Part A

First you will investigate the effect that the kind of surface has on the force of friction.

Clean your lab table thoroughly. Be sure to zero the spring scale while it is in the horizontal position. Then, begin with the wide, covered surface of the friction block in contact with the table (Figure 14.6). Use the spring scale to measure the smallest force that will pull the block slowly across the table. Use only enough force to keep the block barely moving. The procedures that you used in the preceding experiment—calling out the spring scale readings and having your lab partner repeat each measurement—will also be helpful here. Take several readings.

- What is the smallest force that keeps the block moving?
- Should you be concerned about the frictional force between the spring scale and the table? Why or why not?

Repeat the experiment with the wide, uncovered surface of the block in contact with the table.

- What is the smallest force that will keep the block moving now?
- Does the force of friction depend on the types of surfaces that are in contact with each other?

Part B

You can also pull the block when it rests on one of its narrow surfaces. The weight of the block is the same as when it rests on a wide surface. However, the area of contact between the block and the table is now smaller.

With the block resting on one of its narrow surfaces, repeat the two experiments you did in Part A.

- Does the force of friction depend on the area of contact between the block and the table?

13. When a book is resting on a level table and you are not pushing on it, is there a frictional force between the book and the table?

14. Suppose a wooden block is pushed across a table from left to right. In which direction is the frictional force?

15. Would letting a little air out of the tires of the family car increase the car's traction on an icy road? Why or why not?

14.6 Friction and Weight

So far, you have investigated whether the force of friction depends on the kind of surface and the contact area between two objects. What about weight? Does the weight of an object affect the friction for the same surfaces? To study this, we investigated the frictional force on two blocks of different weights, a short (lighter) block and a long (heavier) one (Figure 14.7). Their weights were 1.30 N and 5.05 N. Using the same procedure that you used in the preceding experiment, we found that the least force needed to move the lighter block was 0.50 N. For the heavier block, the least force was 2.00 N. The friction was greater for the heavier block than for the lighter one.

How do you know that the difference in the frictional forces for the two blocks is due to their different weights and not their different surface areas?

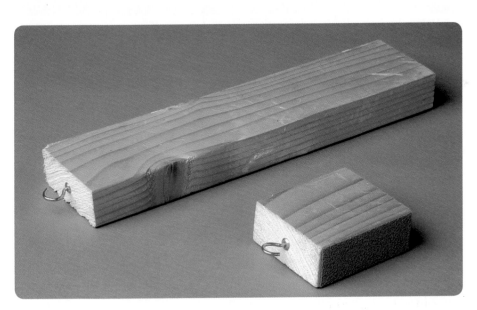

Figure 14.7
Two blocks, a short, lighter one and a long, heavier one. Each has nonskid material on the surface with the largest area.

Figure 14.8

The short, lighter block with added weight.

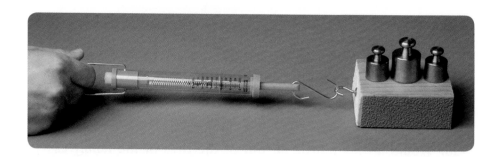

We then placed various weights on the lighter block and measured the force of friction for each combination (Figure 14.8). The results are shown in Table 14.2. These data are then graphed in Figure 14.9. Within the range of the data, the force of friction is proportional to weight. The proportionality constant is called the *coefficient of friction*. It will be different for each pair of surfaces.

Force of friction = (coefficient of friction) · weight

Because both weight and friction are forces, their ratio is a pure number—that is, a number without units—if both are measured in the same units. In Figure 14.9, both forces are expressed in newtons. As a result, the coefficient of friction calculated from the graph is a pure number.

Table 14.2 Data on the Relation Between Frictional Force and the Weight of a Wooden Block				
Block	Weight of block (N)	Added weight (N)	Total weight (N) *	Force of friction (N)
Long	5.05	0.00	5.05	2.00
Short	1.30	0.00	1.30	0.50
Short	1.30	0.49	1.79	0.55
Short	1.30	0.98	2.28	0.90
Short	1.30	1.47	2.77	1.05
Short	1.30	1.96	3.26	1.20
Short	1.30	2.45	3.75	1.40
Short	1.30	2.94	4.24	1.60
Short	1.30	3.43	4.73	1.80
Short	1.30	3.92	5.22	1.90
Short	1.30	4.41	5.71	2.25
Short	1.30	4.90	6.20	2.50

* The total weight in each case is the sum of the weight of the block and any additional weights that were placed on top of it.

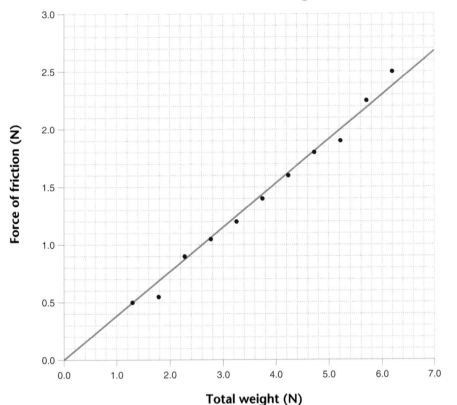

Friction Versus Weight

Figure 14.9
Graph of the results shown in Table 14.2.

Force of friction (N) vs *Total weight (N)*

16. For identical surfaces, how does the force of friction depend on the weight of the object you are trying to move?

17. What is the coefficient of friction for the surfaces used to produce the data in Table 14.2?

18. Why do some motorists keep sand in the trunk of the cars for winter driving?

19. Use the graph in Figure 14.9 to answer the following questions.

   a. What would be the frictional force on the short block if its total weight equaled the weight of the long block?

   b. How does this force compare with the measured force on the long block?

   c. Are you surprised by your answer to part (b)? Why or why not?

14.7 Newton's Third Law

In Experiment 14.5, Sliding Friction, when you just began to pull on the block with a spring scale, the block did not move. The frictional force exerted by the table on the block balanced the force exerted by the spring. Did the block also exert a frictional force on the table in the opposite direction? If so, how big was that force?

You easily measured the frictional force that the table exerted on the block because the block was free to move. Suppose that the table was also free to move. Then, if a frictional force is exerted on the table by the pulled block, we could balance this force using another spring scale attached to the table. This would tell us how large the frictional force on the table is. Obviously, the table is not free to move. There is considerable friction between the legs of the table and the floor. So we cannot answer the question about the frictional force on the table.

However, suppose we place the block on a light cart instead of a table (Figure 14.10). The cart's wheels, which cannot be seen in the photograph, have very good bearings. As a result, there is very little friction between the cart and whatever it sits on. If we now pull on the block, the cart will move with the block. To keep the cart at rest, the frictional force exerted by the block on the cart must be balanced by another force. Pulling on the cart with the second spring scale provides this balancing force.

Note in Figure 14.10 that the cart is pulled to the left and the block is pulled to the right. Let us call the force exerted by the spring on the cart A, and the force exerted by the other spring on the block D. Figure 14.10 clearly shows that these two forces are equal in strength:

$$A = D.$$

What prevents the table from moving?

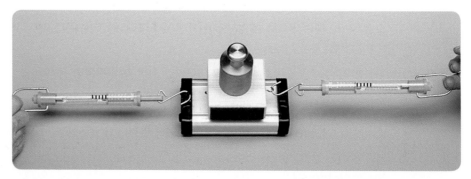

Figure 14.10

A block on a cart. Because of special wheels, there is very little friction between the cart and the table. All three objects are at rest. The cart is pulled to the left and the block is pulled to the right. Note that the readings on both spring scales are the same.

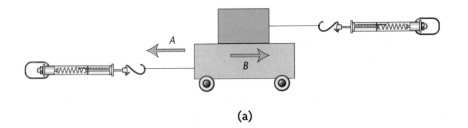

(a)

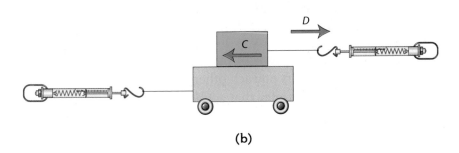

(b)

Now concentrate just on the forces acting on the cart. The spring pulls the cart to the left with a force A. The force of friction exerted by the block pulls the cart to the right with a force B (Figure 14.11(a)). Since the cart is at rest, these two forces must balance each other, so

$$A = B.$$

We now apply the same reasoning to the forces acting on the block. The spring pulls the block to the right with a force D. The force of friction exerted by the cart on the block pulls the block to the left with a force C (Figure 14.11(b)). Since the block is at rest, these two forces balance each other, so

$$D = C.$$

We can now apply the mathematical property known as *transitivity*. If $B = A$ and $A = D$ and $D = C$, then

$$B = C.$$

In words, the strength of the frictional force exerted by the block on the cart (B) equals the strength of the frictional force exerted by the cart on the block (C). These two forces act, of course, in opposite directions.

Now consider another situation. In Experiment 14.4, The Magnetic Force, you measured the force that the lower magnet exerts on the upper magnet. During the experiment, you had to hold the lower magnet in place. Clearly, the upper magnet also exerted a force on the lower magnet. Were the two forces equally strong? You cannot tell on the basis of

Experiment 14.4 because you held the lower magnet down with your hand. However, many experiments have shown that the forces that two magnets exert on each other are equal in strength and opposite in direction.

Finally, let us consider once again the gravitational force. The weight of a rock on the surface of the earth is the force with which the earth pulls the rock down. Does the rock pull the earth up with an equal force? No experiment that you can do in the laboratory can detect the effect of the gravitational force that the rock exerts on the earth. This problem can be eliminated if we look, for example, at the earth and the moon. Studies of the motions of the earth and moon show that the gravitational forces they exert on each other are equal in strength.

In fact, all forces known today that act between two objects along the line that connects them are equal in strength and opposite in direction. This property of forces is known as *Newton's third law*.

Newton's third law may seem strange to you. Is it possible that when a heavy truck collides with a small car, the forces acting between them are equal and opposite? Keep in mind that "equal forces" does not mean the effects of those forces are equal. Obviously, the small car may be completely destroyed, whereas the truck may suffer only minor damage. Newton's third law relates only to forces, not to their effects.

> How does the weight of a rock compare with the force of the rock on the earth?

> Suppose that you kick a soccer ball. Which experiences a greater force— the ball or your foot? Explain.

20. On a copy of Figure B, mark all the horizontal forces acting on the block and all the horizontal forces acting on the cart. Explain which pairs of forces are equal and why.

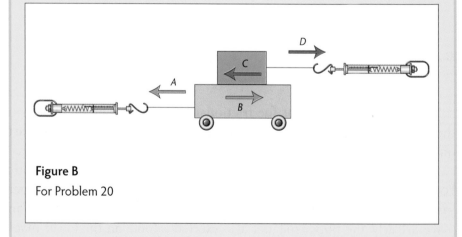

Figure B
For Problem 20

21. Consider two different magnets mounted on two carts with low-friction wheels, as shown in Figure C. The carts are at rest. The forces exerted by the two spring scales are equal and opposite. Explain why the forces that the magnets exert on each other are equal and opposite.

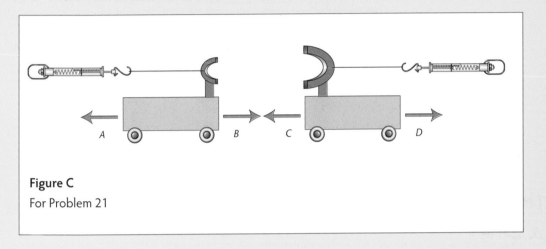

Figure C
For Problem 21

FOR REVIEW, APPLICATIONS, AND EXTENSIONS

22. A heavy plate is placed on top of a vertical spring. The spring is compressed and the plate comes to rest.

   a. What forces are acting on the plate at the moment it is placed on the spring?

   b. What forces are acting on the plate after it has come to rest?

   c. How do the forces in part (b) compare?

23. Suppose a bottle of water weighs 360.00 N in New York City.

   a. If you want the bottle of water to have the same weight in La Paz, Bolivia, should you add or remove some water?

   b. How much water should you add or remove?

24. Most refrigerator doors have a magnetic strip around the edge that holds the door shut. How could you measure the magnetic force holding the door shut? Try it.

25. Not all magnets are permanent. A piece of iron surrounded by a coil of wire becomes a magnet when current flows through the wire. Such a magnet is called an *electromagnet*. In large junkyards, electromagnets are used to lift and move cars.

    a. How much magnetic force is needed to lift a 2,000-lb car?

    b. Express this force in newtons.

    c. Why do you think an electromagnet is used rather than a permanent magnet?

THEME FOR A SHORT ESSAY

Friction is sometimes needed and sometimes to be avoided. Write a short essay titled "The Two Faces of Friction."

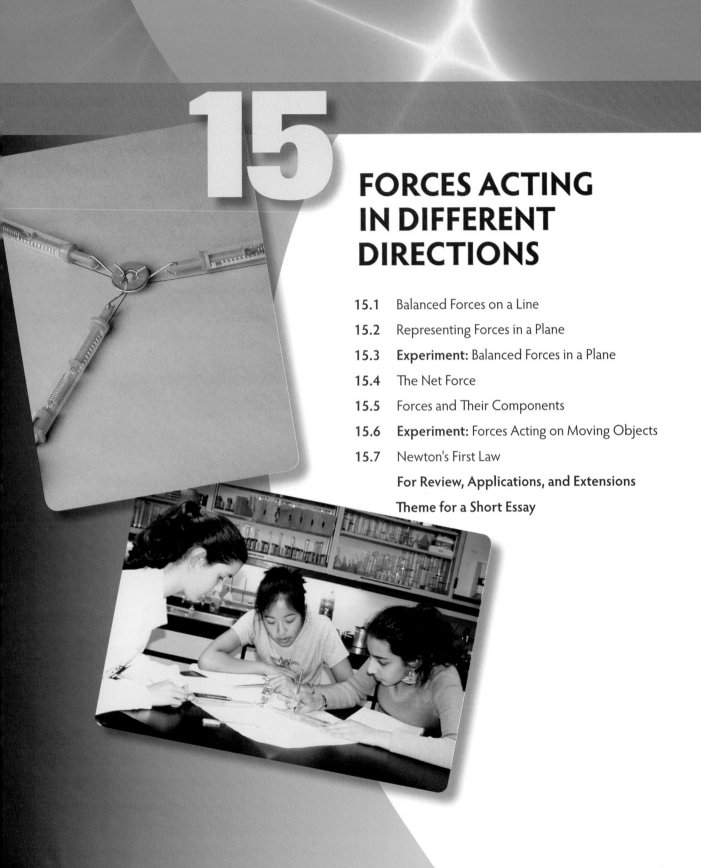

15

FORCES ACTING IN DIFFERENT DIRECTIONS

15.1 Balanced Forces on a Line

In Chapter 14 you learned that if we exert a force on an object and it does not move, there must be another force acting on the object with equal strength in the opposite direction. We say that the forces on the object are *balanced*. For two forces to be balanced, they must be of the same strength and act in opposite directions along the same line (Figure 15.1).

Figure 15.1

Two balanced 8.0-N forces hold a washer at rest above a pushpin. The washer does not touch the pushpin. Since the forces are in opposite directions along the same line, we can call one +8.0 N and the other –8.0 N.

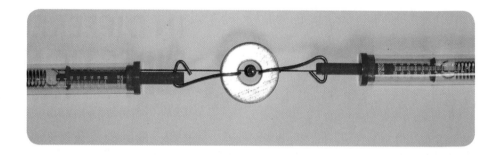

You can also use signed numbers (+ or –) to see whether forces acting along a line are balanced. If one direction is chosen to be negative, then the other direction is positive. The sum of the forces shown in Figure 15.1 is then

$$(-8.0)\ \text{N} + (+8.0)\ \text{N} = 0$$

Forces along the same line are balanced when their sum is zero.

You can tell whether any number of forces along a line are balanced by expressing their directions and strengths as signed numbers and adding in this way. If the sum is zero, the forces are balanced. An example is shown in Figure 15.2. If we choose the direction to the left to be negative and to the right positive, the sum of these forces is

$$(-4.0)\ \text{N} + (-10.0)\ \text{N} + (+14.0)\ \text{N} = 0$$

Figure 15.2

Three forces applied along a line cause the washer to remain at rest above the pushpin. If the direction to the left is chosen to be negative, we have $(-4.0)\ \text{N} + (-10.0)\ \text{N} + (+14.0)\ \text{N} = 0$. The forces are balanced.

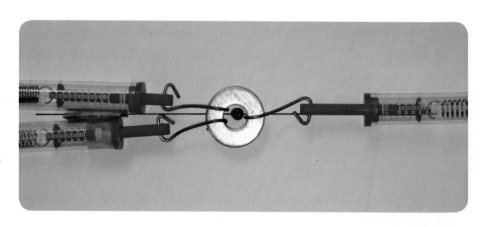

But we could just as well have chosen negative to be to the right. The sum would still be zero.

$$(+4.0) \text{ N} + (+10.0) \text{ N} + (-14.0) \text{ N} = 0$$

Representing the direction and the strength of each force with a signed number is useful when forces are along the same line.

Three forces are exerted on a washer along a single line. The forces are 5 N to the right, 14 N to the left, and 9 N to the right. Are the forces balanced? Explain.

15.2 Representing Forces in a Plane

Although the force of gravity always points down, other forces can be exerted in any direction. For example, you can pull a bag along the floor in any direction. You can also lift it up. For a full description of a force, we need to do more than just state its strength. We also need to state its direction. Such a quantity, described by both its size and its direction, is called a *vector*.

A vector can be represented by an arrow that is drawn to scale and points in the appropriate direction (Figure 15.3). In the case of a force, the direction of the vector indicates the direction of the force, and the length of the vector represents the strength of the force. In other words, the length of the vector is proportional to the force. When using the same proportionality constant, a vector that is twice as long as another vector represents twice as much force, one three times as long represents three times the force, and so on.

To draw a vector that is the proper length to represent a certain force, we must first choose the proportionality constant relating the length of the vector to the strength of the force:

Length (cm) = proportionality constant (cm/N) · force (N)

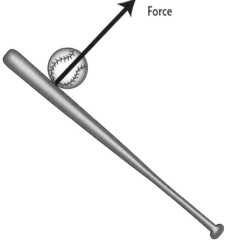

Force

Figure 15.3

When a bat hits a softball, it applies force to the ball. The direction of the vector represents the direction of the force, and the length of the vector represents the strength of the force.

You can choose any value for this proportionality constant, but it will be helpful to choose a constant that is both easy to work with and that results in vectors that fit on your paper. For example, you might choose a proportionality constant of 2 centimeters per newton (2 cm/N). Using this constant, a 1-N force is represented by a vector that is 2 cm long, as shown in Figure 15.4(a):

$$\text{Length} = (2 \text{ cm/N}) \cdot (1 \text{ N}) = 2 \text{ cm.}$$

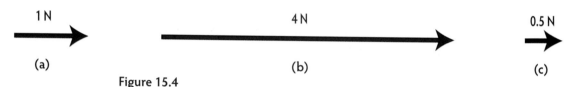

Figure 15.4

(a) Using a proportionality constant of 2 cm/N, the vector that represents a 1-N force is 2 cm long. (b) Using the same proportionality constant, the vector that represents a 4-N force is four times as long, or 8 cm. (c) By this proportionality constant, a 0.5-N force is represented by a vector that is one-half the length of the 1-N arrow, or 1 cm.

Now suppose that you want to use the same 2-cm/N proportionality constant to represent a force of 4 N (Figure 15.4(b)). A 4-N force has four times the strength of a 1-N force. Therefore, the vector drawn to represent the 4-N force is four times as long as the vector that represents the 1-N force:

$$\text{Length} = (2 \text{ cm/N}) \cdot (4 \text{ N}) = 8 \text{ cm.}$$

This is four times the length of the 1-N vector.

If you use the same proportionality constant to represent a force of one-half newton (Figure 15.4(c)), the length of the vector is

$$\text{Length} = (2 \text{ cm/N}) \cdot (0.5 \text{ N}) = 1 \text{ cm.}$$

Suppose we want to determine the strength of the force from the length of the vector. To do this, we rewrite our equation as:

$$\text{Force (N)} = \text{new proportionality constant (N/cm)} \cdot \text{length (cm)}$$

Your original proportionality constant was 2 cm/N. With this value of the proportionality constant, 1 centimeter represents 0.5 newton, giving us a new proportionality constant of 0.5 N/cm.

How many newtons are represented by a vector 6 cm long? You can see that

$$\text{Force} = (0.5 \text{ N/cm}) \cdot (6 \text{ cm}) = 3 \text{ N.}$$

For the given proportionality constant, a 6-cm vector represents a force of 3 N.

1. Using a proportionality constant of 5 cm/N, draw a vector to represent each of the following forces. (Hint: Since the length of a vector represents the size of a force, you must be careful not to make the vectors any longer when you draw the arrow-heads.)

    a. 2 N to the right

    b. 5 N toward the top of the page

    c. 1.5 N toward the top-left corner of the page

2. Using a proportionality constant of 4 N/cm, describe each force represented in Figure A.

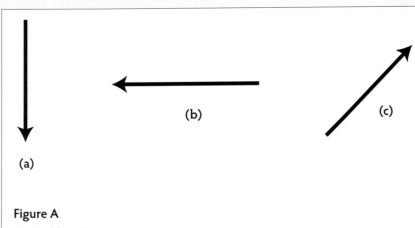

(b)

(c)

(a)

Figure A
For Problem 2

3. Using a proportionality constant of 0.2 cm/N, complete the following chart.

Size of force (N)	Length of vector (cm)
5	?
16	?
?	0.7
?	5.8

4. a. Using a proportionality constant of 5 N/cm, complete the following chart.

   b. Draw each of the vectors specified in the chart.

Length of vector	Size of force	Direction
15 cm	?	Upward
3.4 cm	?	West
?	25 N	North
?	18 N	Downward

5. How long should a vector be to represent a 14-N force if the proportionality constant is 0.5 cm/N? How long should it be if the proportionality constant is 0.2 cm/N?

EXPERIMENT
E

15.3 Balanced Forces in a Plane

Suppose that three forces acting on an object are not along the same line but are in the same plane. If they are not along the same line, they cannot be added like signed numbers. We are no longer able to tell whether they are balanced by seeing if their sum is zero. Instead, we must look for another way to combine the forces to find out whether they are balanced. That is the purpose of this experiment.

Your teacher will provide you with a sheet of paper showing line segments that represent the directions for the forces you will exert. Use it to set up the apparatus shown in Figure 15.5.

After setting up the apparatus, label each line segment with the same letter (X, Y, or Z) that is written on the spring scale you will pull in that direction. Then, with the help of one of your two lab partners, pull the spring scales in the exact directions indicated by the line segments. As you pull, be sure that the washer remains centered and at rest over the pushpin, without touching it.

Why is it important that the washer and the spring scales do not touch the pushpin as you take your force readings?

⚠ CAUTION: Spring scales can be damaged if they are pulled with too much force. As you and your partner pull, be sure that none of the spring scales exceeds 20 N.

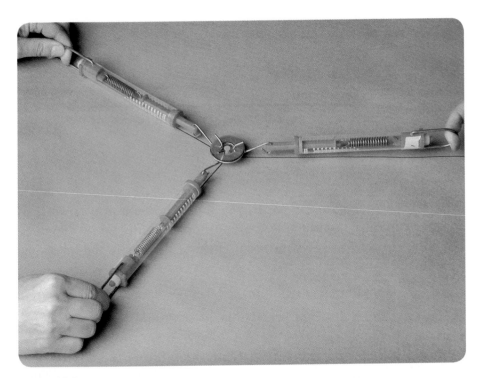

Figure 15.5

The force apparatus. Tape the sheet showing the directions of the forces to a larger piece of paper. Then extend the lines onto the larger paper. Draw arrowheads to indicate the directions that the spring scales will be pulled. Place a thin piece of wood or cardboard under the center of the paper. Then insert a pushpin through the paper and into the wood or cardboard at the point where the lines meet. Slip a large washer over the pushpin and hook three spring scales onto the washer. Pull the spring scales along the lines you have drawn while keeping the washer at rest above the pushpin.

When the washer is steady over the pushpin, your other lab partner (the one who is not holding a spring scale) will carefully read all three spring scales by looking straight down at each one.

Record the force reading from each spring scale next to the appropriate line segment on the paper.

- Are the forces on the washer balanced? How do you know?
- If you represent the three forces as signed numbers, can you find a combination that will add up to zero?

To describe the three forces, you need a way to express both their strengths and their directions. The line segments on the large sheet of paper provide the directions. You still need a way to express the strength, or *magnitude*, of each force.

A simple way to represent the magnitude is to draw a line segment whose length is proportional to the magnitude of the force. To fit all

> What information does the length of each line segment represent?

Figure 15.6

(a) The magnitude of a force can be represented by the length of a line segment. With a proportionality constant of 2 cm/N, the length of a segment representing a 4-N force is 8 cm. (b) By changing the segment to an arrow, we can also show the direction of the force. Note that the head of the arrow is carefully drawn so it does not increase the length of the arrow.

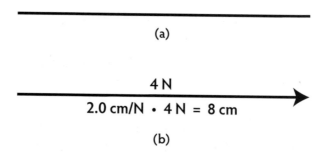

(a)

4 N
2.0 cm/N • 4 N = 8 cm

(b)

three line segments on the paper, you must choose a proportionality constant carefully. For example, a proportionality constant of 2.0 cm/N (Figure 15.6) may satisfy your requirements, giving you the following equation:

$$\text{Length of segment (cm)} = 2.0 \text{ cm/N} \times \text{force (N)}$$

You may find a different proportionality constant more suitable for your data. If you do, use it.

Using your proportionality constant, determine the appropriate lengths for the line segments that will represent the three forces. After removing the pushpin, draw a line segment in each direction on your paper to represent the force measured in that direction. Have one end of each segment touch the hole that was left when the pushpin was removed. On the other end, draw an arrowhead to show the direction of the force. Be careful not to extend the length of the segment when you add the arrowhead.

Figure 15.7 shows the results of an experiment similar to the one you just did. The solid black arrows represent three forces acting on an object much like the forces on the washer in your experiment. The three forces were balanced. The blue arrow, labeled D, represents an imaginary force. This force has the same magnitude as force A, but it is in the opposite direction, so it balances force A.

Force D balances force A.

> Why is it important that you not extend the length of the line segment when you draw the arrowhead?

Figure 15.7

If the three forces are balanced, the sum of forces B and C must balance force A. So the sum of forces B and C must be the same as the force represented by the blue vector D. Notice that this vector is the diagonal of a parallelogram formed using the vectors for forces B and C as two of its sides. For that reason, this procedure for adding forces is known as the *parallelogram method.*

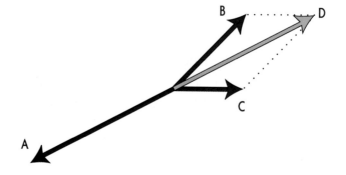

Since all three forces (A, B, and C) are balanced, the sum of forces B and C must also balance force A:

Force B + force C balances force A.

Therefore,

Force B + force C = force D.

Notice that the blue arrow representing force D in Figure 15.7 is also the diagonal of a parallelogram formed from the arrows that represent forces B and C. Is this a coincidence or a general rule that we can use?

To find out, draw a parallelogram using the two arrows representing forces Y and Z on your paper. Then draw an arrow along the diagonal of the parallelogram.

- How does the magnitude of the diagonal arrow that you drew compare with the magnitude of the third arrow, X? Is the diagonal longer, shorter, or the same length as arrow X?

Now extend arrow X backward by drawing a line from the hole left by the pushpin to the edge of your paper.

- How does the direction of the diagonal arrow compare with this extension of arrow X? Does the diagonal arrow point along the extended line, slightly to the right of the extension, or slightly to the left when viewed from the hole left by the pushpin?

Repeat this investigation with the other two pairs of forces on your drawing (X and Y; Z and X) and compare the results with those of your classmates.

- What do you conclude about the way forces add?

Whenever three forces are balanced, the sum of any two must balance the third. If the sum of any two forces does not balance the third, then the three forces are not balanced.

The technique you have just used is called the *parallelogram method*. Forces and other vector quantities are added by the parallelogram method.

---

6. How do you draw two vectors to represent two forces that balance each other?

7. Suppose that you are given a vector diagram representing three forces applied to a soccer ball at rest. When two of the vectors are added, they form a new vector that is the opposite of the third original vector. Will the ball stay at rest? Why or why not?

8. A vector that represents a force of 32 N is 8 cm long. What proportionality constant was used to construct this vector?

9. Copy each vector diagram in Figure B. Then, in each case, draw a vector to represent a third force that balances the two given forces.

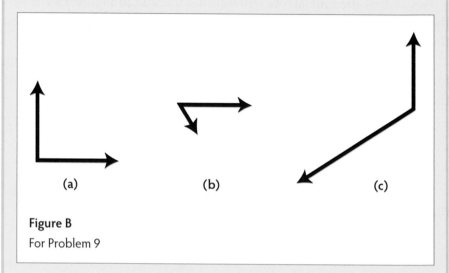

(a)   (b)   (c)

Figure B
For Problem 9

10. Four forces are applied to an object at rest. The forces are balanced. How does the sum of any two of the forces compare with the sum of the other two forces?

15.4 The Net Force

So far, we have shown that if two forces acting in different directions are balanced by a third force, we can add them using the parallelogram method. Do unbalanced forces add in the same way? The answer is yes. If only forces B and C in Figure 15.7 (on page 310) were acting on an object at rest, the object would start moving in the direction of force D. Force D, in this case, would be called the *net force*—that is, the vector sum of the two forces acting on the object.

The parallelogram method can be applied, two forces at a time, to add any number of forces acting on the same object. Figure 15.8(a), for example, shows three forces acting on the same object. Figure 15.8(b) shows the addition of forces B and C, resulting in force D. Figure 15.8(c) shows the addition of forces D and A to obtain force E—the net force. If these forces were applied to an object that was initially at rest, the object would begin to move in the direction of this net force E.

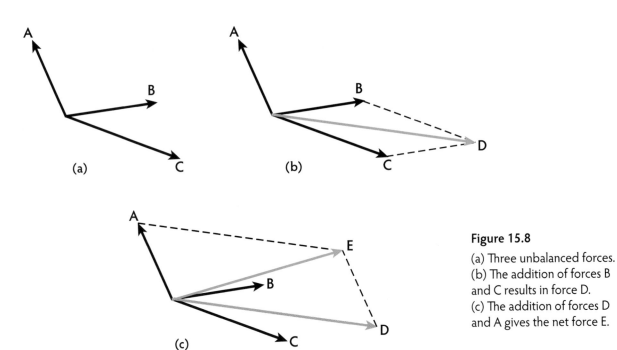

Figure 15.8

(a) Three unbalanced forces.
(b) The addition of forces B and C results in force D.
(c) The addition of forces D and A gives the net force E.

11. In Figure C, the sets of vectors represent forces applied to objects that are initially at rest. Determine the net force on each object.

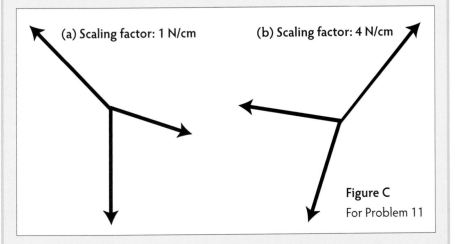

(a) Scaling factor: 1 N/cm

(b) Scaling factor: 4 N/cm

Figure C
For Problem 11

12. Suppose an iron washer is pulled east by a magnet with a force of 5 N, and north by a spring with a force of 2 N. How would the magnitude and direction of the net force be affected if the spring, rather than the magnet, pulled the washer east with a force of 5 N, and the magnet pulled the washer north with a force of 2 N?

13. **A book on a table is pulled horizontally with a force of 0.1 N. The book remains at rest.**

   a. **What is the net force on the book?**

   b. **What are all the forces that make up the net force?**

15.5 Forces and Their Components

What do we call the two forces that add to form a single force?

In the preceding sections, you saw that forces are vectors and that vectors can be added using the parallelogram method. So all of the forces acting on an object can be added to find the net force on the object. For example, in Figure 15.9, forces 1 and 2 add to form the net force. Looking at this in reverse, we can think of any single force as being of the result of the addition of two other forces. As an example, we can think of the net force in Figure 15.9 as having been formed from the addition of forces 1 and 2. Forces 1 and 2 are *components* of the net force.

Figure 15.9

The net force is the sum of forces 1 and 2. Forces 1 and 2 are components of the net force.

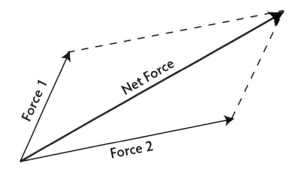

It is often useful to think of a single force as being made up of two perpendicular components. To find the components of a given force along two perpendicular directions, begin by drawing a vector that represents the original force. Then draw two lines in perpendicular directions (Figure 15.10(a)). By drawing two more lines, you can complete a rectangle that has the original force as its diagonal (Figure 15.10(b)). The sides of the rectangle represent the components of the original force along the two perpendicular directions (Figure 15.10(c)).

As an application, consider the following situation. A deliveryman has to load a heavy cart onto a truck. Rather than lift the cart straight up, he wants to pull it up a ramp (Figure 15.11). How does the magnitude of the force needed to pull the cart up the ramp compare with the magnitude of the force needed to lift the cart straight up and onto the truck?

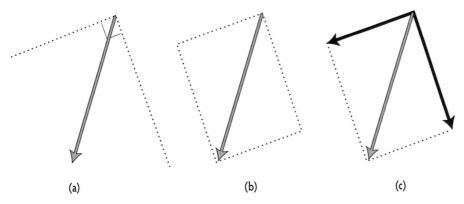

(a)   (b)   (c)

Figure 15.10

(a) The blue vector represents a force. The dotted lines specify two perpendicular directions. (b) Completing the rectangle determines the size of the components in the two perpendicular directions. (c) The black vectors represent the perpendicular components of the original force.

To answer this question, we can think of the weight of the cart as a sum of two perpendicular components. One component is parallel to the ramp and one is perpendicular to the ramp (Figure 15.12). When the cart is at rest, we know that the net force on it is zero. That means that there must be two additional forces acting on the cart—one balancing force 1 and one balancing force 2.

Force 1 is balanced by the pull of the rope. Force 2 is balanced by the ramp itself pushing against the wheels of the cart. By drawing vectors to represent the forces, we can see that the magnitude of the force needed to pull the cart up the ramp (force 1) is less than the magnitude of the force needed to lift the cart straight up (the weight of the cart).

> Why might a delivery person use a ramp to load a cart rather than simply lifting the cart onto a truck?

Figure 15.11

A heavy cart being slowly lowered from a truck. A rope held by a person on the truck controls the motion of the cart.

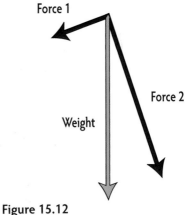

Figure 15.12

Looking at the weight of the cart as the sum of two forces, one parallel to and one perpendicular to the ramp.

14. A force of 5.0 N is applied to a rolling suitcase as shown in Figure D. The force on the handle is directed at an angle of 40° above horizontal.

   a. Draw a vector representing this force using a proportion-ality constant of 1 cm/N.

   b. What are the horizontal and vertical components of this force?

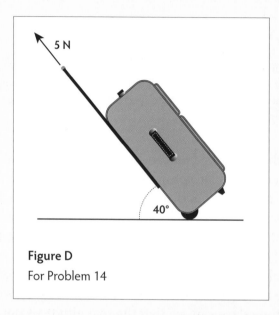

Figure D
For Problem 14

15. Suppose Figure 15.12 represents the forces shown in Figure 15.11. Assume that the value of the proportionality constant is 1 cm/100 N.

   a. What is the weight of the cart?

   b. What force must the rope exert on the cart to balance force 1?

   c. Could you lift the cart?

16. Suppose that the cart in Figure 15.11 is replaced by a box of equal weight. Now friction cannot be ignored.

   a. What is the direction of the frictional force when the box is pulled up the ramp?

   b. How will the frictional force affect the force that must be exerted by the rope?

17. In Section 14.6, Friction and Weight, you learned that the force of friction on an object is proportional to the weight of the object. On a ramp, the force of friction is proportional to the component of the weight that is perpendicular to the ramp.

   a. Will the force of friction on the box used in Problem 16 increase or decrease if the ramp in Figure 15.11 is made steeper?

   b. Will the component of the weight of the box parallel to the ramp increase or decrease if the ramp is made steeper?

   c. Use your answers to (a) and (b) to explain why an object will slide down a ramp if the ramp is steep enough.

EXPERIMENT E   15.6 Forces Acting on Moving Objects

You have worked with both balanced and unbalanced forces on objects that are initially at rest. Now suppose that you apply a force for a short time to an object that is already moving. What will the motion of the object look like after the force ends? Will the object slow down after the force stops? Will it move in the direction of the force, or will it move in some other direction? To study these questions, you will use an air puck and a platform, such as those shown in Figure 15.13.

> What is the advantage of using the air puck in this experiment?

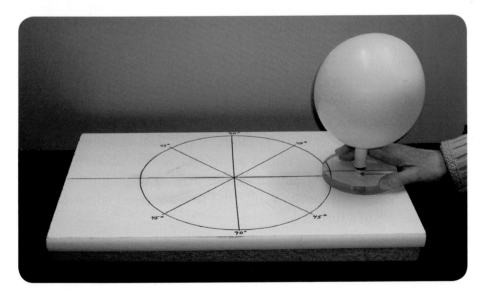

Figure 15.13

The assembled air puck apparatus and platform.

Figure 15.14

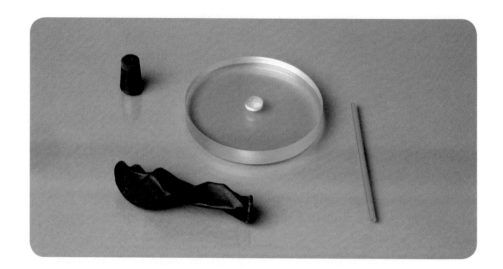

The platform must be cleaned and leveled before the experiment is started. This may have been done in advance by your teacher. To prepare the puck, assemble the balloon and stopper apparatus as instructed in the caption for Figure 15.14.

> **CAUTION: For health reasons, if more than one person will be blowing up the balloon, each should have his or her own coffee stirrer.**

Hold the mouth of the balloon over the large end of the stopper as you blow into the coffee stirrer. When the balloon is inflated, remove the coffee stirrer and place your finger over the hole in the stopper to prevent air from escaping. Then, using a slight twisting motion, quickly press the small end of the stopper into the hole on the top of the air puck. To keep the bottom of the puck clean and dry, touch it as little as possible.

Immediately position the air puck on the platform. By pressing down slightly on the air puck, you can prevent air from escaping from the balloon until you are ready to make observations.

Place the air puck at the center of the platform and release it. If the platform is not sufficiently level, the puck will drift downhill. You can now make very small adjustments to the feet so that when the puck is released, it remains practically at rest. In making this adjustment, it is best to turn only one foot at a time and to make small adjustments of only about 1/8 of a turn or less.

To apply forces to the puck in a uniform way you will use short, strong puffs of air directed toward the center of the puck (Figure 15.15) just as it reaches the center of the platform. These puffs can be produced

How can you use the air puck to determine when the platform is level?

How will you know when the platform is level?

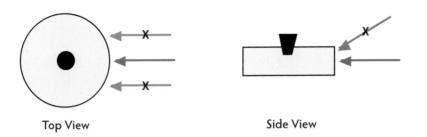

Top View   Side View

Figure 15.15
Two views of the air puck (without the balloon). Each puff should be directed toward the center of the base of the air puck. In the diagrams, the blue arrows show the correct direction for the puff. The red arrows show incorrect directions.

by squeezing an empty shampoo bottle as shown in Figure 15.16 or by blowing briefly through a straw as shown in Figure 15.17. In each trial, direct a single puff toward the center of the pattern on the platform from a position on the outer circle (Figure 15.17). Keep each puff as short as possible, and try to make each puff the same strength.

Have your lab partner place the center of the air puck at the point where the outer circle crosses the straight line running along the length of the platform. She or he can then tap the puck lightly with one finger so that it moves very slowly toward the center of the circular pattern.

• Does the puck move at a constant speed?

Figure 15.16
The student is ready to use an empty shampoo bottle to direct a short puff toward the air puck's base when the puck reaches the center of the circle. The angled lines are used to aim the puff toward the center of the pattern from a position on the outer circle. They can also be used to determine the direction that the puck moves after the force is applied.

Figure 15.17
As an alternative, short puffs can be directed toward the air puck using a straw rather than a shampoo bottle. Here the student is ready to produce a puff when the puck reaches the center of the circle. Notice that the puff can be sent from either the right or the left side of the air puck platform.

Just as the air puck reaches the center, hit it with a single, short, strong puff of air and watch what happens.

- When you apply a force with a single, short puff in a direction opposite to the puck's direction of motion, what happens to the speed of the puck?
- After the puff is over, does the speed of the puck continue to change, or does the puck move at a constant speed?
- What happens when you apply a force to the puck with a single, short puff in the same direction that it is already moving?
- After the puff is over, does the speed of the puck continue to change, or does the puck move at a constant speed?

Now apply a puff at an angle to the motion of the puck, for example, the angle as shown in Figure 15.17.

- Do the direction of motion and the speed of the puck change?
- After the puff is over, does the speed of the puck continue to change, or does the puck move at a constant speed?
- After the puff is over, does the direction of the puck continue to change, or does the puck move in the same direction?

15.7 Newton's First Law

The air puck that you used in the preceding experiment allowed you to almost eliminate friction. The absence of friction is hardly the type of situation that you encounter in daily life. Nevertheless, we can learn much by studying nature under such simplified conditions—in this case by eliminating friction and applying a force for only a very short time interval.

When the air puck is placed on a level, smooth platform, it remains at rest. The net force on it is zero. If the puck is then given a short push, it starts moving. But when the push ends, the net force is again zero. Although no net force is acting on the puck, it continues to move in a straight line with a constant speed. If the puck is already moving when it is given a short push, it may change its speed and direction. But once the push has ended and the net force is again zero, the puck will continue to move at a constant speed in a straight line. These observations and many others similar to them lead to two conclusions:

(1) When the net force on an object at rest is zero, the object will remain at rest.

(2) When the net force on a moving object is zero, the object will continue to move in a straight line at a constant speed.

The combination of these two conclusions is known as *Newton's first law*. We arrived at this law by observing what happens after a short puff. However, we can think of a force of longer duration as a rapid succession of very short puffs. Once the net force ends, Newton's first law holds.

Newton's first law may seem strange to you. It appears to contradict your daily experience. It says that a moving object will continue to move in a straight line at a constant speed even though the net force on it is zero. But you are used to applying a force just to keep things moving! For example, you cannot keep a shopping cart moving at a constant speed unless you keep pushing it. How can the net force on the cart be zero if you are pushing it?

The answer is that in daily life, friction is always present. If the cart is moving in a straight line at a constant speed, the force you are applying just balances the frictional force. As a result, the net force on the shopping cart is zero, just as Newton's first law implies.

When you exerted a force on the puck in Experiment 15.5, you did so with a short burst of air. As you applied this force, the net force on the puck was not zero. But before and after the puff, the net force on the puck was almost zero because the force of friction was almost zero and the platform was nearly level. This made it easier to observe the effect of your force alone on the motion of the puck.

18. When a car is allowed to coast on a level road, it slows down and stops. Is this a violation of Newton's first law? Explain.

FOR REVIEW, APPLICATIONS, AND EXTENSIONS

19. Consider a Boeing 777 flying in a straight horizontal line at an altitude of 10,000 m. It is flying at a constant speed when the plane's engines provide a total forward force (thrust) of 640,000 N. The vertical force (lift) holding the plane up is 2,500,000 N.

    a. What is the net force on the plane?

    b. Draw a vector that represents the sum of the thrust and the lift.

    c. There are two additional forces on the plane. One is the downward force due to gravity (weight) and the other is the force due to friction with the air (drag). How can you find the sum of these two forces?

20. Form a team of three to do the following experiment. Two of you pull on the ends of a 3-m-long rope to keep it as taut as you can. The third student pushes down on the rope near the middle.

    a. Why is it so difficult to resist the downward push?

    b. Copy Figure E. Assume that each student holding the rope applies a force of 200 N, as shown in the figure. Is the strength of the downward force applied by the third student to hold the rope down greater than, less than, or equal to 200 N?

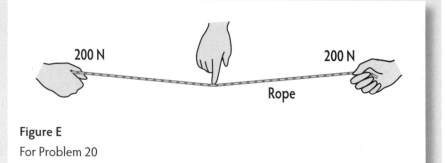

200 N   200 N

Rope

Figure E
For Problem 20

21. As you bicycle along a straight, level path, you must keep pedaling to maintain a constant speed.

    a. What is the net force on the bicycle?

    b. Under what condition would you not have to pedal to maintain a constant speed?

    c. In the case you just described, what forces are added to give a net force of zero?

THEME FOR A SHORT ESSAY

In daily life, we count on the presence of forces. When a needed force is absent, the effect may be harmful. For example, a car may hit a patch of ice on a curve and skid off the road. Describe a situation from your own experience when a missing force resulted in an unexpected motion.

16

FORCE AND MOTION IN A STRAIGHT LINE

16.1 The Motion Detector

Your observations of the motion of an air puck in the preceding chapter were mostly qualitative. In this chapter, you will extend your study of motion to determine the quantitative effects of a constant net force.

We begin with measurements of position and time. To measure these quantities, you will use a motion detector connected to a computer, as shown in Figure 16.1.

But before you can trust the motion detector and computer to measure positions and time, you must convince yourself that they provide the same measurements that you would obtain with other devices that you already trust. You could easily check the accuracy of the computer's internal clock by comparing it with a stopwatch or a classroom clock, but computers are trusted for their accuracy so this will not be necessary.

To see if the motion detector reads positions correctly, begin by using another device that you already trust—a meter stick—to measure 0.00, 1.00, 2.00, and 3.00 meters along a line extending outward from the edge

> **What two things must be checked before you can trust the data provided by the motion detector and the computer?**

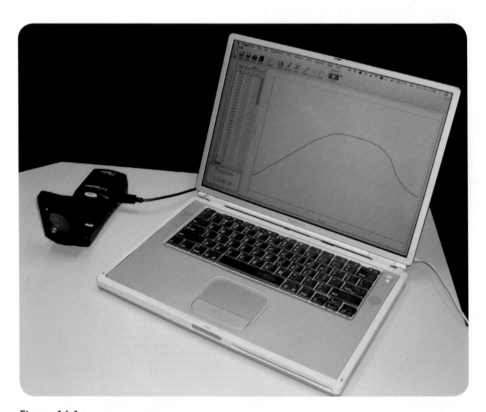

Figure 16.1

The motion detector and computer. The screen shows a graph of distance versus time taken by this assembly.

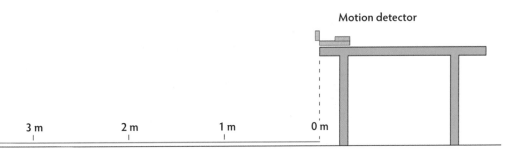

Figure 16.2

The experimental setup, showing the motion detector pointing along the line that has been created on the floor.

of your lab table (Figure 16.2). You may want to use masking tape to mark these distances on the floor. (To make each piece of tape easier to remove, fold one end onto itself to create a tab that will not stick to the floor. You can then use this tab to remove the tape when you have finished the experiment.)

 CAUTION: Masking tape bonds strongly to the wax used on many tile floors. If it is left in place overnight or longer, removal becomes very difficult. For this reason, be sure to remove the tape from the floor at the end of your class period.

Now set the motion detector on your lab table, and point it horizontally in the direction of the line you have just created. Then stand straight and still with your heels at the 2.00-m mark, facing away from the detector. (Alternatively, you can hold a piece of cardboard or a book at the 2.00-m mark.) To prevent interference, be sure no other objects are within a meter on either side of the line.

Have your lab partner operate the motion detector as directed by your teacher. The motion detector is taking readings when you hear it clicking. As it takes readings, a graph is produced that shows your distance from the detector on the vertical axis and time on the horizontal axis.

- Why is it important to measure the distance to the 2.00-m mark as accurately as possible?
- Why is it important to stand straight and still at the 2.00-m mark?
- Why does the graph show a horizontal line?

If the horizontal line on the graph is not at 2.00 m, move the motion detector forward or back until the graph reads 2.00 m when you stand at the 2.00-m mark. When you are sure that the motion detector reads

2.00 m, tape it to the table so it will not move during the remainder of this checking procedure.

Next, you need to see if the motion detector produces divisions that are the correct size. In other words, will you still obtain a correct reading if you change your distance from the detector? To check this, stand now at the 3.00-m mark while your partner operates the motion detector.

- Does the motion detector read 3.00 m?
- How does the graph show that you increased your distance from the detector by 1.00 m?

To test the sensitivity of the motion detector, you can find out how far an object must move for its motion to be detected. Stand at the 2.00-m mark while your partner operates the motion detector. During the 10-s interval that the detector is on, lean slightly forward and then back without moving your feet.

- Estimate how far forward you or your partner leaned.
- Can you detect the leaning motion on the graph?
- How did your estimated distance compare with the distance shown by the graph?

You saw that when you stand still in front of a motion detector, a horizontal line appears on the distance-time graph. This line is the result of many nearly identical position measurements taken by the motion detector.

Now, beginning at the 1.00-m mark, move slowly away from the detector using shuffling "baby steps" until you reach the 3.00-m mark. If you get a very rough, jagged graph, just try again. It only takes a few seconds! (Hint: To avoid such a "noisy" graph, you might try holding a piece of cardboard or a book between you and the motion detector.)

- How can you tell which portion of the graph represents your motion as you were walking?

When you look at a motion graph, you need to concentrate on the relevant region of the graph—that is, the portion of the graph that you want to analyze. In this experiment, that portion is a straight line.

- What are the beginning and end times for the relevant portion of your motion graph?

Now shuffle back from the 3.00-m mark to the 1.00-m mark at about the same speed.

- How would you describe the differences between the last two graphs?

Because the motion detector measures positions only in one direction, all positions are expressed by positive numbers. A change in position, however, can be either away from the detector or toward the detector. A *change in position* is calculated like any other change: the later value minus the earlier value. A change in position, called a *displacement*, is positive displacement if you move away from the motion detector. If you move toward the detector, the displacement is negative.

- What was your displacement from the beginning to the end of each of your two walks?

Next, starting from the same 1.00-m mark, collect data as you walk away from the motion detector at a slightly faster pace. Then repeat this procedure once more while walking at this new pace in the opposite direction.

- How are these last two graphs different from the earlier pair of graphs?

1. **In Figure A, how far from the motion detector was the person standing?**

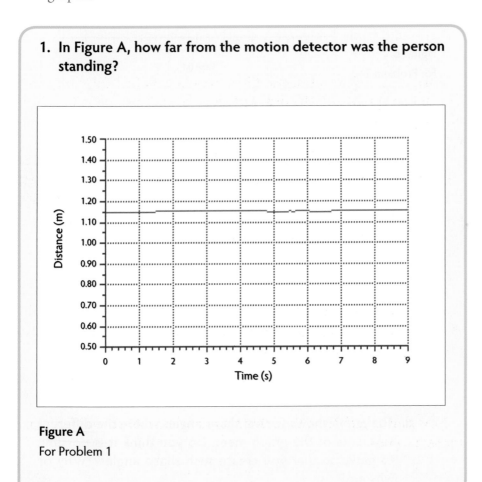

Figure A

For Problem 1

2. Describe what you think may have happened to produce the graph shown in Figure B.

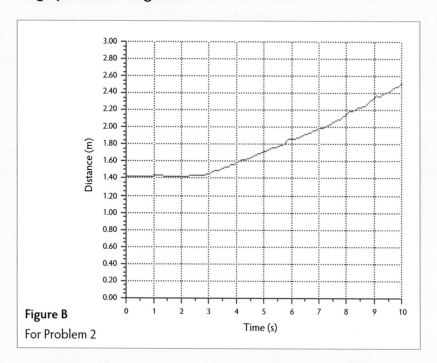

Figure B
For Problem 2

3. Describe in detail how you should walk to make a graph similar in shape to the one shown in Figure C.

4. Figure D shows the motion graph for a fictitious "walk" in front of a motion detector.

   a. During which segment, II or IV, must you move faster to reproduce the motion shown by the graph? How is this shown on the graph?

   b. Look at segments IV and VI on the graph. Which segment represents motion away from the detector and which represents motion toward it? How is this difference shown on the graph?

   c. Imagine that you are trying to tell someone how to move in front of the motion detector in order to reproduce this graph. What instructions should you give?

   d. The graph shows several sharp angles where the different segments of the graph meet. Do you think it is possible to move so that you create such sharp angles? Why or why not?

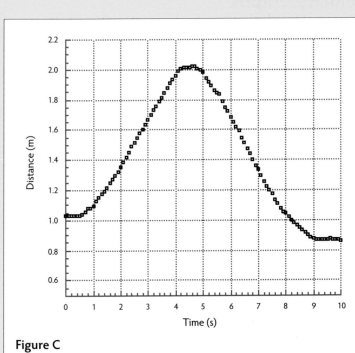

Figure C

For Problem 3

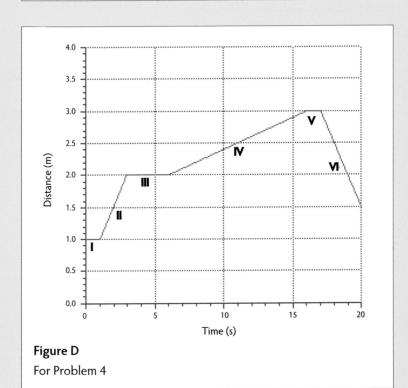

Figure D

For Problem 4

16.2 Velocity Graphs

The speed of a moving object tells us the distance it covers per unit time. For example, Olympic runners have achieved speeds of 10 m/s.

The distance between two points A and B is the same whether one moves from A to B or from B to A. If we want to state not only how fast an object moves but also in which direction along a line, we have to calculate the displacement per unit time, called *velocity*.

The motion detector provides us with positions of a moving object at 0.05-s intervals. As an example, consider the position-time graph of a walk in front of the motion detector (Figure 16.3). As you can see, there are many positions too close together to easily read the graph.

Figure 16.4 is a magnification of a small section near the top on the left side of the graph shown in Figure 16.3. To calculate the velocity at point B, read the displacement from point A to point C using the vertical axis and divide by the time interval that you read on the horizontal axis. In this case

$$\text{Velocity at point B} = \frac{1.823 \text{ m} - 1.777 \text{ m}}{2.10 \text{ s} - 2.00 \text{ s}} = \frac{0.046 \text{ m}}{0.10 \text{ s}} = 0.45 \text{ m/s}$$

To repeat such calculations for every data point shown on the position-time graph in Figure 16.3 would be very tedious. But a computer

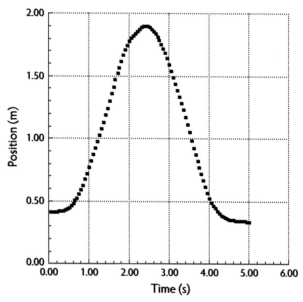

Figure 16.3

A position-time graph showing a walk in front of the motion detector.

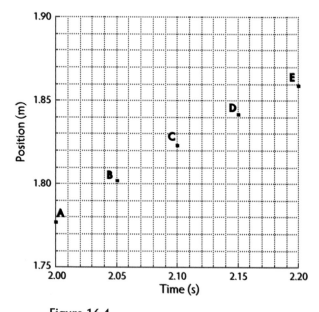

Figure 16.4

A close-up of a portion of the graph shown in Figure 16.3.

can perform all the necessary calculations in less than a second. When the velocities at all of the various positions are plotted as a function of time, the result is a velocity-time graph, shown in Figure 16.5. Let us examine the general features of the position-time and the velocity-time graphs.

From the position-time graph (Figure 16.3), we can see that for about 0.2 s after the motion detector started operating, the person's position did not change; he stood still. After about 0.2 s, he began to walk away from the detector. Between 0.8 s and 1.8 s, his velocity appears to be constant, although this is difficult to judge exactly. At around 2.0 s, he began to slow down. He came briefly to rest at about 2.4 s, then walked back toward the detector, and stopped at about 4.6 s. His final position was closer to the detector than his initial position.

What can we learn from the velocity-time graph (Figure 16.5)? For the first 0.2 s, until the person began to walk, the velocity was zero. Then it increased rapidly. Between 1.0 s and 1.8 s, the velocity was about at its greatest. There are some wiggles, which were not noticeable on the position-time graph. This is typical of velocity graphs. They are more sensitive to changes in velocity than are position-time graphs. At about 1.8 s, the velocity begins to decrease, just as we saw on the position graph. At 2.4 s, the velocity goes through zero and becomes negative; the person begins to move back toward the motion detector. After 3.5 s, the velocity becomes less negative, showing that the person is slowing down. He comes to rest at about 4.6 s.

You will use velocity-time graphs extensively in the next two experiments.

> What does the position-time graph look like if velocity is constant?

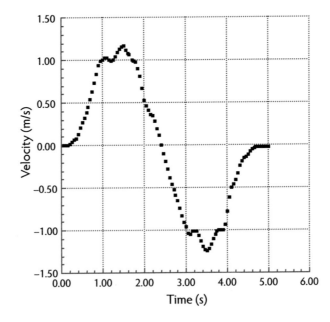

Figure 16.5

A velocity-time graph for the same walk that was graphed in Figure 16.3.

5. Using Figure 16.4, calculate the velocities at points C and D, and plot a velocity-time graph for points B, C, and D.

6. Does a negative velocity also mean that displacement is negative?

7. Can you tell from Figure 16.5 that the person ended up closer to the detector than when he started his walk? Why or why not?

8. How would Figures 16.3 and 16.5 look if the person stopped and stood still at the farthest point instead of coming back toward the motion detector? Make sketches of the position-time and velocity-time graphs for this new situation.

EXPERIMENT
E

16.3 Motion Under a Constant Net Force: The Effect of Time

When no net force is acting on an object, the object will either remain at rest or move in a straight line with a constant speed (Section 15.7, Newton's First Law). How will a constant net force change the velocity of an object? To find out, we will calculate the *change in velocity* of the object from the beginning to the end of a time interval during which the force was acting. Like a change in position, a change in velocity is found by subtracting the velocity at the beginning from the velocity at the end of a time interval.

To find out how a constant net force will change the velocity of an object, we will split the question into three more specific questions:

(1) How is the change in velocity of an object related to the length of time that a constant force is applied to the object?

(2) How is the change in velocity of an object related to the magnitude of the force acting on the object when different forces are applied for equal time intervals?

(3) How is the change in velocity of an object related to the mass of the object when the same constant force is applied for the same time interval?

The first of these questions will be addressed in this experiment. The other two questions will be investigated in Sections 16.4 and 16.6.

Your moving object will be a cart, and you will use a motion detector to produce a velocity-time graph. The simplest way to determine the force on the cart would be to pull the cart with a spring scale, just as

In a certain time interval, the velocity of an object changes from 1.0 m/s to 5.0 m/s. What is the change in velocity of the object?

What two quantities must be kept constant if you want to study how the time that a force is applied affects the change in velocity of an object?

you did in Experiment 14.5, Sliding Friction. But because the cart moves faster and faster, it is hard to maintain a constant force. You may want to test this for yourself. Try to pull the cart with a constant force of 0.5 N.

• Were you able to keep the force constant?

You will use the setup shown in Figure 16.6 to provide a constant force. The force will be applied to the cart as the weight falls. To measure the force applied to the cart, you will use a spring scale that is attached to the cart. Since you will be using the spring scale in a horizontal position, remember to first zero it in the horizontal position.

Are there any other forces that might affect the motion of the cart? From Chapter 14 you know that as soon as the cart begins to move, friction will play a part. Fortunately, you can use what you have learned about Newton's first law to compensate for the friction.

From Section 15.7, Newton's First Law, you know that when the net force on a moving object is zero, the object will continue to move at a constant velocity.

Before we compensate for friction, we need to level the ramp in the side-to-side direction. To do so, place the cart sideways on the ramp and load it with 1 kg of additional mass. Then use the two adjustable feet at one end of the ramp to roughly level the ramp in the side-to-side direction. You will know when the ramp is roughly level when the cart no longer rolls to one side or the other.

> What is the net force on the cart when it rolls at a constant velocity?

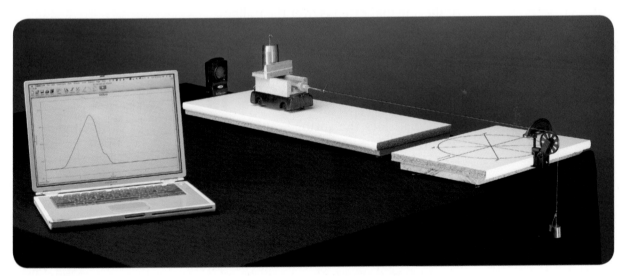

Figure 16.6

The experimental setup. Fishing line extends over a pulley that is mounted to the air puck platform. The line connects the spring scale on the cart to falling weights. A wooden superstructure and larger weights sit on the cart. When released, the cart moves away from the motion detector.

Now, to compensate for friction, turn the cart 90° so that it points along the length of the ramp. Then use the single adjustable foot at the other end of the ramp to adjust the slope of the ramp. Adjust the slope until the cart, after being given a light tap to get it started, appears to travel at a slow, constant velocity toward the pulley. The motion detector can provide a velocity-time graph to help you determine whether the cart is actually moving at a constant velocity. If it does, you have balanced the force of friction.

REMINDER: If you are unable to adjust the single foot far enough to cause the cart to move at a constant velocity, turn the ramp 180° and begin the adjustment process again.

- What does the velocity-time graph look like when the cart moves at a constant velocity?
- Why is it important to prepare the ramp in this way before beginning the experiment?

You are now ready for the main part of the experiment. To study how the change in velocity is affected by the amount of time that a constant force is applied, you will use the same cart and the same 1 kg of additional mass that you used to adjust the ramp.

Attach the fishing line to the spring scale, and hang 60 g from the end of the line that extends over the pulley.

- What force does the spring scale read before you release the cart?

Now release the cart from rest without giving it even the slightest push forward or backward.

- What does the spring scale read while the cart is moving? Is the force the same as it was before the cart was released?

Release the cart again while the motion detector is collecting data and creating a velocity-time graph.

We performed a run similar to the one you have just completed. A graph of our data is shown in Figure 16.7. Although your graph may look different in some details, it should show the four distinct regions shown in Figure 16.7.

- What was happening to the cart in each region of the graph?
- Which region of the graph shows the motion of the cart when the spring scale provided the net force on the cart?

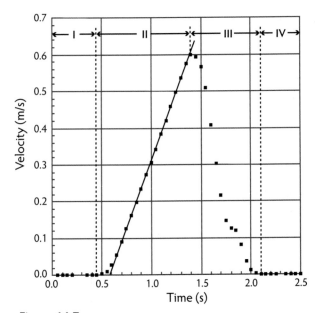

Figure 16.7

A typical graph of velocity as a function of time for a cart pulled by a constant force.

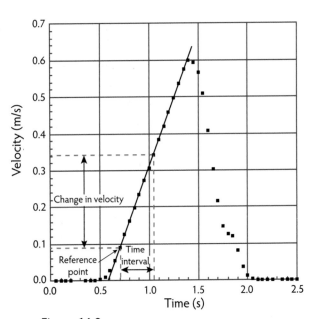

Figure 16.8

A reference point is chosen in the lower portion of the straight region. The change in velocity and the time interval between two points can then be determined.

To answer the question raised at the beginning of this section, we will concentrate entirely on this part of the graph, where the constant force was acting on the cart. On a printout of your graph, draw a straight line through this part of the graph.

To see how the velocity changes as the time interval increases, you can pick any reference point on the straight section, preferably near the lower end (Figure 16.8). Then record several different time intervals and their corresponding changes in velocity, always starting from the reference point you have chosen. Using these data, make a graph of the change in velocity as a function of the time interval.

- How would you describe your graph?
- What do you conclude about the relation between an object's change in velocity and the time interval during which a constant force acts on the object?

Suppose you had picked a different reference point on the straight portion of your original graph to find the relation between the change in velocity and the length of the time interval.

- Would the graph of the change in velocity as a function of the time interval be any different? (If you are not sure of your answer, do it.)
- What do you conclude?

9. Would it be better to use a 20-N spring scale in this experiment instead of the 5-N spring scale? Why or why not?

10. If the time interval during which a constant net force is applied to an object is tripled, how will the change in velocity of that object be affected?

11. Suppose that a net force of 1.0 N is applied to a loaded cart for 1.0 second. As a result, the cart's velocity changes by 1.2 m/s. What will be the change in velocity if the same force is applied for 2.0 seconds? For 4.0 seconds?

12. Suppose that the surface of your ramp is not completely flat. If it has a dip in the middle, how would that change the velocity-time graph for the motion of the cart?

13. In this experiment, is it necessary that the pulley be very light? Why or why not?

14. Suppose that there were a lot of friction in the pulley.

    a. How would this affect the results of your experiment?

    b. How would it affect your conclusion?

EXPERIMENT

E

16.4 Motion Under a Constant Net Force: The Effect of the Magnitude of the Force

You have now seen that the change in velocity of a cart is proportional to the time interval during which a constant force acts on it. How does the change in velocity over a given time interval depend on the magnitude of the force? To investigate this effect, you must be able to vary the force without changing the mass of the cart.

To determine the effect of the magnitude of the force, you will vary the falling mass. Remember that you must keep both the time interval and the mass of the cart constant while you change the force. The velocity-time graph of the data will allow you to select equal time intervals.

Adjust the slope of the ramp to balance the frictional force, just as you did in Experiment 16.3.

Now, beginning with a falling mass of close to 50 g, use the motion detector to create and save a velocity-time graph of the cart's motion. Repeat this procedure using various falling masses in a range from 50 g to 100 g until you have at least four different velocity-time graphs. On each graph, identify the region that shows the movement of the cart as the constant force acts on it. Using points separated by equal time inter-

What two quantities must be kept constant if you want to study how the magnitude of the force on an object affects the change in velocity of the object?

vals on each graph, record the mass of the cart, the force on the cart, the time interval, and the change in velocity.

Next, plot a graph of the change in velocity as a function of the force.

- Should you include the origin as an experimental point?
- How would you describe this graph?
- If the mass of the cart and the length of time that the force is applied remain constant, how is the change in velocity related to the magnitude of the force applied?

---

15. A net force acts on an object for a certain time interval. If the net force on the object is increased by a factor of 5, what will happen to its change in velocity during the same time interval? What will happen if the force is cut in half?

16. Which of the following would cause the greatest change in velocity for a cart of given mass?

   A. A 3.0-N force applied for 2.5 seconds

   B. A 6.0-N force applied for 1.6 seconds

   C. A 9.0-N force applied for 1.0 second

16.5 Free Fall and the Effect of Mass: A Prediction

You are now ready to find out how a change in the velocity of an object depends on the mass of the object when the time interval and force are kept constant. To do so, we will first try to make a prediction based on common observations.

Suppose that gravity provides the net force on an object. This is the case when we simply drop the object. As you learned in Section 14.2, the gravitational force on an object—its weight—is proportional to its mass. This means that we cannot change the mass of an object without also changing its weight; when we double the mass we also double the weight.

In Experiment 16.4 you took care to change only the magnitude of the force, keeping the mass unchanged. So the results of that experiment tell us nothing about what happens to the change in velocity when both the force and the mass change.

You may conclude from Experiment 16.4 that since an object's change in velocity is proportional to the force acting on it—in this case, the weight of the object—the change in velocity will be greater for a heavier,

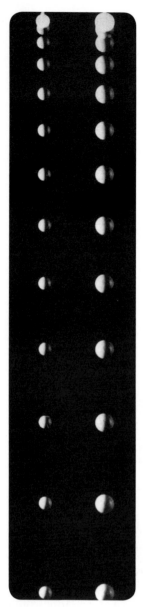

Figure 16.9

Two steel spheres of different mass are released simultaneously from the same height and photographed at equal time intervals. The changes in velocity in each time interval are clearly equal.
(From the collection of H. Nakagone, M. Hotta, T. Takahashi, published by Ködansha, 1966)

more-massive object. But you also know from your own experience that it is harder to push a very massive object, such as a boulder, than it is to push a small rock. This observation may lead you to a different conclusion. You may conclude that if you exert the same net force on two objects having different masses, the change in velocity during any time interval will be less for the more-massive object than it will be for the less-massive object. But these two possible conclusions contradict each other! Which outcome is correct? Nature provides the answer.

Consider the multiple-exposure photograph in Figure 16.9. It shows two steel spheres of different mass that have been dropped from rest under conditions of negligible air resistance. Vertical motion under such conditions is called *free fall*. As you can see from the equal distances covered between exposures, the change in velocity in any time interval is exactly the same for both spheres.

Perhaps the most dramatic demonstration of this experiment was done on the moon, where there is no air. The commander of *Apollo 15* held a hammer in one hand and a feather in the other, and dropped them simultaneously from the same height. Both the hammer and the feather changed velocity by the same amount. As a result, they covered the same distance and reached the surface of the moon at the same time. Apparently, in free fall, the effect that greater weight has on the change in velocity is exactly canceled by the effect of the inevitable, accompanying increase in mass.

How can we account for these observations? Let's look again at the relation between weight and mass (Section 14.2).

$$\text{Weight} = \text{constant} \cdot \text{mass}$$

Dividing both sides of this equation by mass, we see that the ratio of weight to mass is constant:

$$\frac{\text{Weight}}{\text{mass}} = \text{constant}$$

Suppose that the change in velocity during free fall is proportional to the ratio of weight to mass.

$$\text{Change in velocity is proportional to } \frac{\text{weight}}{\text{mass}}.$$

Since this ratio is constant, this would account for the observations: The change in velocity in free fall is the same for all objects, independent of their mass.

Does this relation also hold for forces other than the gravitational force? For example, will it also be valid when a constant force is exerted by a spring? One way to answer this question is to make a prediction, and then test that prediction. We predict that the proportionality will be valid for all forces.

$$\text{Change in velocity is proportional to } \frac{\text{force}}{\text{mass}}.$$

This proportionality says, for example, that if the mass is doubled, the change in velocity is cut in half, provided the force and time interval remain the same. If the mass is cut in half, the change in velocity is doubled. In the next experiment, you will test whether this prediction can be generalized to apply to any force.

---

17. Everybody knows that when a pebble and a sheet of paper are released from the same height at the same time, the pebble reaches the ground first. Does this observation contradict the result shown in Figure 16.9? Why or why not?

EXPERIMENT E

16.6 Testing a Prediction: The Relation Between Mass and Change in Velocity

To test the prediction made at the end of the last section, you will need to make several runs using the same equipment that you used in the previous two experiments. Be sure the slope of the platform is properly adjusted so that the force of the spring scale will be the net force. In each run, although the cart will have a different total mass, the force and time interval will be the same. For the first run, add 500 g to the cart. Then change the total mass of the cart for each new run, so that you end up with at least five or six runs having masses over a range from 0.500 kg to 1.700 kg. When recording the total mass of the cart, remember to include the mass of the cart assembly and spring scale, along with the added masses.

For each run, use the velocity-time graph obtained by the motion detector to find the change in velocity during a set time interval. Then create a new graph showing the change in velocity in each of the runs as a function of the corresponding total mass of the cart. Draw a smooth curve close to the plotted points.

• How would you describe this graph?

To test the prediction, pick two points on your graph that have a mass ratio of 2:1. Read the change in velocity for each of these points.

What two quantities must be kept constant if you want to study how the mass of an object affects the change in velocity of the object when a force is applied?

- What is the ratio of the changes in velocity?
- Was the prediction correct?

Create a table by picking several pairs of points from your graph. For each pair, record the ratio of the changes in velocity and the corresponding ratio of masses.

- How is the change in velocity related to the reciprocal of the total mass of the cart?
- Are your results consistent with the prediction that the change in velocity is proportional to the reciprocal of the mass?

---

18. Trucks A and B have the same mass when empty. Suppose that Truck B is loaded with enough cargo to double its mass. How will the changes in velocity of these two trucks compare if the same net force is applied to both for the same length of time?

16.7 Newton's Second Law

In the last three experiments, you have studied how a force on a cart, the time interval during which the force is applied, and the total mass of the cart affect changes in the cart's velocity. In each experiment, you varied one quantity while keeping the other two constant. The results of these experiments can be summarized as follows:

(1) The change in velocity is proportional to the time interval when force and mass remain constant (Experiment 16.3).

> Change in velocity is proportional to time interval.

(2) The change in velocity is proportional to the magnitude of the force when the time interval and the mass remain constant (Experiment 16.4).

> Change in velocity is proportional to force.

(3) The change in velocity is proportional to the reciprocal of the mass when the force and the time interval remain constant (Section 16.6).

> Change in velocity is proportional to $\dfrac{1}{\text{mass}}$.

Recall that if a quantity is proportional to more than one other quantity, it is proportional to the product of these quantities (Appendix 2).

Therefore,

$$\text{Change in velocity is proportional to } \frac{\text{force} \cdot (\text{time interval})}{\text{mass}}.$$

Then, inserting a proportionality constant, we have

$$\text{Change in velocity} = \text{constant} \cdot \frac{\text{force} \cdot (\text{time interval})}{\text{mass}}.$$

As we have seen before, the value of a proportionality constant depends on the units being used. As a reminder, you expressed the velocity change in meters per second, the time interval in seconds, the force in newtons, and the mass in kilograms. If you make a histogram of the values of the proportionality constant calculated from your class results, you may obtain a histogram similar to that shown in Figure 16.10. Most values are within a few percent of 1. This is no coincidence. The newton was defined by choosing a value of 1 for this proportionality constant. Therefore the constant in the previous equation is 1.

With this choice, the last equation simplifies to

$$\text{Change in velocity} = \frac{\text{force} \cdot (\text{time interval})}{\text{mass}}.$$

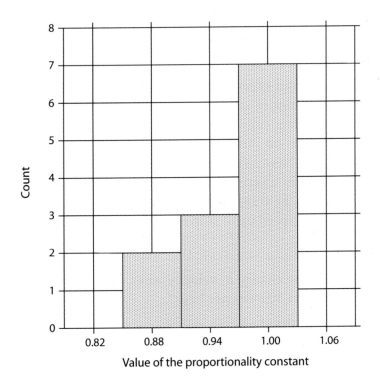

Figure 16.10

A histogram of the values of the proportionality constant and the product of force and time interval divided by mass.

State Newton's second law in your own words.

Multiplying both sides of this equation by the mass and reversing the order of the equation, we have

$$\text{Force} \cdot (\text{time interval}) = \text{mass} \cdot (\text{change in velocity}).$$

This equation is known as *Newton's second law*. It has been tested over a wide range of masses, velocities, forces, and time intervals. When generalized to motion in three dimensions, Newton's second law has been applied to such varied tasks as sending a spacecraft to Mars and to producing clear pictures on old picture-tube television screens. In this section and in the problems that follow it, we will try to give you a feel for the variety of situations that can be understood using Newton's second law.

For example, why are air bags installed in cars? In a collision, a moving car stops quickly. Its change in velocity equals the negative of its initial velocity (zero velocity minus the velocity at the instant of the collision).

A collision can take place in about a tenth of a second. The force exerted on the driver and passengers during such a collision is rather large—often larger than the human body can sustain without injury. Is there any way that we can reduce the forces on the driver and passengers in a car accident? No matter what we do, the product of the car's mass and its change in velocity during the collision cannot be changed. If we want to reduce the force on the driver and passengers, there is only one quantity in Newton's second law that can be changed—the time interval of the collision. This is what air bags do; they lengthen the time of the collision by cushioning the driver and passengers. As a result, less force is applied for a longer period of time to stop the people in the car.

Another example of an application of Newton's second law can be found in the light rail systems that are being built in many urban and suburban areas. Trains in such areas are expected to be quite fast, and they have to stop frequently. The time interval for the train to reach its cruising speed must be short, and it must be able to stop quickly. To satisfy these needs, Newton's second law requires either a very powerful engine and brakes, or a very light train. The less expensive alternative is used—the mass of the train is made as small as possible. With a small mass, less force can speed up or stop the train in a short time interval.

19. **a. What is the change in velocity when a car starts from rest and reaches 50 miles per hour?**

   b. What will the change in velocity be when a car cruising at 60 miles per hour comes to rest?

20. In an emergency, which will take a longer time interval to stop—a car that contains only the driver, or the same car containing the driver and five passengers? Explain your answer in terms of Newton's second law.

21. Use Newton's second law to explain why a light sports car, starting from rest, will reach 60 miles per hour in less time than a heavy sedan having the same kind of engine.

22. As a rocket burns its fuel, the mass of the rocket decreases. Assuming that the rocket's engines continue to provide the same force, how will this affect the change in velocity that takes place each second?

FOR REVIEW, APPLICATIONS, AND EXTENSIONS

23. A truck traveling at 50 miles per hour is carrying a heavy box sitting near the rear end of the truck bed.

    a. What force will prevent the box from continuing to move at 50 miles per hour when the truck stops at a traffic light?

    b. Explain what happens if the truck comes to a stop abruptly. Use Newton's second law.

    c. Where would a thoughtful driver place the box in the first place? What additional force would keep the box from continuing to move at 50 miles per hour?

24. A child can drive a nail into a wooden board by repeated hits with a hammer. Yet a full-grown man cannot push a nail into the board by leaning on it, even if he uses a piece of wood between his hand and the head of the nail for protection. Does the child really exert a greater force on the nail? To help you answer this question, here are some realistic numbers.

    a. Consider the head of a hammer, with a mass of 0.50 kg, hitting the nail at a downward velocity of 10 m/s. Assume that it takes 0.005 s for the head of the hammer to come to rest. What was the upward force exerted by the nail on the hammer to stop it?

    b. According to Newton's third law, what was the downward force exerted by the head of the hammer on the nail?

c. Suppose a man has a mass of 80 kg (about 180 lb). What is his weight in newtons?

d. Suppose he succeeds in putting half his weight on the nail. What is the downward force that he exerts on the nail?

e. What is the ratio of the force exerted by the child with the hammer to the force exerted by leaning man?

25. Even when a force is not constant, Newton's second law gives us information about the average force over the time interval being studied. A Lexus automobile has a mass of 1,748 kg. Starting from rest, it is able to reach a velocity of 26.8 m/s (about 60 miles per hour) in 7.5 seconds. A Chevrolet Corvette has a mass of 1,645 kg. If it starts from rest, it can reach 26.8 m/s in 7.8 seconds.

a. What is the average force applied to the Lexus as it goes from 0 to 26.8 m/s?

b. What is the average force applied to the Corvette as it goes from 0 to 26.8 m/s?

26. When the U.S. space shuttle is launched, the whole assembly has a mass of about 2,040,000 kg. During the first few seconds after liftoff, the engines provide a total thrust of about 34,600,000 N.

a. Ignoring air resistance, what is the net force acting on the whole assembly during the first 5.0 seconds?

b. Assuming that during the first 5.0 seconds the rocket moves straight up, what will be the shuttle's velocity at the end of 5.0 seconds?

27. Sprinters in the 100-meter race want to reach their highest velocity in the shortest possible time.

a. What does this tell you about the force propelling the sprinter forward?

b. Suppose the runners start off on plain gravel. What limits the force that pushes them forward?

c. Why are starting blocks (Figure E) used in races?

Figure E
For Problem 27

We can think of Newton's second law as a general principle when it comes to making a change in anything, not just velocity. For example, a change in a field from being full of rocks to being ready for planting depends on the amount of time devoted to it, the number of people working in the field, and the size of the field. If you translate the variables in Newton's second law to the variables in this situation, you may find that Newton's law applies. Write a brief essay on this subject using an example of your choice.

THEME FOR A SHORT ESSAY

Epilogue

As this course comes to an end, you may ask yourself: "What have I learned this year in science?" We hope that you will think of several things, some specific and some more general.

During the year we tried to familiarize you with some of the basic facts and ideas of physical science. You saw the evidence for the facts, and the usefulness of the ideas. Contrary to what you may have expected, science does not deal with absolute truths. The specific facts we find in the laboratory, such as density, melting points, solubilities, and half-lives are all subject to the limitations of our measurements.

Scientific laws are generalizations based on measurements made many times under controlled conditions to assure their validity. Yet these generalizations also have their limitations. If this is the case in science, how careful must you be about the facts and generalizations in your daily life? Do you ask for evidence to support what you read and hear? If this introduction to science has made you a more critical reader, a more careful observer, and a sharper thinker, your work during the year was worthwhile.

Appendix 1
Calculating in Scientific Notation

Part 1 Scientific Notation

The number of atoms in a piece of iron is very large. The mass of one atom in grams is a very small number. Scientific notation simplifies calculations made with large and small numbers by eliminating the need to use zeros as placeholders. Scientific notation thus enables us to write only the significant digits of a number.

The numbers in shorthand in Table A.1 are called *powers of ten*. The small numeral at the right of 10 is called the *exponent*. You can see that the exponent of 10 equals the number of zeros in the standard notation. Numbers larger than 1 have trailing zeros and numbers smaller than 1 have leading zeros. In order to distinguish between the two types of numbers, we write a negative sign before the exponent for numbers smaller than 1.

Table A.1			
Words	Standard numerals	Written shorthand	Spoken shorthand
million	1,000,000	10^6	"ten to the sixth"
hundred thousand	100,000	10^5	"ten to the fifth"
ten thousand	10,000	10^4	"ten to the fourth"
thousand	1,000	10^3	"ten cubed"
hundred	100	10^2	"ten squared"
ten	10	(10^1)	(shorthand not used)
one	1	(10^0)	(shorthand not used)
tenth	0.1	10^{-1}	"ten to the negative one"
hundredth	0.01	10^{-2}	"ten to the negative two"
thousandth	0.001	10^{-3}	"ten to the negative three"

Any number can be written as a product of a number between 1 and 10, and a power of ten. The following examples show how this is done.

$$3{,}000 = 3 \times 1{,}000 = 3 \times 10^3$$
$$3{,}200 = 3.2 \times 1{,}000 = 3.2 \times 10^3$$
$$0.05 = 5 \times 0.01 = 5 \times 10^{-2}$$
$$0.058 = 5.8 \times 0.01 = 5.8 \times 10^{-2}$$

The number multiplying a power of ten (5.8 in the last example) is called a *coefficient*. A number written as a product of a coefficient between 1 and 10 and a power of ten is said to be in *scientific notation*.

You can think of the process of separating a number into a coefficient and a power of ten in the following way. Moving a decimal point three places to the left divides a number by 1,000; for example,

$$3,200 \div 1,000 = 3.2.$$

To keep the value of the original number unchanged, you have to multiply 3.2 by 1,000. Hence $3,200 = 3.2 \times 1,000$. (In 3,200 the decimal point after the last zero is not written.)

Moving a decimal point two places to the right multiplies a number by 100. To keep the number 0.058 unchanged after moving the decimal point two places to the right, you must divide the new form—5.8—by 100, or multiply it by 0.01. Hence $0.058 = 5.8 \times 10^{-2}$.

1. Write the following numbers as numerals with exponents.

   a. hundred million   b. billion   c. ten thousand

   d. millionth   e. ten millionth   f. billionth

   (*Hint:* For numbers smaller than one, always include the zero to the left of the decimal point; for example, 0.01, not .01.)

2. Write the following numbers as standard numerals and in words.

   a. 10^7 b. 10^{10} c. 10^{-5} d. 10^{-7}

3. Write the following numbers in scientific notation.

   a. 8,000,000   b. 400,000   c. 370,000

   d. 5,610   e. 423   f. 9,060

4. Write the following numbers in scientific notation.

   a. 0.6   b. 0.07   c. 0.004

   d. 0.0506   e. 0.00042   f. 0.612

5. Write the following numbers as standard numerals.

   a. 3×10^6 b. 4.02×10^8 c. 6.52×10^7

   d. 8×10^{-5} e. 7.2×10^{-3} f. 4.07×10^{-4}

Part 2 Multiplying and Dividing in Scientific Notation: Significant Digits

As a preparation for multiplying numbers in scientific notation, let us look first at products of powers of ten:

$$10^3 \times 10^2 = 1,000 \times 100 = 100,000 = 10^5$$
$$10^6 \times 10^{-4} = 1,000,000 \times 0.0001 = 100 = 10^2$$
$$10^1 \times 10^{-1} = 10 \times 0.1 = 1 = 10^0$$
$$10^{-2} \times 10^{-5} = 0.01 \times 0.00001 = 0.0000001 = 10^{-7}$$

You can work out other examples, which will lead to the general rule: To multiply powers, add the exponents (with their proper signs!). Thus, in the preceding examples, we could have found the exponents of the products by addition:

$$3 + 2 = 5$$
$$6 + (-4) = 2$$
$$1 + (-1) = 0$$
$$(-2) + (-5) = -7$$

To multiply numbers in scientific notation, change the order of the factors in a product. For example:

$$(3 \times 10^5) \times (2 \times 10^4) = (3 \times 2) \times (10^5 \times 10^4) = 6 \times 10^9$$
$$(1.5 \times 10^{-2}) \times (3.0 \times 10^6) = (1.5 \times 3.0) \times (10^{-2} \times 10^6) = 4.5 \times 10^4$$

In general, to multiply two or more numbers in scientific notation, multiply the coefficients and the powers of ten separately.

Since powers of ten are multiplied by adding their exponents, it is reasonable to expect that powers of ten are divided by subtracting their exponents. The following examples illustrate this rule.

$$\frac{10^7}{10^4} = \frac{10,000,000}{10,000} = 1,000 = 10^3 \qquad\qquad 7 - 4 = 3$$

$$\frac{10^{-2}}{10^3} = \frac{0.01}{1,000} = 0.00001 = 10^{-5} \qquad\qquad (-2) - 3 = 5$$

$$\frac{10^2}{10^{-2}} = \frac{100}{0.01} = 10,000 = 10^4 \qquad\qquad 2 - (-2) = 4$$

$$\frac{10^{-3}}{10^{-2}} = \frac{0.001}{0.01} = 0.1 = 10^{-1} \qquad\qquad (-3) - (-2) = -1$$

To divide numbers in scientific notation, rearrange the numbers in a way similar to that used in multiplication.

$$\frac{6 \times 10^7}{2 \times 10^5} = \frac{6}{2} \times \frac{10^7}{10^5} = 3 \times 10^2$$

$$\frac{4.5 \times 10^2}{1.5 \times 10^4} = \frac{4.5}{1.5} \times \frac{10^{-2}}{10^{-4}} = 3.0 \times 10^2$$

In general, to divide numbers in scientific notation, divide the coefficients and the powers of ten separately.

Note that when two numbers in scientific notation are multiplied or divided, the product or quotient is not automatically given in scientific notation. For example,

$$(5 \times 10^2) \times (7 \times 10^4) = 35 \times 10^6$$

Here the coefficient, 35, is not between 1 and 10. However, we can move the decimal point one place to the left, and compensate for this by multiplying the number by 10:

$$35 \times 10^6 = 3.5 \times 10 \times 10^6 = 3.5 \times 10^7$$

Here is another example:

$$\frac{4 \times 10^5}{8 \times 10^2} = 0.5 \times 10^3$$

To change the coefficient to a number between 1 and 10, in this case you move the decimal point one place to the right, and compensate for this by dividing by 10 (or multiplying by 10^{-1}):

$$0.5 \times 10^3 = 5 \times 10^{-1} \times 10^3 = 5 \times 10^2$$

Scientific notation eliminates the need for zeros as placeholders. It removes any doubt about the significance of zeros in a measured number. For example, how many significant digits are there in 3,600 cm^2? Is this measurement accurate to the nearest 100 cm^2, 10 cm^2, or 1 cm^2? If standard numerals are used, there is no way of telling. In scientific notation, however, you write 3.6×10^3 cm^2 to indicate two significant digits, and 3.60×10^3 cm^2 to indicate three significant digits. Thus, you would write 3.60×10^3 cm^2 if the measurement 3,600 cm^2 were reliable to the nearest 10 cm^2.

You are likely to use scientific notation mostly for calculations with measurements. You should therefore use the rule given in Section 3.4 for the number of digits to be written when multiplying or dividing the coefficients: The result should have as many significant digits as the measurement with the smallest number of significant digits.

6. Multiply the following numbers.
   a. $10^8 \times 10^6$ b. $10^9 \times 10^{-5}$ c. $10^{-2} \times 10^6$
   d. $10^{-3} \times 10^{-3}$ e. $10^4 \times 10^{-7}$ f. $10^{-10} \times 10^{-12}$

7. Multiply the following numbers and express the results in scientific notation.
   a. $(2 \times 10^7) \times (3 \times 10^{-4})$ b. $(4 \times 10^3) \times (4 \times 10^3)$
   c. $(5 \times 10^{-2}) \times (1 \times 10^{-6})$ d. $(7 \times 10^3) \times (5 \times 10^{-2})$
   e. $(2.5 \times 10^4) \times (3 \times 10^5)$ f. $(6 \times 10^7) \times (1.5 \times 10^8)$

8. Divide the following numbers.
   a. $\dfrac{10^7}{10^3}$ b. $\dfrac{10^4}{10^8}$ c. $\dfrac{10^{12}}{10^{-2}}$

   d. $\dfrac{10^{-6}}{10^{-8}}$ e. $\dfrac{10^{-4}}{10^3}$ f. $\dfrac{10^{-4}}{10^{-2}}$

9. Divide the following numbers.
   a. $\dfrac{6 \times 10^5}{4 \times 10^3}$ b. $\dfrac{2 \times 10^7}{5 \times 10^{-8}}$ c. $\dfrac{7 \times 10^{-4}}{1 \times 10^{-6}}$

   d. $\dfrac{2 \times 10^8}{8 \times 10^4}$ e. $\dfrac{3 \times 10^{-2}}{6 \times 10^4}$ f. $\dfrac{7 \times 10^5}{2 \times 10^2}$

10. Write the following measurements in scientific notation.
    a. 6,500 g to the nearest 100 g
    b. 6,500 g to the nearest 1 g
    c. 6,500 g to the nearest 0.1 g
    d. 200 cm^3 to the nearest 1 cm^3
    e. 5,040 cm^3 to the nearest 10 cm^3
    f. 70,000 cm^3 to the nearest 1,000 cm^3

11. What is the area of a rectangular piece of land having sides of the following lengths?
    a. 3.5×10^3 m and 1.2×10^3 m
    b. 6.3×10^2 m and 4.7×10^4 m

12. Calculate the mass of 2.0×10^4 cm^3 of oxygen. (See Table 3.1 on page 55 for the density of oxygen.)

13. Suppose that a 3.2×10^{-3} g sample of a radioactive element produces 4.5×10^4 helium atoms per minute. How many helium atoms would be produced by 1.00 g of the element in 60.0 minutes?

Appendix 2
Proportionality

Consider the following ratios:

$$\frac{8}{2}, \quad \frac{16}{4}, \quad \frac{40}{10}, \text{ and } \frac{48}{12}.$$

You can see by inspection or by simplifying that all these ratios equal 4. This fact can also be expressed by the following equations:

$$8 = \mathbf{4} \times 2$$
$$16 = \mathbf{4} \times 4$$
$$40 = \mathbf{4} \times 10$$
$$48 = \mathbf{4} \times 12.$$

Think of the factor 4 in each equation as the number of sides of a square, and the other factor as the length of each side of that square. The product is then equal to the perimeter of a square. This relationship can be presented in a table (Table A.2).

The relationship between the length of a side and the perimeter of a square also can be expressed by a formula:

Perimeter of square $= 4 \cdot$ (length of one side).

The data in Table A2.1 can be represented by a graph (Figure A2.1). Notice that the graph is a straight line through the origin.

Table A.2	
Length of one side	Perimeter
2	8
4	16
10	40
12	48
⋮	⋮

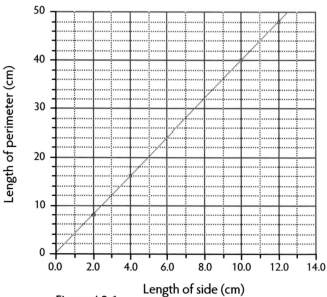

Figure A2.1

There are many situations in which one quantity equals a constant times another quantity:

$$\text{Quantity 2} = \text{constant} \cdot (\text{Quantity 1}).$$

We call such a relationship a *proportionality*. The constant factor is the *proportionality constant.*

When two quantities are proportional to each other, their ratio remains constant and equals the proportionality constant. Also, the graph of any proportionality has two very identifiable characteristics:

(1) It is a straight line.

(2) The line goes through the origin.

To be able to say that a graph shows that two quantities are proportional, both these conditions must be met.

1. **How can you tell that neither of the two graphs below represents a proportionality?**

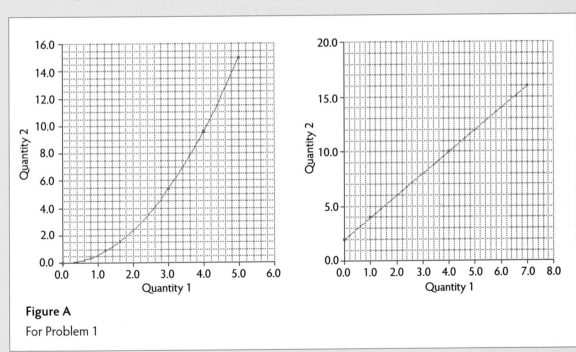

Figure A

For Problem 1

2. **Make a table for the perimeter of an equilateral triangle of sides 0, 1, 2, 3, 4, and 6 cm. Is the relation between the length of the perimeter and the length of one side a proportionality? If so, why?**

Usually, the two proportional quantities have units. In our example, both the side length and the perimeter have units of length, such as meters or centimeters. Because the proportionality constant is the ratio of the two quantities, its units will be the ratio of the units of the two quantities. In our example, the length of one side and the perimeter of a square have the same units. So, their ratio is a number without units.

The situation is quite different when the two quantities have different units. Suppose for example, that the cost per liter of milk is constant. Then the cost of milk is proportional to the volume of milk. If we express the cost of milk in dollars and the volume in liters,

Cost (dollars) = proportionality constant · volume (liter)

Thus, the proportionality constant is expressed in units of dollars/liter. If the cost of the same amount of milk were expressed in pennies, the number expressing the cost would be 100 times greater, and so would the proportionality constant.

3. The cost of filling a car's gas tank is proportional to the volume of gasoline that you buy. If the cost is expressed in dollars and the volume of the gasoline in gallons, what are the units of the proportionality constant?

4. a. The cost of eggs at the supermarket is proportional to the number of eggs bought. If the cost is expressed in dollars and the number of eggs in dozens, what are the units of the proportionality constant?

   b. What would be the proportionality constant be if the number of eggs were expressed by the number of individual eggs rather than in dozens?

   c. How are these two proportionality constants related to each other?

5. As you can see in Figure B, the height of a stack of pennies is proportional to the number of pennies.

   a. Measure the height of a few pennies and calculate the proportionality constant in millimeters per penny. Does your answer depend on the number of pennies you used?

   b. What would be the value of the proportionality constant if you chose the thickness of one penny as your unit of height?

Figure B

For Problem 5

In Chapters 15 and 16, you will encounter situations in which a quantity is independently proportional to each of two variables. Here is a familiar example. Suppose you want to cover a rectangular area with carpet. For a given width, the cost of the carpet will be proportional to the length of the rectangle. By the same reasoning, for a given length, the cost of the carpet will also be proportional to the width of the rectangle.

Cost = proportionality constant · length (for a given width)

Cost = proportionality constant · width (for a given length).

You already know that the cost of the carpet is proportional to the area to be covered. But the area of a rectangle equals the product of length and width. Therefore, the cost of the carpet is proportional to the product of length and width:

Cost = new proportionality constant · length · width .

This result can be generalized: when a quantity is proportional to each of two variables, it is proportional to their product.

6. Suppose that a rectangular room requires 10 tiles to cover its width and 15 tiles to cover its length. The cost of one tile is $3.00. Which of these three numbers is the proportionality constant? Which are quantities that the cost of covering the floor is proportional to?

7. Consider a bunch of identical glass marbles. The mass of the bunch is proportional to product to the density of the glass and the number of marbles. If you measure the mass in grams and the density in grams per cubic centimeter, what is the value of the proportionality constant?

Acknowledgments from the First Edition

The following members of the Educational Services Incorporated staff in addition to myself were involved in the development of the course; John B. Coulter, on leave from Pakuranga College, Howick, New Zealand; Judson B. Cross; John H. Dodge; Robert W. Estin, on leave from Roosevelt University, Chicago, Illinois; Malcolm H. Forbes; Ervin H. Hoffart; Gerardo Melcher, on leave from the University of Chile, Santiago, Chile; Harold A. Pratt, on leave from Jefferson County Public Schools, Lakewood, Colorado; Louis E. Smith, on leave from San Diego State College, San Diego, California; Darrel W. Tomer, on leave from Hanford Union High School, Hanford, California; and James A. Walter.

For the summer of 1963, we were joined by Elmer L. Galley, Mott Program of the Flint Public Schools, Flint, Michigan; Edward A. Shore, The Putney School, Putney, Vermont; and Byron L. Youtz, Reed College, Portland, Oregon.

Later on, considerable time was devoted to this project by others who joined us during the summers or consulted on a part-time basis throughout the following years; Gilbert H. Daenzer, Lutheran High School Central, St. Louis, Missouri Thomas J. Dillon, Concord- Carlisle High School, Concord, Massachusetts; Winslow Durgin, Xavier High School, Concord, Massachusetts; Alan Holden, Bell Telephone Laboratories, Murray Hill, New Jersey; Robert Gardner, Salisbury School, Salisbury, Connecticut; Father John Kerdiejus, S.J. Xavier High School, Concord, Massachusetts; Herman H. Kirkpatrick, Roosevelt High School, Des Moines, Iowa; Elisabeth Lincoln, Dana Hall School, Wellesley, Massachusetts; John V. Manuelian, Warren Junior High School, Newton, Massachusetts; John N. Meade, Newman Junior High School, Needham, Massachusetts; Paul Meunier, Marshfield High School, Marshfield, Massachusetts; Father Patrick Nowlan, O.S.A., Monsignor Bonner High School, Drexel Hill, Pennsylvania; Frank Oppenheimer, University of Colorado, Boulder, Colorado; Charles M. Shull, Jr., Colorado School of Mines, Golden Colorado; Malcolm K. Smith, Massachusetts Institute of Technology, Cambridge, Massachusetts; Moddie D. Taylor, Howard University, Washington, D.C.; Carol A. Wallbank, Dighton-Rehoboth Regional High School, Rehoboth, Massachusetts; Richard Whitney, Roxbury Latin School, West Roxbury, Massachusetts; Marvin Williams, Bell

Junior High School, Golden, Colorado; M. Kent Wilson, Tufts University, Medford, Massachusetts; and Carl Worster, Belmont Junior High School, Lakewood, Colorado.

I also wish to acknowledge the invaluable services of George D. Cope and Joan E. Hamblin in photography; R. Paul Larkin as art director for the preliminary edition; Barbara Griffin, Nancy Nelson, and Gertrude Rogers in the organization of feedback from the pilot schools; Nathaniel C. Burwash and John W. DeRoy in apparatus construction and design; Benjamin T. Richards for production; and Andrea G. Julian for editorial assistance. Much of the administrative work was done by Geraldine Kline.

Throughout the entire project I benefited from the advice and criticism of M. Kent Wilson. Valuable assistance in coordinating various group efforts in the summers of 1963 and 1966 was provided by Byron L. Youtz. In editing this edition of the course, I was specially aided by Judson B. Cross and by Harold A. Pratt, who was responsible for the group summarizing the feedback.

I wish to thank the editorial and art staff of the Educational Book Division of Prentice-Hall, Inc., for their help in preparing the final form of this edition.

Constant sources of encouragement and constructive criticism were the pilot teachers, who voluntarily spent many extra hours relating to us their classroom experience. Without them, the course could not have been developed to this point.

The initial stage of the Introductory Physical Science Program was funded by Educational Services Incorporated. Since then, it has been supported by a grant from the National Science Foundation. This financial support is gratefully acknowledged.

Uri Haber-Schaim
March 1967

Index

S

Salt. *See* rock salt; sodium chloride.
Sand, volume of, measuring, 12–13
Saturated solution, 72–73, 74–75
Scale, boiler, 92
Scales
    for counting, 6
    reading, 9–10
Scientific notation, 347–351 (*See also*
    Powers–of–10 notation.)
Sensitivity of a balance, 20–21, 28
Separation
    by flotation, 102
    of gases by condensing, 101–102,
      108–109
    of insoluble solids, 102–103
    of liquids by fractional distillation,
      96–98, 101–102
    of soluble solids in mixtures,
      104–106
Significant digits, 48–49
Silver
    compounds of, 212
    density of, 51
Sinkhole, 89
Sliding friction, 293–297
    definition of, 296
    force of, 293¬294
    and weight, 295–297
Sludge test, 114
Sodium
    discovery of, 131, 209
    properties of, 211–212, 215
    spectrum of, 170–171
Sodium carbonate, 117–118
    properties of, 113
    separating, 113
Sodium chloride (table salt)
    boiling point of, 66
    precipitating, 113
    purifying, 104
    solubility of, 79, 104–106
Sodium nitrate, solubility, 79
Solids, density of, measuring, 50–51
Solubility (*See also* concentration;
    fractional crystallization;
      precipitate.)
    and separation of substances,
      104–106
    and temperature, 77–79

    as characteristic property, 76, 83
    definition of, 75
    graphs of, 78–79
    measuring, 84–86
    of carbon dioxide, 84–86
    of gases, table of, 87
Solute(s)
    definition of, 73
    in drinking water, 90-91
Solution(s), 72–73
    acidic, 89
    concentration
      definition of, 73
      measuring, 74–76
    saturated, 72–73, 74–75
Solvent, definition of, 73
Space shuttle, 344
Specific heat, 248, 250–251
    definition of, 248
    of water, 248
    table of, 251
Spectral analysis (spectroscopy),
    170–172
    of polonium, 172
    of sunlight, 171
    uses of, 172
Spectra of elements, 169
Spectroscope, 169
Spectroscopy. (*See* spectral analysis.)
Spectrum of light, 169, 171
Speed
    of a spinning wheel, 270
    of molecules, 183–184,
      195–198
Sphere-gas machine, 184–186, 195–196
Spring, energy of, 278, 282
Spring scale(s)
    calibration marks, 285
    definition of, 285
    limits of, 305
    use of, 285, 292, 305, 332–334,
      336, 339
    zeroing, 285, 292
Strontium, spectrum, 171
Substances (*See also* compounds and
    elements.)
    distinguished from objects, 44
    identifying, 65–66
    pure, 111, 131
Sugar, measuring volume of, 14